HOW HUMANS EVOLVED

EIGHTH EDITION

ROBERT BOYD · JOAN B. SILK

PRIMATE ECOLOGY EDITION

NORTON
CUSTOM

W. W. NORTON & COMPANY, INC.

NEW YORK · LONDON

D1300562

W. W. Norton & Company has been independent since its founding in 1923, when William Warder Norton and Mary D. Herter Norton first published lectures delivered at the People's Institute, the adult education division of New York City's Cooper Union. The Nortons soon expanded their program beyond the Institute, publishing books by celebrated academics from America and abroad. By mid-century, the two major pillars of Norton's publishing program—trade books and college texts—were firmly established. In the 1950s, the Norton family transferred control of the company to its employees, and today—with a staff of four hundred and a comparable number of trade, college, and professional titles published each year—W. W. Norton & Company stands as the largest and oldest publishing house owned wholly by its employees.

Editor: Katie Hannah
Director of custom strategy: Susan Brennan
Managing editor, College: Marian Johnson
Project editor: Hannah Bachman
Assistant editor: Laura Dragonette
Assistant editor: Alexandra Gakos
Production manager: Jeremy Burton
Production assistant: Lindsay Fischer
Design director: Rubina Yeh
Custom cover designer: Tiani Kennedy
Text permissions manager: Megan Schindel
Photo permissions manager: Aga Millhouse

The Library of Congress has cataloged an earlier edition as follows:

Library of Congress Cataloging-in-Publication Data
Names: Boyd, Robert (Professor of cultural evolution), author. | Silk, Joan B., author.
Title: How humans evolved / Robert Boyd and Joan B. Silk, Arizona State University.
Description: Eighth edition. | New York : W. W. Norton & Company, [2018] | Includes bibliographical references and index.
Identifiers: LCCN 2017021652 | ISBN 9780393603453 (pbk.)
Subjects: LCSH: Human evolution.
Classification: LCC GN281 .B66 2018 | DDC 599.93/8—dc23 LC record available at
https://lccn.loc.gov/2017021652

ISBN: 978-0-393-69227-3

W. W. Norton & Company, Inc., 500 Fifth Avenue, New York, NY 10110
www.wwnorton.com
W. W. Norton & Company, Ltd., Castle House, 75/76 Wells Street, London W1T3QT

1 2 3 4 5 6 7 8 9 0

EIGHTH EDITION

HOW HUMANS EVOLVED

EIGHTH EDITION

HOW HUMANS EVOLVED

Robert Boyd and Joan B. Silk

Arizona State University

W. W. NORTON & COMPANY
NEW YORK • LONDON

W. W. Norton & Company has been independent since its founding in 1923, when William Warder Norton and Mary D. Herter Norton first published lectures delivered at the People's Institute, the adult education division of New York City's Cooper Union. The firm soon expanded its program beyond the Institute, publishing books by celebrated academics from America and abroad. By midcentury, the two major pillars of Norton's publishing program—trade books and college texts—were firmly established. In the 1950s, the Norton family transferred control of the company to its employees, and today—with a staff of four hundred and a comparable number of trade, college, and professional titles published each year—W. W. Norton & Company stands as the largest and oldest publishing house owned wholly by its employees.

Editor: Jake Schindel
Associate Managing Editor, College: Carla Talmadge
Assistant Editor: Rachel Goodman
Managing Editor, College: Marian Johnson
Managing Editor, College Digital Media: Kim Yi
Associate Director of Production, College: Benjamin Reynolds
Media Editors: Tacy Quinn and Miryam Chandler
Associate Media Editor: Mary Williams
Media Project Editor: Rachel Mayer
Media Editorial Assistant: Sarah Rose Aquilina
Digital Production: Lizz Thabet
Marketing Manager, Anthropology: Katie Sweeney
Designer: Lissi Sigillo
Photo Editor: Ted Szczepanski
Permissions Manager: Megan Schindel
Permissions Clearing: Bethany Salminen
Composition: Brad Walrod/Kenoza Type, Inc.
Illustrations: Imagineering Art
Manufacturing: Transcontinental

Permission to use copyrighted material is included in the back matter.

Library of Congress Cataloging-in-Publication Data

Names: Boyd, Robert (Professor of cultural evolution), author. | Silk, Joan B., author.
Title: How humans evolved / Robert Boyd and Joan B. Silk, Arizona State University.
Description: Eighth edition. | New York : W. W. Norton & Company, [2018] | Includes bibliographical references and index.
Identifiers: LCCN 2017021652 | **ISBN 9780393603453 (pbk.)**
Subjects: LCSH: Human evolution.
Classification: LCC GN281 .B66 2018 | DDC 599.93/8—dc23 LC record available at https://lccn.loc.gov/2017021652

W. W. Norton & Company, Inc., 500 Fifth Avenue, New York, NY 10110
wwnorton.com
W. W. Norton & Company Ltd., 15 Carlisle Street, London W1D 3BS

1 2 3 4 5 6 7 8 9 0

ABOUT THE AUTHORS

ROBERT BOYD

has written widely on evolutionary theory, focusing especially on the evolution of cooperation and the role of culture in human evolution. His book *Culture and the Evolutionary Process* received the J. I. Staley Prize. He is the coauthor of *Not by Genes Alone* and several edited volumes. He has also published many articles in scientific journals and edited volumes. He is a professor in the School of Human Evolution and Social Change at Arizona State University.

JOAN B. SILK

has conducted extensive research on the social lives of monkeys and apes, including extended fieldwork on chimpanzees at Gombe Stream Reserve in Tanzania and on baboons in Kenya and Botswana. She is also interested in the application of evolutionary thinking to human behavior. She is the coeditor of *The Evolution of Primate Societies* and has published many articles in scientific journals and edited volumes. She is a professor in the School of Human Evolution and Social Change at Arizona State University.

CONTENTS

Preface xiii
Prologue: Why Study Human Evolution? xviii

Part One: How Evolution Works

CHAPTER 1: Adaptation by Natural Selection 2

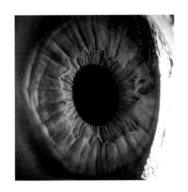

Explaining Adaptation before Darwin 3
Darwin's Theory of Adaptation 5
    Darwin's Postulates 6
    An Example of Adaptation by Natural Selection 7
    Individual Selection 11
The Evolution of Complex Adaptations 12
    Why Small Variations Are Important 12
    Why Intermediate Steps Are Favored by Selection 14
Rates of Evolutionary Change 17
Darwin's Difficulties Explaining Variation 21

Part Two: Primate Ecology and Behavior

CHAPTER 5: Primate Diversity and Ecology 108

Two Reasons to Study Primates 109
   Primates Are Our Closest Relatives 110
   Primates Are a Diverse Order 110
Features That Define the Primates 111
Primate Biogeography 114
A Taxonomy of Living Primates 115
A CLOSER LOOK 5.1 Teeth and Guts: You Are What You Can Chew 116
Primate Diversity 118
   The Strepsirrhines 118
   The Haplorrhines 119
Primate Ecology 125
   The Distribution of Food 125
   Activity Patterns 130
   Ranging Behavior 131
   Predation 132
Primate Sociality 134
Primate Conservation 135
A CLOSER LOOK 5.2 Forms of Social Groups among Primates 136

CHAPTER 6: Primate Mating Systems 142

The Language of Adaptive Explanations 144
The Evolution of Reproductive Strategies 145
Reproductive Strategies of Females........................... 147
    Sources of Variation in Female Reproductive Performance 148
A CLOSER LOOK 6.1 Dominance Hierarchies.................. 151
    Reproductive Trade-offs 154
Sexual Selection and Male Mating Strategies 155
    Intrasexual Selection.................................... 156
Male Reproductive Tactics 159
    Investing Males 159
    Male–Male Competition in Groups without Pair Bonds 160
    Infanticide.. 163

CHAPTER 7: The Evolution of Cooperation......... 168

Altruism: A Puzzle....................................... 169
Mutualism 170
The Problem with Group-Level Explanations 171
Kin Selection 172
A CLOSER LOOK 7.1 Group Selection...................... 173
    Hamilton's Rule 174
    Kin Recognition 176
    Kin Biases in Behavior 179
A CLOSER LOOK 7.2 How Relationships Are Maintained 180
    Parent–Offspring Conflict................................ 184
Reciprocal Altruism...................................... 184

CHAPTER 8: Primate Life Histories and the Evolution of Intelligence 188

Big Brains and Long Lives 189
Life History Theory....................................... 190
Selective Pressures Favoring Large Brains in Monkeys and Apes......... 193
What Do Monkeys Know about One Another?.................... 197
The Value of Studying Primate Behavior 202

Part Four: Evolution and Modern Humans

CHAPTER 15: Evolution and Human Behavior 386

Why Evolution Is Relevant to Human Behavior 387

Understanding How We Think 390

Inbreeding Avoidance 391

Human Mate Preferences 395

Social Consequences of Mate Preferences 401

Kipsigis Bridewealth 402

How Much Does Evolution Explain about Human Behavior? 403

CHAPTER 16: Culture, Cooperation, and Human Uniqueness 406

Evolution and Human Culture 408

Culture Is an Adaptation... 414

Cooperation 417

Is Human Evolution Over? 425

Epilogue: There Is Grandeur in This View of Life... 427

Appendix: The Skeletal Anatomy of Primates A-1

Glossary... G-1

Credits C-1

Index I-1

PREFACE

How Humans Evolved focuses on the processes that have shaped human evolution. This approach reflects our training and research interests. As anthropologists, we are interested in the evolutionary history of our own species, *Homo sapiens*, and the diversity of contemporary human societies. As evolutionary biologists, we study how evolution works to shape the natural world. In this book, we integrate these two perspectives. We use current theoretical and empirical work in evolutionary theory, population genetics, and behavioral ecology to interpret human evolutionary history. We describe the changes that have occurred as the human lineage has evolved, and we consider why these changes may have happened. By focusing on the processes that generate change, create adaptations, and shape bodies and behavior, we try to give life to the creatures that left the bones and made the artifacts that paleontologists and archaeologists painstakingly excavate. We also pay serious attention to the role of evolution in shaping contemporary human behavior. There is considerable controversy over evolutionary approaches to human behavior within the social sciences, but we think it is essential to confront these issues clearly and openly. Positive responses to the first seven editions of *How Humans Evolved* tell us that many of our colleagues endorse this approach.

One of the problems in writing a textbook about human evolution is that there is considerable debate on many topics. Evolutionary biologists disagree about how new species are formed and how they should be classified; primatologists argue about whether large primate brains are adaptations to social or ecological challenges and whether reciprocity plays an important role in primate societies; paleontologists disagree about the taxonomic relationships among early hominin species and the emergence of modern humans; and people who study modern humans disagree about the meaning and significance of race, the role of culture in shaping human behavior and psychology, the adaptive significance of many aspects of modern human behavior, and several other things. Sometimes multiple interpretations of the same data can be defended; in other cases, the facts seem contradictory. Textbook writers can confront this kind of uncertainty in two ways. They can weigh the evidence, present the ideas that best fit the available evidence, and ignore the alternatives. Or they can present opposing ideas, evaluate the logic underlying each idea, and explain how existing data support each of the positions. We chose the second alternative, at the risk of complicating the text and frustrating readers looking for simple answers. We made this choice because we believe that this approach is essential for understanding how science works. Students need to see how theories are developed, how data are accumulated, and how theory and data interact to shape our ideas about how the world works. We hope that students remember this long after they have forgotten many of the facts that they will learn in this book.

We wrote this book with undergraduates in mind and have designed several features to help students use the book effectively. We have retained the "key idea" statements (now printed in blue-green type), and we recommend that students use these key ideas to keep track of important concepts and facts and to structure their review of the material. Important terms that may be unfamiliar are set in boldface type when they first appear. Readers can find definitions for these terms in the Glossary. Discussion questions appear at the end of each chapter. These questions are meant to help students synthesize material presented in the text. Some of the questions are designed to help students review factual material, but most are intended to help students think about the processes or theoretical principles they have learned. Some questions are open-ended and meant to encourage students to apply their own values and judgment to the material presented in the text. Students tell us that they find these questions useful as they attempt to master the material and prepare for exams. The list of references for further reading at the end of each chapter provides a starting point for students who want to delve more deeply into the material covered in that chapter.

The book is richly illustrated with photographs, diagrams, figures, and graphs. These illustrations provide visual information to complement the text. For some subjects, a picture is clearly worth a thousand words—no amount of description can enable students to conjure up an image of an aye-aye or appreciate how much more similar the australopith pelvis is to the modern human pelvis than to the chimpanzee pelvis. The diagrams of evolutionary processes that appear in Part One are designed to help students visualize how natural selection works. The figures depicting the hominin fossils are drawn to scale, so each is presented in the same orientation and to the same scale. This should help students compare one hominin specimen with another. We have often been advised that you cannot put graphs in an undergraduate textbook, but we think that the graphs help students understand the evidence more fully. For us, it is easier to remember data that are portrayed graphically than to recall verbal descriptions of results.

New in the Eighth Edition

The study of human evolution is a dynamic field. No sooner do we complete one edition of this book than researchers make new discoveries that fundamentally change our view of human evolution. New developments in human evolutionary studies require regular updates of the textbook. Although we have made several changes throughout the book to reflect new findings, clarify concepts, and improve the flow of the text, readers familiar with prior editions will find the most substantive changes in Part Three, "The History of the Human Lineage."

In Part Three, we reorganized the treatment of early *Homo*, the development of stone tools, and the evolution of the distinctive human life history. Although the earliest stone tools now date to 3.3 million years ago (Ma), such tools don't become common in the archaeological record until about 2 Ma. These findings, combined with new analyses of brain size in early *Homo* species, suggest that flaked stone tools became a crucial part of human adaptation with the advent of early *Homo*, which also coincided with the evolution of larger brains and a slower life history. As usual, new fossil and archaeological finds have been incorporated into Part Three. For example, Chapter 10 discusses the tools found at Lomekwi and Chapter 11 includes a description of the morphology of *Homo naledi*. Chapter 13 has been extensively revised to reflect new insights from analyses of genetic data. We now have complete genomes for several late Pleistocene modern human fossils dating from 35 thousand years ago (ka) to 45 ka. In addition, we have complete sequences for a large, worldwide sample of living people, and these data provide rich information about the expansion of modern humans across the globe and about their interactions with Neanderthals and Denisovans. It now seems that modern humans interbred with these earlier hominins for thousands of years. New archaeological evidence suggests that the spread of modern humans across Eurasia may have occurred in several waves, perhaps beginning as early as 120 ka.

Ancillary Materials for Teaching and Learning

Visit wwnorton.com/instructors to download resources.

INQUIZITIVE
Prepared by Ashley Hurst, University of Texas—San Antonio.

InQuizitive is a formative, adaptive learning tool that improves student understanding of important learning objectives by personalizing quiz questions for each student. Engaging, gamelike elements built into InQuizitive motivate students as they learn.

InQuizitive includes a variety of question types that test student knowledge in different ways and enrich the user experience. Performance-specific feedback creates teaching moments that help students understand their mistakes and get back on the right track. Animations, videos, and other resources built into InQuizitive allow students to review core concepts as they answer questions.

InQuizitive is easy to use. Instructors can assign InQuizitive out of the box or use intuitive tools to customize the learning objectives they want students to work on. Students can access InQuizitive on computers, tablets, and smartphones, making it easy to study on the go.

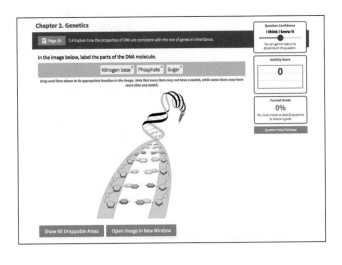

Student Access Codes

Student access codes to InQuizitive are automatically included with all new texts in any format. InQuizitive access can also be inexpensively purchased as a stand-alone option at **digital.wwnorton .com/howhumans8**. Contact your W. W. Norton sales rep, or visit inquizitive.wwnorton .com to learn more.

New Interactive Instructor's Guide

All the resources you need to create a rich and engaging course experience are included in one place with the new Interactive Instructor's Guide: iig.wwnorton.com/ howhumans8/full. Easily search by keyword, topic, or chapter to find and download videos, animations, in-class activity suggestions, PowerPoints, and more on this new site.

Physical Anthropology Animations and Videos

Animations of key concepts from the text, as well as curated real-world videos, are available to instructors and students in several ways, including via the coursepack, in the Interactive Instructor's Guide, and at **digital.wwnorton.com/ howhumans8**. These features are brief, easy to use, and great for explaining and helping students better visualize and understand concepts, either in class or as a self-study tool.

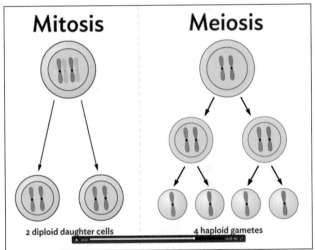

Coursepacks

Prepared by Tracy Betsinger, State University of New York at Oneonta.

Available at no cost to professors and students, Norton Coursepacks for online or hybrid courses are available in a variety of formats, including Blackboard, WebCT, Moodle, Canvas, and D2L. With just a simple download from the Norton instructor website, instructors can bring high-quality Norton digital media into a new or existing online course (no extra student passwords required). Content includes the full suite of animations and streaming videos that accompanies the text, available here to integrate into your lectures or for students to view outside of class. Engaging visual questions are specially designed for the distance or blended learning environment. Norton test banks and chapter quizzes are also all available for your use, and vocabulary flash cards are included for student self-study. Additionally, if InQuizitive will be in use, contact your local Norton representative to learn about our easy integration options for a single-sign-on and gradebook-reporting experience with your Norton Coursepack. All visual materials in Norton Coursepacks are ADA compliant.

PowerPoint Package
Prepared by Melissa Torpey, University of North Carolina—Wilmington.

The PowerPoint slides for this edition retain their richly illustrated format and extensive lecture notes. Designed to cover the core material in a highly visual way by using photography and art from the text, these PowerPoint slides bring the concepts in each chapter to life with additional photography and design. These slides also include a lecture script in the notes field. Download these resources from wwnorton.com/instructors or from the Interactive Instructor's Guide.

Update PowerPoint Service
To help cover what is new in the discipline, each semester Norton will provide a new set of supplemental lectures, notes, and assessment material covering current and breaking research. Prepared by Laurie Reitsema (University of Georgia), this material will be available for download at wwnorton.com/instructors and in the Interactive Instructor's Guide.

JPEGs of Art
To help you improve your class, JPEGs of all the art and photographs are available for download from the Norton instructor website.

Instructor's Manual
Prepared by Susan Kirkpatrick Smith, Kennesaw State University.

The Instructor's Manual provides an overview of each chapter's key concepts with additional explanation for topics that students may find more challenging as well as answers to the end-of-chapter Study Questions found in the text. The Instructor's Manual is available for download at the Norton instructor website.

Test Bank
Prepared by Greg Laden, Century College.

The Test Bank offers teachers approximately 60 multiple-choice and essay questions (organized by difficulty level and topic) for each chapter. Every question is keyed according to Bloom's knowledge types and the corresponding learning objective from the textbook. The Test Bank is available in downloadable formats in the Exam View Assessment Suite, as a PDF, and in formats compatible with MS Word and other word processors.

Ebook: Same Great Book, a Fraction of the Price
An affordable and convenient alternative, Norton Ebooks retain the content and design of the print book and allow students to highlight and take notes with ease, print chapters as needed, read online or offline, and search the text. Instructors can even take notes in their ebooks that can be shared with their students.

Acknowledgments

Over the last 25 years, many of our colleagues have provided new information, helpful comments, and critical perspectives that have enriched this book. We are grateful for all those who have responded to our requests for photographs, clarifications, references, and opinions. For the Eighth Edition, we are grateful to our ASU colleagues, particularly William Kimbel, Kaye Reed, and Gary Schwartz, for their generous help with revisions of Part Three. We also thank Melissa Wilson Sayers and Luca Pagani for their assistance with material in Chapter 13. For the Seventh Edition we thank Curtis Marean for reviewing Chapter 13 and Kim Hill for reading Chapter 16. For the Sixth Edition, we thank Christopher Kirk for reviewing Chapter 5, Leanne Nash for reviewing Chapters 4 and 8, Roberto Delgano for reviewing Chapters 6 and 7, and Carol Ward and Jeremy DeSilva for help with Chapter 9. For the Fourth Edition, Laura MacLatchy provided help with the Miocene apes in Chapter 10, Dan Fessler and David Schmitt gave us access to material for Chapter 16, and Kermyt Anderson dug up original data for figures in Chapter 17. Steven Reznik reviewed our discussion of the rapid evolution of placentas in the minnows he studies and kindly provided an image. Leslie Aiello helped with our discussion of hominin developmental rates. For help with the Third Edition, we thank Carola Borries, Colin Chapman, Richard Klein, Cheryl Knott, Sally McBrearty, Ryne Palombit, Steve Pinker, Karin Stronswold, and Bernard Wood. For help with the Second Edition, we also thank Tom Plummer, Daniel Povinelli, Beverly Strassman, and Patricia Wright. We remain grateful for the help we received for the First Edition from Leslie Aiello, Monique Borgerhoff Mulder, Scott Carroll, Dorothy Cheney, Glenn Conroy, Martin Daly, Robin Dunbar, Lynn Fairbanks, Sandy Harcourt, Kristin Hawkes, Richard Klein, Phyllis Lee, Nancy Levine, Jeff Long, Joseph Manson, Henry McHenry, John Mitani, Jocelyn Peccei, Susan Perry, Steve Pinker, Tom Plummer, Tab Rasmussen, Mark Ridley, Alan Rogers, Robert Seyfarth, Frank Sulloway, Don Symons, Alan Walker, Tim White, and Margo Wilson.

Several people have provided reviews of all or parts of the text and accompanying resource suite. We thank the following: Stephanie Anestis, Thad Bartlett, AnnMarie Beasley, Rene Bobe, Barry Bogin, Doug Broadfield, Bryce Carlson, Joyce Chan, Margaret Clarke, Steve Corbett, Julie Cormack, Douglas Crews, Roberto Delgado, Arthur Durband, Charles Edwards, Donald Gaff, Renee Garcia, Susan Gibson, Peter Gray, Mark Griffin, Corinna Guenther, Sharon Gursky, Kim Hill, Kevin Hunt, Andrew Irvine, Trine Johansen, Andrea Jones, Barbara King, Richard Klein, Sam Kobari, Jeremy Koster, Kristin Krueger, Darrell La Lone, Clark Larsen, Lynette Leidy, Joseph Lorenz, Laura MacLatchy, Lara McCormick, Elizabeth Miller, Shannon Mills, John Mitani, Gilliane Monnier, Peer Moore-Jansen, M. J. Mosher, Martin Muller, Marilyn Norconk, Ann Palkovich, Amanda Wolcott Paskey, James Paterson, Michael Pietrusewsky, Mindy Pitre, Barbara Quimby, Corey Ragsdale, Kristin Rauch, Ulrich Reichard, Laurie Reitsema, Michael Robertson, Stacey Rucas, Michael Schillaci, Eric Schnicter, Liza Shapiro, Beth Shook, Eric Smith, K. Elizabeth Soluri, Craig Stanford, Horst Steklis, Joan Stevenson, Mark Stoneking, Rebecca Storey, Rebecca Stumpf, Roger Sullivan, Yanina Valdos, Timothy Weaver, Elizabeth Weiss, Jill Wenrick, Patricia Wright, and Alexandra Zachwieja. Although we are certain that we have not satisfied all those who read and commented on parts of the book over the years, we have found all the comments helpful as we revised the text.

Richard Klein provided us with many exceptional drawings of fossils that appear in Part Three—an act of generosity that we continue to appreciate. We also give special thanks to Neville Agnew and the Getty Conservation Institute for granting us permission to use images of the Laetoli conservation project for the cover of the Second Edition.

We also acknowledge the thousands of students and dozens of teaching assistants at ASU and UCLA who have used various versions of this material over the years. Student evaluations of the original lecture notes, the first draft of the text, and the first seven editions were helpful as we revised and rewrote various parts of the book. The teaching assistants helped us identify many parts of the text that needed to be clarified, corrected, or reconsidered.

We thank all the people at Norton who helped us produce this book, particularly our current editor, Jake Schindel, and his predecessors, Leo Wiegman, Pete Lesser, Aaron Javsicas, and Eric Svendsen. We are also grateful to the assistant editor, Rachel Goodman, and project editor, Carla Talmadge. We also thank all the other people who saw the book through the production and marketing process, including Sarah Rose Aquilina, Tacy Quinn, Donna Ranieri, Benjamin Reynolds, Bethany Salminen, Megan Schindel, Lissi Sigillo, Katie Sweeney, and Ted Szczepanski.

PROLOGUE

WHY STUDY HUMAN EVOLUTION?

Origin of man now proved—Metaphysics must flourish—He who understand baboon would do more toward metaphysics than Locke.

—*Charles Darwin*, M Notebook, *August 1838*

In 1838, Charles Darwin discovered the principle of evolution by natural selection and revolutionized our understanding of the living world. Darwin was 28 years old, and it was just two years since he had returned from a five-year voyage around the world as a naturalist on the HMS *Beagle* (**Figure P.1**). Darwin's observations and experiences during the journey had convinced him that biological species change through time and that new species arise by the transformation of existing ones, and he was avidly searching for an explanation of how these processes worked.

In late September of the same year, Darwin read Thomas Malthus's *Essay on the Principle of Population*, in which Malthus (**Figure P.2**) argued that human populations invariably grow until they are limited by starvation, poverty, and disease. Darwin realized that Malthus's logic also applied to the natural world, and this intuition inspired the conception of his theory of evolution by natural selection. In the intervening century and a half, Darwin's theory has been augmented by discoveries in genetics and amplified by studies of the evolution of many types of organisms. It is now the foundation of our understanding of life on Earth.

This book is about human evolution, and we will spend a lot of time explaining how natural selection and other evolutionary processes have shaped the human species. Before we begin, it is important to consider why you should care about this topic. Many of you will be working through this book as a requirement for an undergraduate class in biological anthropology and will read the book in order to earn a good grade. As instructors of a class like this ourselves, we approve of this motive. However, there is a much better reason to care about the processes that have shaped human evolution: Understanding how humans evolved is the key to understanding why people look and behave the way they do.

The profound implications of evolution for our understanding of humankind were apparent to Darwin from the beginning. We know this today because he kept notebooks in which he recorded his private thoughts about various topics. The quotation that begins this prologue is from the *M Notebook*, begun in July 1838, in which Darwin jotted down his ideas about humans, psychology, and the philosophy of science. In the nineteenth century, metaphysics involved the study of the human mind. Thus Darwin was saying that because he believed humans evolved from a creature something like a baboon, it followed that an understanding of the mind of a baboon would contribute more to an understanding of the human mind than would all the works of the great English philosopher John Locke.

Darwin's reasoning was simple. Every species on this planet has arisen through the same evolutionary processes. These processes determine why organisms are the way they are by shaping their morphology, physiology, and behavior. The traits that characterize the human species are the result of the same evolutionary processes that created all other species. If we understand these processes and the conditions under which the human species evolved, then we will have the basis for a scientific understanding of human nature. Trying to comprehend the human mind without an understanding of human evolution is, as Darwin wrote in another notebook that October, "like puzzling at astronomy without mechanics." By this, Darwin meant that his theory of evolution could play the same role in biology and psychology that Isaac Newton's laws of motion had played in astronomy. For thousands of years, stargazers, priests, philosophers, and mathematicians had struggled to understand the motions of the planets without success. Then, in the late 1600s, Newton discovered the laws of mechanics and showed how all the intricacies in the dance of the planets could be explained by the action of a few simple processes (**Figure P.3**).

In the same way, understanding the processes of evolution enables us to account for the stunning sophistication of organic design and the diversity of life and to understand why people are the way they are. As a consequence, understanding how natural selection and other evolutionary processes shaped the human species is relevant to all the academic disciplines that are concerned with human beings. This vast intellectual domain includes medicine, psychology, the social sciences, and even the humanities. Beyond academia, understanding our own evolutionary history can help us answer many questions that confront us in everyday life. Some of these questions are relatively trivial: Why do we sweat when hot or nervous? Why do we crave salt, sugar, and fat, even though large amounts of these substances cause disease (**Figure P.4**)? Why are we better marathon runners than mountain climbers? Other questions are more profound: Why do only women nurse their babies? Why do we grow old and eventually die? Why do people around the world look so different? As you will see, evolutionary theory provides answers or insights about all these questions. Aging, which eventually leads to death, is an evolved characteristic of humans and most other creatures. Understanding how natural selection shapes the life histories of organisms tells us why we are mortal, why our life span is about 70 years, and why other species live shorter lives. In an age of horrific ethnic conflicts and growing respect for multicultural diversity, we are constantly reminded of the variation within the human species. Evolutionary analyses tell us that genetic differences between human groups are relatively minor and that our notions of race and ethnicity are culturally constructed categories, not biological realities.

FIGURE P.1

When this portrait of Charles Darwin was painted, he was about 30 years old. He had just returned from his voyage on the HMS *Beagle* and was still busy organizing his notes, drawings, and vast collections of plants and animals.

FIGURE P.2

Thomas Malthus was the author of *An Essay on the Principle of Population*, a book Charles Darwin read in 1838 that profoundly influenced the development of his theory of evolution by natural selection.

FIGURE P.3

Sir Isaac Newton discovered the laws of celestial mechanics, a body of theory that resolved age-old mysteries about the movements of the planets.

FIGURE P.4

A strong appetite for sugar, fat, and salt may have been adaptive for our ancestors, who had little access to these foods. We have inherited these appetites and now have easy access to sugar, fat, and salt. As a consequence, many of us suffer from obesity, high blood pressure, diabetes, and heart disease.

FIGURE P.5

One of the great debates in Western thought focuses on the essential elements of human nature. Are people basically moral beings corrupted by society or fundamentally amoral creatures socialized by cultural conventions, social strictures, and religious beliefs?

All these questions deal with the evolution of the human body. However, understanding evolution is also an important part of our understanding of human behavior and the human mind. The claim that understanding evolution will help us understand contemporary human behavior is much more controversial than the claim that it will help us understand how human bodies work. But it should not be. The human brain is an evolved organ of great complexity, just like the endocrine system, the nervous system, and all the other components of the human body that regulate our behavior. Understanding evolution helps us understand our mind and behavior because evolutionary processes forged the brain that controls human behavior, just as they forged the brain of the chimpanzee and the salamander.

One of the great debates in Western thought centers on the essence of human nature. One view is that people are basically honest, generous, and cooperative creatures who are corrupted by an immoral economic and social order. The opposing view is that we are fundamentally amoral, egocentric beings whose antisocial impulses are held in check by social pressures. This question turns up everywhere. Some people believe that children are little barbarians who are civilized only through sustained parental effort; others think that children are gentle beings who are socialized into competitiveness and violence by exposure to negative influences such as toy guns and violent TV programs (**Figure P.5**). The same dichotomy underpins much political and economic thought. Economists believe that people are rational and selfish, but other social scientists, particularly anthropologists and sociologists, question and sometimes reject this assumption. We can raise an endless list of interesting questions about human nature: Does the fact that, in most societies, women rear children and men make war mean that men and women differ in their innate predispositions? Why do men typically find younger women attractive? Why do some people neglect and abuse their children, whereas others adopt and lovingly raise children who are not their own?

Understanding human evolution does not reveal the answers to all these questions or even provide a complete answer to any one of them. As we will see, however, it can provide useful insights about all of them. An evolutionary approach does not imply that behavior is genetically determined or that learning and culture are unimportant. In fact, we will argue that learning and culture play crucial roles in human behavior. Behavioral differences among peoples living in different times and places result mainly from flexible adjustments to different social and environmental conditions. Understanding evolution is useful precisely because it helps us understand why humans respond in different ways to different conditions.

Overview of the Book

Humans are the product of organic evolution. By this we mean that there is an unbroken chain of descent that connects every living human being to a bipedal, apelike creature that walked through the tall grasses of the African savanna 3 million years ago (Ma); to a monkeylike animal that clambered through the canopy of great tropical forests covering much of the world 35 Ma; and, finally, to a small, egg-laying, insect-eating mammal that scurried about at night during the age of the dinosaurs 100 Ma. To understand what we are now, you have to understand how this transformation took place. We tell this story in four parts.

Part One: How Evolution Works

More than a century of hard work has given us a good understanding of how evolution works. The transformation of apes into humans involved the assembly of many new, complex adaptations. For example, for early humans to walk upright on two legs, there had to be coordinated changes in many parts of their bodies, including their feet, legs, pelvis, backbone, and inner ear. Understanding how natural selection gives rise to such complex structures and why the genetic system plays a crucial role in this process is essential for understanding how new species arise. Understanding these processes also allows us to reconstruct the history of life from the characteristics of contemporary organisms.

Part Two: Primate Ecology and Behavior

In the second part of the book, we consider how evolution has shaped the behavior of nonhuman primates—an exercise that helps us understand human evolution in two ways. First, humans are members of the primate order: We are more similar to other primates, particularly the great apes, than we are to wolves, raccoons, or other mammals. Studying how primate morphology and behavior are affected by ecological conditions helps us determine what our ancestors might have been like and how they may have been transformed by natural selection. Second, we study primates because they are an extremely diverse order and are particularly variable in their social behavior. Some are solitary, others live in pair-bonded groups, and some live in large groups that contain many adult females and males. Data derived from studies of these species help us understand how social behavior is molded by natural selection. We can then use these insights to interpret the hominin fossil record and the behavior of contemporary people (**Figure P.6**).

Part Three: The History of the Human Lineage

General theoretical principles are not enough to understand the history of any lineage, including our own. The transformation of a shrewlike creature into the human species involved many small steps, and each step was affected by specific environmental and biological circumstances. To understand human evolution, we have to reconstruct the actual history of the human lineage and the environmental context in which these events occurred. Much of this history is chronicled in the fossil record. These bits of mineralized bone, painstakingly collected and reassembled by paleontologists, document the sequence of organisms that links early mammals to modern humans. Complementary work by geologists, biologists, and archaeologists allows us to reconstruct the environments in which the human lineage evolved (**Figure P.7**).

Part Four: Evolution and Modern Humans

Finally, we turn our attention to modern humans and ask why we are the way we are. Why is the human species so variable? How do we acquire our behavior? How has evolution shaped human psychology and behavior? How do we choose our mates? Why do people commit infanticide? Why have humans succeeded in inhabiting every corner of Earth when other species have more limited ranges? We will explain how an understanding of evolutionary theory and a knowledge of human evolutionary history provide a basis for addressing such questions.

The history of the human lineage is a great story, but it is not a simple one. The relevant knowledge is drawn from many disciplines in the natural sciences, such as physics, chemistry, biology, and geology, and from the social sciences, mainly anthropology, psychology, and economics. Learning this material is an ambitious task, but it offers a very satisfying reward. The better you understand the processes that have shaped human evolution and the historical events that took place in the human lineage, the better you will understand how we came to be and why we are the way we are.

FIGURE P.6

We will draw on information about the behavior of living primates, such as this chimpanzee, to understand how behavior is molded by evolutionary processes, to interpret the hominin fossil record, and to draw insights about the behavior of contemporary humans.

FIGURE P.7

Fossils painstakingly excavated from many sites in Africa, Europe, and Asia provide us with a record of our history as a species. Two million years ago in Africa, there were several apelike species that walked bipedally but still had ape-size brains and apelike developmental patterns. These are the fossilized remains of *Homo habilis*, a species that some think is ancestral to modern humans.

1

PART ONE

HOW EVOLUTION WORKS

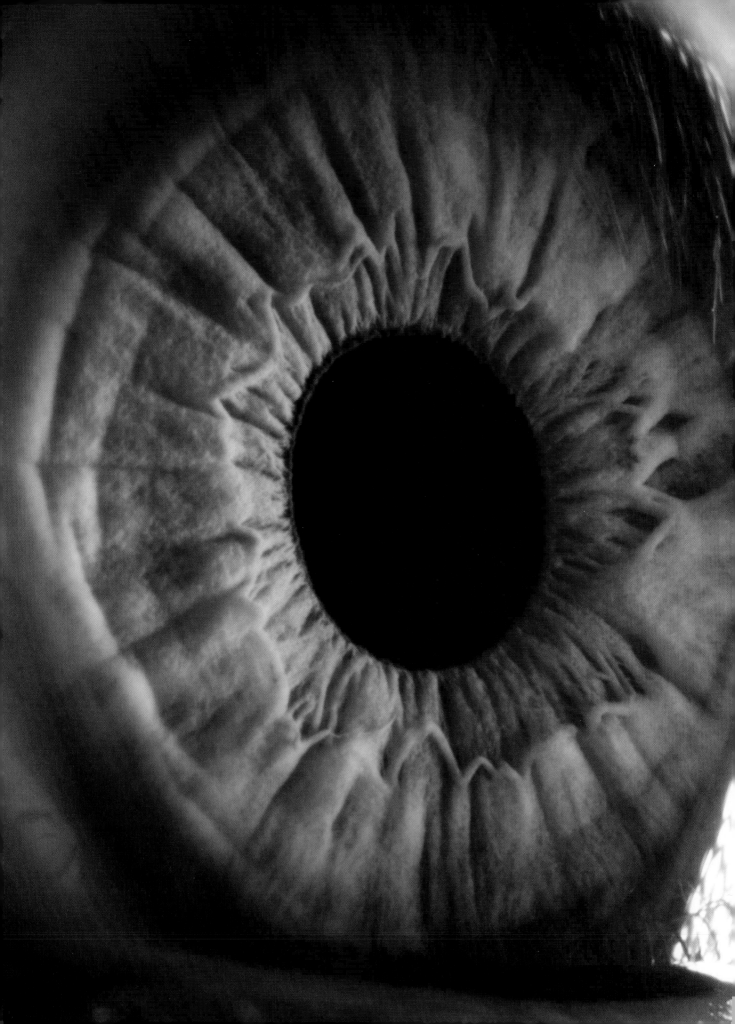

1

- **Explaining Adaptation before Darwin p. 3**
- **Darwin's Theory of Adaptation p. 5**
- **The Evolution of Complex Adaptations p. 12**
- **Rates of Evolutionary Change p. 17**
- **Darwin's Difficulties Explaining Variation p. 21**

ADAPTATION BY NATURAL SELECTION

CHAPTER OBJECTIVES

By the end of this chapter you should be able to

A. Describe why our modern understanding of the diversity of life is based on the ideas of Charles Darwin.

B. Explain how competition, variation, and heritability lead to evolution by natural selection.

C. Explain why natural selection sometimes causes species to become better adapted to their environments.

D. Explain why natural selection can produce change or cause species to remain the same over time.

E. Describe how natural selection can produce very complex adaptations such as the human eye.

F. Assess why natural selection usually works at the level of the individual, not at the level of the group or species.

Explaining Adaptation before Darwin

Animals and plants are adapted to their conditions in subtle and marvelous ways. Even the casual observer can see that organisms are well suited to their circumstances. For example, fish are clearly designed for life underwater, and certain flowers are designed to be pollinated by particular species of insects. More careful study reveals that organisms are more than just suited to their environments: They are complex machines, made up of many exquisitely constructed components, or **adaptations**, that interact to help the organism survive and reproduce.

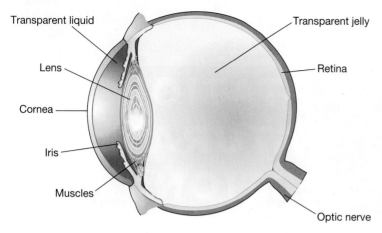

FIGURE 1.1

A cross section of the human eye.

The human eye provides a good example of an adaptation. Eyes are amazingly useful: They allow us to move confidently through the environment, to locate critical resources such as food and mates, and to avoid dangers such as predators and cliffs. Eyes are extremely complex structures made up of many interdependent parts (**Figure 1.1**). Light enters the eye through a transparent opening, then passes through a diaphragm called the iris, which regulates the amount of light entering the eye and allows the eye to function in a wide range of lighting conditions. The light then passes through a lens that projects a focused image on the retina on the back surface of the eye. Several kinds of light-sensitive cells then convert the image into nerve impulses that encode information about spatial patterns of color and intensity. These cells are more sensitive to light than the best photographic film. The detailed construction of each of these parts of the eye makes sense in terms of the eye's function: seeing. If we probed into any of these parts, we would see that they, too, are made of complicated, interacting components whose structure is understandable in terms of their function.

Differences between human eyes and the eyes of other animals make sense in terms of the types of problems each creature faces. Consider, for example, the eyes of fish and humans (**Figure 1.2**). The lens in the eyes of humans and other terrestrial mammals is much like a camera lens; it is shaped like a squashed football and has the same index of refraction (a measure of light-bending capacity) throughout. In contrast, the lens in fish eyes is a sphere located at the center of the curvature of the retina, and the index of refraction of the lens increases smoothly from the surface of the lens to the center. It turns out that this kind of lens, called a spherical gradient lens, provides a sharp image over a full 180° visual field, a very short focal length, and high light-gathering power—all desirable properties. Terrestrial creatures like us cannot use this design because light is bent when it passes from the air through the cornea (the transparent cover of the pupil), and this fact constrains the design of the remaining lens elements. In contrast, light is not bent when it passes from water through the cornea of aquatic animals, and the design of their eyes takes advantage of this fact.

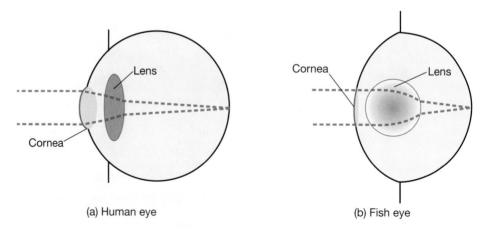

(a) Human eye (b) Fish eye

FIGURE 1.2

(a) Like those of other terrestrial mammals, human eyes have more than one light-bending element. A ray of light entering the eye (*dashed lines*) is bent first as it moves from the air to the cornea and then again as it enters and leaves the lens. (b) In contrast, fish eyes have a single lens that bends the light throughout its volume. As a result, fish eyes have a short focal length and high light-gathering power.

Before Darwin there was no scientific explanation for the fact that organisms are well adapted to their circumstances.

As many nineteenth-century thinkers were keenly aware, complex adaptations such as the eye demand a different kind of explanation from other natural objects. This is not simply because adaptations are complex, since many other complicated objects exist in nature. Adaptations require a special kind of explanation because they are complex in a particular, highly improbable way. For example, the Grand Canyon, with its maze of delicate towers intricately painted in shades of pink and gold, is byzantine in its complexity (**Figure 1.3**). Given a different geological history, however, the Grand Canyon might be quite different—different towers in different hues—yet we would still recognize it as a canyon. The particular arrangement of painted towers of the Grand Canyon is improbable, but the existence of a spectacular canyon with a complex array of colorful cliffs in the dry sandstone country of the American Southwest is not unexpected at all; and in fact, wind and water produced many such canyons in this region. In contrast, any substantial changes in the structure of the eye would prevent the eye from functioning, and then we would no longer recognize it as an eye. If the cornea were opaque or the lens on the wrong side of the retina, then the eye would not transmit visual images to the brain. It is highly improbable that natural processes would randomly bring together bits of matter having the detailed structure of the eye because only an infinitesimal fraction of all arrangements of matter would be recognizable as a functioning eye.

In Darwin's day, most people were not troubled by this problem because they believed that adaptations were the result of divine creation. In fact, the theologian William Paley used a discussion of the human eye to argue for the existence of God in his book *Natural Theology,* published in 1802. Paley argued that the eye is clearly *designed* for seeing, and where there is design in the natural world, there certainly must be a heavenly designer.

Although most scientists of the day were satisfied with this reasoning, a few, including Charles Darwin, sought other explanations.

FIGURE 1.3

Although an impressive geological feature, the Grand Canyon is much less remarkable in its complexity than the eye.

Darwin's Theory of Adaptation

Charles Darwin was expected to become a doctor or clergyman, but instead he revolutionized science.

Charles Darwin was born into a well-to-do, intellectual, and politically liberal family in England. Like many prosperous men of his time, Darwin's father wanted his son to become a doctor. But after failing at the prestigious medical school at the University of Edinburgh, Charles went on to Cambridge University, resigned to becoming a country parson. He was, for the most part, an undistinguished student—much more interested in tramping through the fields around Cambridge in search of beetles than in studying Greek and mathematics. After graduation, one of Darwin's botany professors, John Stevens Henslow, provided him with a chance to pursue his passion for natural history as a naturalist on the HMS *Beagle.*

The *Beagle* was a Royal Navy vessel whose charter was to spend two to three years mapping the coast of South America and then to return to London, perhaps by circling the globe (**Figure 1.4**). Darwin's father forbade him to go, preferring that Charles get serious about his career in the church, but Darwin's uncle (and future father-in-law) Josiah Wedgwood II intervened. The voyage was the turning point in Darwin's life. His work during the voyage established his reputation as a skilled naturalist. His observations of living and fossil animals ultimately convinced him that plants and animals sometimes change slowly through time and that such evolutionary change is the key to understanding how new species come into existence. This view was rejected by most scientists of the time and was considered heretical by the general public.

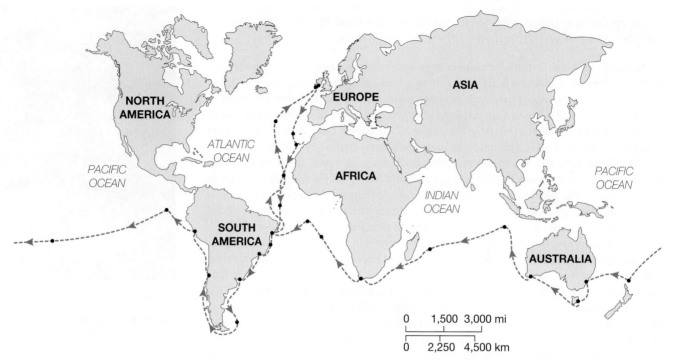

FIGURE 1.4

Darwin circumnavigated the globe during his five-year voyage on the HMS *Beagle*.

Darwin's Postulates

Darwin's theory of adaptation follows from three postulates: (1) the struggle for existence, (2) the variation in fitness, and (3) the inheritance of variation.

In 1838, shortly after the *Beagle* returned to London, Darwin formulated a simple mechanistic explanation for *how* species change through time. His theory follows from three postulates:

1. The ability of a population to expand is infinite, but the ability of any environment to support populations is always finite.

2. Organisms within populations vary, and this variation affects the ability of individuals to survive and reproduce.

3. This variation is transmitted from parents to offspring.

Darwin's first postulate means that populations grow until they are checked by the dwindling supply of resources in the environment. Darwin referred to the resulting competition for resources as "the struggle for existence." For example, animals require food to grow and reproduce. When food is plentiful, animal populations grow until their numbers exceed the local food supply. Because resources are always finite, it follows that not all individuals in a population will be able to survive and reproduce. According to the second postulate, some individuals will possess traits that enable them to survive and reproduce more successfully (producing more offspring) than others in the same environment. The third postulate holds that if the advantageous traits are inherited by offspring, then these traits will become more common in succeeding generations. Thus traits that confer advantages in survival and reproduction are retained in the population, and traits that are disadvantageous disappear. When Darwin coined the term **natural selection** for this process, he was making a deliberate analogy to the artificial selection practiced by animal and plant breeders of his day. A much more apt term would be "evolution by variation and selective retention."

(a)

(b)

FIGURE 1.5

(a) The islands of the Galápagos, which are located off the coast of Ecuador, house a variety of unique species of plants and animals. (b) Cactus finches from Charles Darwin's *The Zoology of the Voyage of H.M.S. Beagle* (1840).

An Example of Adaptation by Natural Selection

Contemporary observations of Darwin's finches provide a particularly good example of how natural selection produces adaptations.

In his autobiography, first published in 1887, Darwin claimed that the curious pattern of adaptations he observed among the several species of finches that live on the Galápagos Islands off the coast of Ecuador—now referred to as "Darwin's finches"—was crucial in the development of his ideas about evolution (**Figure 1.5**). Some evidence suggests that Darwin was actually confused about the Galápagos finches during his visit, and they played little role in his discovery of natural selection. Nonetheless, Darwin's finches hold a special place in the minds of most biologists.

Peter and Rosemary Grant, biologists at Princeton University, conducted a landmark study of the ecology and evolution of one particular species of Darwin's finches on one of the Galápagos Islands. The study is remarkable because the Grants were able to directly document how Darwin's three postulates led to evolutionary change. The island, Daphne Major, is home to the medium ground finch (*Geospiza fortis*), a small bird that subsists mainly by eating seeds (**Figure 1.6**). The Grants and their colleagues caught, measured, weighed, and banded nearly every finch on the island each year of their study—some 1,500 birds in all. They also kept track of critical features of the birds' environment, such as the distribution of seeds of various sizes, and they observed the birds' behavior.

A few years into the Grants' study, a severe drought struck Daphne Major (**Figure 1.7**). During the drought, plants produced far fewer seeds, and the finches soon depleted the stock of small, soft, easily processed seeds, leaving only large, hard seeds that were difficult to process (**Figure 1.8**). The bands on the birds' legs enabled the Grants to track the fate of individual birds during the drought, and the regular measurements that they had made of the birds allowed them to compare the traits of birds that survived the drought with the traits of those that perished. The Grants also kept detailed records of the environmental conditions, which allowed them to determine how the drought affected the birds' habitat. It was this vast body of data that enabled the Grants to document the action of natural selection among the finches of Daphne Major.

FIGURE 1.6

The medium ground finch, *Geospiza fortis*, uses its beak to crack open seeds.

(a)

(b)

FIGURE 1.7

Daphne Major (a) after a year of good rains, and (b) after a year of very little rain.

FIGURE 1.8

During the two-year drought, the size and hardness of seeds available on Daphne Major increased because birds consumed all of the desirable small, soft seeds, leaving mainly larger and harder seeds. Each point on this plot represents an index of seed size and hardness at a given time.

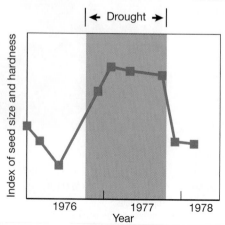

The Grants' data show how the processes identified in Darwin's postulates lead to adaptation.

The events on Daphne Major embodied all three of Darwin's postulates. First, the supply of food on the island was not sufficient to feed the entire population, and many finches did not survive the drought. From the beginning of the drought in 1976 until the rains came nearly two years later, the population of medium ground finches on Daphne Major declined from 1,200 birds to only 180.

Second, beak depth (the top-to-bottom dimension of the beak) varied among the birds on the island, and this variation affected the birds' survival. Before the drought began, the Grants and their colleagues had observed that birds with deeper beaks were able to process large, hard seeds more easily than birds with shallower beaks. Deep-beaked birds usually concentrated on large seeds, whereas shallow-beaked birds normally focused their efforts on small seeds. The open bars in the histogram in **Figure 1.9a** show what the distribution of beak sizes in the population was like before the drought. The height of each open bar represents the number of birds with beaks in a given range of depths—for example, 8.8 to 9.0 mm, or 9.0 to 9.2 mm. During the drought, the relative abundance of small seeds decreased, forcing shallow-beaked birds to shift to larger and harder seeds. Shallow-beaked birds were then at a distinct disadvantage because it was harder for them to crack the seeds. The distribution of individuals within the population changed during the drought because finches with deeper beaks were more likely to survive than were finches with shallow beaks (**Figure 1.9b**). The shaded portion of the histogram in Figure 1.9a shows what the distribution of beak depths would have been like among the survivors. Because many birds died, there were fewer remaining in each category. However, mortality was not random. The proportion of shallow-beaked birds that died greatly exceeded the proportion of deep-beaked birds that died. As a result, the shaded portion of the histogram shows a shift to the right, which means that the average beak depth in the population increased. Thus, the average beak depth among the survivors of the drought was greater than the average beak depth in the same population before the drought.

Third, parents and offspring had similar beak depths. The Grants discovered this by capturing and banding nestlings and recording the identity of the nestlings' parents. When the nestlings became adults, the Grants recaptured and measured them. The Grants found that, on average, parents with deep beaks produced offspring with deep beaks (**Figure 1.10**). Because parents were drawn from the pool of individuals that survived the drought, their beaks were, on average, deeper than those of the original residents of the island, and because offspring resemble their parents, the average beak depth of the survivors' offspring was greater than the average beak depth before the drought.

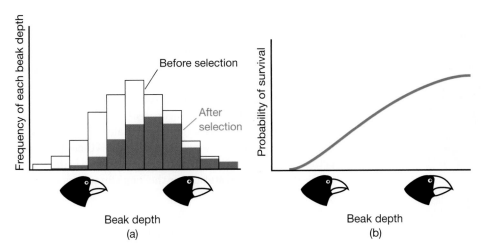

Beak depth
(a)

Beak depth
(b)

FIGURE 1.9

How directional selection increased mean beak depth among medium ground finches on Daphne Major. (a) The heights of the bars represent the numbers of birds whose beak depths fall within each of the intervals plotted on the *x* axis, with beak depth increasing to the right. The open bars show the distribution of beak depths before the drought began. The shaded bars show the distribution of beak depths after a year of drought. Notice that the number of birds in each category has decreased. Because birds with deep beaks were less likely to die than birds with shallow beaks, the peak of the distribution shifted to the right, indicating that the mean beak depth had increased. (b) The probability of survival for birds of different beak depths is plotted. Birds with shallow beaks are less likely to survive than are birds with deep beaks.

This means that, through natural selection, the average **morphology** (an organism's size, shape, and composition) of the bird population changed so that birds became better adapted to their environment. This process, operating over approximately two years, led to a 4% increase in the mean beak depth in this population (**Figure 1.11**).

Selection preserves the status quo when the most common type is the best adapted.

So far, we have seen how natural selection led to adaptation as the population of finches on Daphne Major evolved in response to changes in their environment. Will this process continue forever? If it did, eventually all the finches would have deep enough beaks to efficiently process the largest seeds available. However, large beaks have disadvantages as well as benefits. The Grants showed, for instance, that birds with large beaks are less likely to survive the juvenile period than are birds with small beaks, probably because large-beaked birds require more food (**Figure 1.12**). Evolutionary theory predicts that, over time, selection will increase the average beak depth in the population until the costs of larger-than-average beak size exceed the benefits. At this point, finches with the average beak size in the population will be the most likely to survive and reproduce, and finches with deeper or shallower beaks than the new average will be at a disadvantage. When this is true, beak size does not change, and we say that an **equilibrium** exists in the population in regard to beak size. The process that produces this equilibrium state is called **stabilizing selection**. Notice that even though the average characteristics of the beak in the population will not change in this situation, selection is still going on. Selection is required to change a population, and selection is also required to keep a population the same.

FIGURE 1.10

Parents with deeper-than-average beaks tend to have offspring with deeper-than-average beaks. Each point represents one offspring. Offspring beak depth is plotted on the vertical axis (deeper beaks farther up the axis), and the average of the two parents' beak depths is plotted on the horizontal axis (deeper beaks farther to the right).

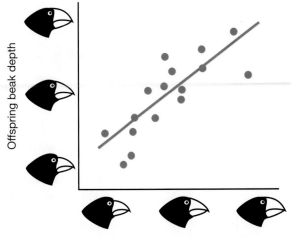

Average parental beak depth

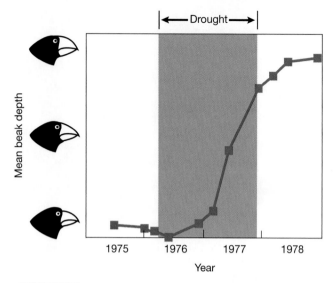

It might seem that beak depth would also remain unchanged if this trait had no effect on survival (or put another way, if there were no selection favoring one type of beak over another). Then all types of birds would be equally likely to survive from one generation to the next, and beak depth would remain constant. This logic would be valid if selection were the only process affecting beak size. However, real populations are also affected by other processes that cause **traits**, or **characters**, to change in unpredictable ways. We will discuss these processes further in Chapter 3. The point to remember here is that populations do not remain static over the long run unless selection is operating.

Evolution need not always lead to change in the same direction.

Natural selection has no foresight; it simply causes organisms to change so that they are better adapted to their current environment. Often environments fluctuate over time, and when they do, selection may track these fluctuations. We see this kind of pattern in the finches of the Galápagos Islands over the last 25 years. During this time there have been dry periods (1976–1978), but there have also been wet periods (1983–1985), when small, soft, easily processed seeds were exceedingly abundant. During wet years, selection favors smaller beaks, reversing the changes in beak size and shape wrought by natural selection during the drought years. As **Figure 1.13** shows, beak size has wobbled up and down during the Grants' long study of the medium ground finch on Daphne Major.

Species are populations of varied individuals that may or may not change through time.

As the Grants' work on Daphne Major makes clear, a species is not a fixed type or entity. Species change in their general characteristics from generation to generation according to the postulates Darwin described. Before Darwin, however, people thought

FIGURE 1.11

The average beak depth in the population of medium ground finches on Daphne Major increased during the drought of 1976–1977. Each point plots an index of average beak depth of the population in a particular year. Deeper beaks are plotted higher on the y axis.

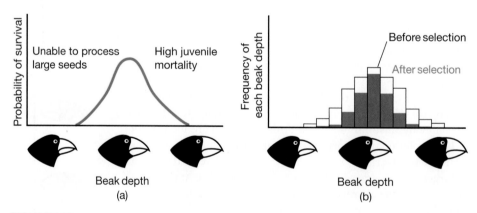

FIGURE 1.12

When birds with the most common beak depth are most likely to survive and reproduce, natural selection keeps the mean beak depth constant. (a) Birds with deep or shallow beaks are less likely to survive than are birds with average beaks. Birds with shallow beaks cannot process large, hard seeds, and birds with deep beaks are less likely to survive to adulthood. (b) The open bars represent the distribution of beak depths before selection, and the shaded bars represent the distribution after selection. As in Figure 1.9, notice that there are fewer birds in the population after selection. Because birds with average beaks are most likely to survive, however, the peak of the distribution of beak depths does not shift and mean beak depth remains unchanged.

of species as unchanging categories, much the same way that we think of geometrical figures: A finch could no more change its properties than a triangle could. If a triangle acquired another side, it would not be a modified triangle, but rather a rectangle. In much the same way, to biologists before Darwin, a changed finch was not a finch at all. Ernst Mayr, a distinguished evolutionary biologist, called this pre-Darwinian view of immutable species "essentialism." According to Darwin's theory, a **species** is a dynamic *population* of individuals. The characteristics of a particular species will be static, or unchanged, over a long time only if the most common type of individual is consistently favored by stabilizing selection. Both **stasis** (staying the same) and change result from natural selection, and both require explanation in terms of natural selection. Stasis is not the natural state of species.

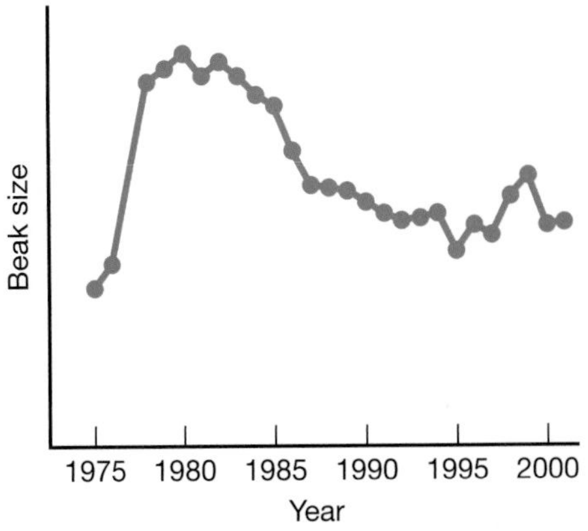

Individual Selection

Adaptation results from the competition among individuals, not between entire populations or species.

Selection produces adaptations that benefit *individuals*. Such adaptation may or may not benefit the population or species. In the case of simple morphological characters such as beak depth, selection probably does allow the population of finches to compete more effectively with other populations of seed predators. However, this need not be the case. Selection often leads to changes in behavior or morphology that increase the reproductive success of individuals but decrease the average reproductive success of the group, population, and species.

The fact that almost all organisms produce many more offspring than are necessary to maintain the species provides an example of the conflict between individual and group interests. Suppose that a female monkey, on average, produces 10 offspring during her lifetime (**Figure 1.14**). In a stable population, only two of these offspring will survive and reproduce on average. From the point of view of the species, the other eight

FIGURE 1.13

An index of mean beak size on Daphne Major for 1975–2001.

FIGURE 1.14

A female blue monkey holds her infant.

are a waste of resources. They compete with other members of their species for food, water, and sleeping sites. The demands of a growing population can lead to serious overexploitation of the environment, and the species as a whole might be more likely to survive if all females produced fewer offspring. This does not happen, however, because natural selection among individuals favors females who produce many offspring.

To see why selection on individuals will lead to this result, let's consider a simple hypothetical case. Suppose the females of a particular species of monkey are maximizing individual reproductive success when they produce 10 offspring. Females that produce more than or less than 10 offspring will tend to leave fewer descendants in the next generation. Further suppose that the likelihood of the species becoming extinct would be lowest if females produced only two offspring apiece. Now suppose that there are two kinds of females. Most of the population is composed of low-fecundity females that produce just two offspring each, but a few high-fecundity females produce 10 offspring each. (**Fecundity** is the term demographers use for the ability to produce offspring.) High-fecundity females have high-fecundity daughters, and low-fecundity females have low-fecundity daughters. The proportion of high-fecundity females will increase in the next generation because such females produce more offspring than do low-fecundity females. Over time, the proportion of high-fecundity females in the population will increase rapidly. As fecundity increases, the population will grow rapidly and may deplete available resources. The depletion of resources, in turn, will increase the chance that the species becomes extinct. However, this fact is irrelevant to the evolution of fecundity before the extinction because natural selection results from competition among individuals, not competition among species.

The idea that natural selection operates at the level of the individual is a key element in understanding adaptation. In discussing the evolution of social behavior in Chapter 7, we will encounter several additional examples of situations in which selection increases individual success but decreases the competitive ability of the population.

The Evolution of Complex Adaptations

The example of the evolution of beak depth in the medium ground finch illustrates how natural selection can cause adaptive change to occur rapidly in a population. Deeper beaks enabled the birds to survive better, and deeper beaks soon came to predominate in the population. Beak depth is a fairly simple character, lacking the intricate complexity of an eye. As we will see, however, the accumulation of small variations by natural selection can also give rise to complex adaptations.

Why Small Variations Are Important

There are two categories of variation: continuous and discontinuous.

It was known in Darwin's day that most variation is continuous. An example of **continuous variation** is the distribution of heights in people. Humans grade smoothly from one extreme to the other (short to tall), with all the intermediate types (in this case, heights) represented. However, Darwin's contemporaries also knew about **discontinuous variation**, in which several distinct types exist with no intermediates. In humans, height is also subject to discontinuous variation. For example, a genetic condition called achondroplasia causes affected individuals to be much shorter than other people, have proportionately shorter arms and legs, and bear a variety of other distinctive features (Peter Dinklage, who plays Tyrion Lannister in *Game of Thrones*, has this condition). Discontinuous variants are usually quite rare in nature. Nonetheless, many of Darwin's contemporaries who were convinced of the reality of evolution believed that new species arise as discontinuous variants.

Discontinuous variation is not important for the evolution of complex adaptations because complex adaptations are extremely unlikely to arise in a single jump.

Unlike most of his contemporaries, Darwin thought that discontinuous variation did not play an important role in evolution. A hypothetical example, described by the Oxford University biologist Richard Dawkins in his book *The Blind Watchmaker*, illustrates Darwin's reasoning. Dawkins recalls an old story in which an imaginary collection of monkeys sits at typewriters happily typing away. Lacking the ability to read or write, the monkeys strike keys at random. Given enough time, the story goes, the monkeys will reproduce all the great works of Shakespeare. But Dawkins points out that this is not likely to happen in the lifetime of the universe, let alone the lifetime of one of the monkey typists. To illustrate why it would take so long, Dawkins presents these illiterate monkeys with a much simpler problem: reproducing a single line from *Hamlet*, "Methinks it is like a weasel" (III.ii). To make the problem even simpler for the monkeys, Dawkins ignores the difference between uppercase and lowercase letters and omits all punctuation except spaces. There are 28 characters (including spaces) in the phrase. Because there are 26 characters in the alphabet and Dawkins is keeping track of spaces, each time a monkey types a character, there is only a 1-in-27 chance that it will type the right character. There is also only a 1-in-27 chance that the second character will be correct. Again, there is a 1-in-27 chance that the third character will be right, and so on, up to the twenty-eighth character. Thus the chance that a monkey will type the correct sequence at random is 1/27 multiplied by itself 28 times, or

$$\underbrace{\frac{1}{27} \times \frac{1}{27} \times \frac{1}{27} \times \cdots \times \frac{1}{27}}_{28 \text{ times}} \approx 10^{-40}$$

This is a *very* small number. To get a feeling for how small a chance there is of the monkeys typing the sentence correctly, suppose a very fast computer could generate 100 billion (10^{11}) characters per second and run for the lifetime of Earth—about 4 billion years, or 10^{17} seconds. Even at that pace and given that much time, the chance of the computer randomly typing the line "Methinks it is like a weasel" even once during the whole of Earth's history would be about 1 in 1 trillion! Typing the whole play is obviously astronomically less likely, and although *Hamlet* is a very complicated thing, it is much less complicated than a human eye. There's no chance that a structure like the human eye would arise by chance in a single trial. If it did, it would be, as the astrophysicist Sir Frederick Hoyle is reported to have said, like a hurricane blowing through a junkyard and chancing to assemble a Boeing 747.

Complex adaptations can arise through the accumulation of small random variations by natural selection.

Darwin argued that continuous variation is essential for the evolution of complex adaptations. Once again, Richard Dawkins provides an example that makes Darwin's reasoning clear. Again imagine a room full of monkeys and typewriters, but now the rules of the game are different. The monkeys type the first 28 characters at random, and then during the next round they attempt to copy the same initial string of letters and spaces. Most of the sentences are just copies of the previous string, but because monkeys sometimes make mistakes, some strings have small variations, usually in only a single letter. During each trial, the monkey trainer selects the string that most resembles Shakespeare's phrase "Methinks it is like a weasel" as the string to be copied by all the monkeys in the next trial. This process is repeated until the monkeys come up with the correct string. Calculating the exact number of trials required to generate the correct sequence of characters is quite difficult, but it is easy to simulate the process on a computer. Here's what happened when Dawkins performed the simulation. The initial random string was

```
WDLMNLT DTJBKWIRZREZLMQCO P
```

After one trial Dawkins got

```
WDLMNLT DTJBSWIRZREZLMQCO P
```

After 10 trials:

```
MDLDMNLS ITJISWHRZREZ MECS P
```

After 20 trials:

```
MELDINLS IT ISWPRKE Z WECSEL
```

After 30 trials:

```
METHINGS IT ISWLIKE B WECSEL
```

After 40 trials:

```
METHINKS IT IS LIKE I WEASEL
```

The exact phrase was reached after 43 trials. Dawkins reports that it took his 1985-vintage Macintosh only 11 seconds to complete this task.

Selection can give rise to great complexity starting with small random variations because it is a *cumulative* process. As the typing monkeys show us, it is spectacularly unlikely that a single random combination of keystrokes will produce the correct sentence. However, there is a much greater chance that some of the many *small* random changes will be advantageous. The combination of reproduction and selection allows the typing monkeys to accumulate these small changes until the desired sentence is reached.

Why Intermediate Steps Are Favored by Selection

The evolution of complex adaptations requires all of the intermediate steps to be favored by selection.

There is a potent objection to the example of the typing monkeys. Natural selection, acting over time, can lead to complex adaptations, but it can do so only if each small change along the way is itself adaptive. Although it is easy to assume that this is true in a hypothetical example of character strings, many people have argued that it is unlikely for every one of the changes necessary to assemble a complex organ such as the eye to be adaptive. An eye is useful, it is claimed, only after all parts of the complexity have been assembled; until then, it is worse than no eye at all. After all, what good is 5% of an eye?

Darwin's answer, based on the many adaptations for seeing or sensing light that exist in the natural world, was that 5% of an eye *is* often better than no eye at all. It is quite possible to imagine that a very large number of small changes—each favored by selection—led cumulatively to the wonderful complexity of the eye. Living mollusks, which display a broad range of light-sensitive organs, provide examples of many of the likely stages in this process:

1. Many invertebrates have a simple light-sensitive spot. Photoreceptors of this kind have evolved many times from ordinary epidermal (surface) cells—usually cells with microscopic hairlike projections (cilia) whose biochemical

machinery is light sensitive. Those individuals whose cells are more sensitive to light are favored when information about changes in light intensity is useful. For example, a drop in light intensity may often indicate that a predator is in the vicinity.

2. The second step is for the light-sensitive spot to form a depression (**Figure 1.15a**). When the cells form a depression, the light does not hit all of the cells at the same time, which provides information about the direction from which the light is coming. The surface of organisms is variable, and those individuals whose photoreceptors are in depressions will be favored by selection in environments in which such information is useful. For example, mobile organisms may need better information about what is happening in front of them than do immobile ones.

3. Through a series of small steps, the depression could deepen (**Figure 1.15b**), and each step could be favored by selection because better directional information would be available with the deepening depression.

4. If the depression got deep enough (**Figure 1.15c**), it could form images on the light-sensitive tissue, much the way pinhole cameras form images on photographic film. In settings in which detailed images are useful, selection could then favor the elaboration of the neural machinery necessary to interpret the image.

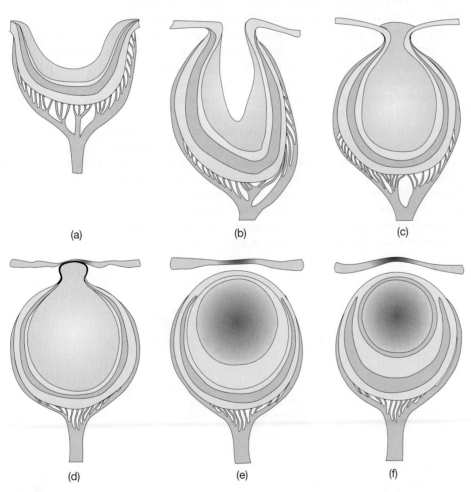

(a)   (b)   (c)

(d)   (e)   (f)

FIGURE 1.15

Living gastropod mollusks illustrate all of the intermediate steps between a simple eye cup and a camera-type eye. (a) The eye pit of a limpet, *Patella* sp.; (b) the eye cup of Beyrich's slit shell, *Pleurotomaria beyrichii*; (c) the pinhole eye of a California abalone, *Haliotis* sp.; (d) the closed eye of a turban shell, *Turbo creniferus*; (e) the lens eye of the spiny dye-murex, *Murex brandaris*; (f) the lens eye of the Atlantic dog whelk, *Nucella lapillus*. (Lens is shaded in e and f.)

5. The next step is the formation of a transparent cover (**Figure 1.15d**). This change might be favored because it protects the interior of the eye from parasites and mechanical damage.

6. A lens could evolve through gradual modification of either the transparent cover or the internal structures within the eye (**Figure 1.15e** and **f**).

Notice that evolution produces adaptations like a tinkerer, not an engineer. New organisms are created by small modifications of existing organisms, not by starting with a clean slate. Clearly many beneficial adaptations will not arise because they are blocked at some step along the way when a particular variation is not favored by selection. Darwin's theory explains how complex adaptations can arise through natural processes, but it does not predict that every possible adaptation, or even most, will occur. This is not the best of all possible worlds; it is just one of many possible worlds.

Sometimes distantly related species have independently evolved the same complex adaptation, absent in their common ancestor, suggesting that the evolution of complex adaptations by natural selection is not a matter of mere chance.

The fact that natural selection constructs complex adaptations like a tinkerer might lead you to think that the assembly of complex adaptations is a chancy business. If even a single step were not favored by selection, the adaptation could not arise. Such reasoning suggests that complex adaptations are mere coincidence. Although chance does play a very important role in evolution, the power of cumulative natural selection should not be underestimated. The best evidence that selection is a powerful process for generating complex adaptations comes from a phenomenon called **convergence**, the evolution of similar adaptations in unrelated groups of animals.

The similarity between the marsupial faunas of Australia and South America and the placental faunas of the rest of the world provides a good example of convergence. In most of the world, the mammalian fauna is dominated by **placental mammals**, which nourish their young in the uterus during long pregnancies. Both Australia and South America, however, became separated from an ancestral supercontinent, known as Pangaea, long before placental mammals evolved. In Australia and South America, **marsupials** (nonplacental mammals, like kangaroos, that rear their young in external pouches) came to dominate the mammalian fauna, filling all available mammalian niches. Some

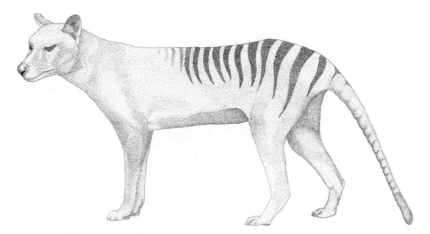

FIGURE 1.16

The marsupial wolf that lived in Tasmania until early in the twentieth century (drawn from a photograph of one of the last living animals). Similarities with placental wolves of North America and Eurasia illustrate the power of natural selection to create complex adaptations. Their last common ancestor was probably a small insectivorous shrewlike creature.

CHAPTER 1: Adaptation by Natural Selection

(a)

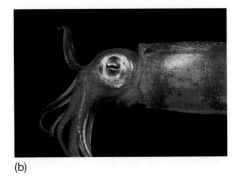
(b)

FIGURE 1.17

Complex eyes with lenses have evolved independently in several kinds of aquatic animals, including the (a) moon wrasse and (b) squid.

of these marsupial mammals were quite similar to the placental mammals on the other continents. For example, there was a marsupial wolf in Australia that looked very much like placental wolves of Eurasia, even sharing subtle features of their feet and teeth (**Figure 1.16**). These marsupial wolves became extinct in the 1930s. Similarly, in South America a marsupial saber-toothed cat independently evolved many of the same adaptations as the placental saber-toothed cat that stalked North America 10,000 years ago. These similarities are more impressive when you consider that the last common ancestor of marsupial and placental mammals was a small, nocturnal insectivorous creature, something like a shrew, that lived about 120 million years ago (Ma). Thus selection transformed a shrew step by small step, each step favored by selection, into a saber-toothed cat—and it did it twice. This cannot be coincidence.

The evolution of eyes provides another good example of convergence. Remember that the spherical gradient lens is a good lens design for aquatic organisms because it has good light-gathering ability and provides a sharp image over the full 180° visual field. Complex eyes with lenses have evolved independently eight times in distantly related aquatic organisms: once in fish, once in cephalopod mollusks such as squid, several times among gastropod mollusks such as the Atlantic dog whelk, once in annelid worms, and once in crustaceans (**Figure 1.17**). These are very diverse creatures whose last common ancestor was a simple creature that did not have a complex eye. Nonetheless, in every case they have evolved very similar spherical gradient lenses. Moreover, no other lens design is found in aquatic animals. Despite the seeming chanciness of assembling complex adaptations, natural selection has achieved the same design in every case.

Rates of Evolutionary Change

Natural selection can cause evolutionary change that is much more rapid than we commonly observe in the fossil record.

In Darwin's day, the idea that natural selection could change a primate into a human, much less that it might do so in just a few million years, was unthinkable. Even though people are generally more accepting of evolution today, many still think of evolution by natural selection as a glacially slow process that requires many millions of years to accomplish noticeable change. Such people often doubt that there has been enough time for selection to accomplish the evolutionary changes observed in the fossil record. And yet, as we will see in later chapters, most scientists now believe that humans evolved from an apelike creature in only 5 million to 10 million years. In fact, some of the rates of selective change observed in contemporary populations are far faster than necessary for such a transition. The puzzle is not whether there has been enough time for natural selection to produce the adaptations that we observe. The real puzzle is why the change observed in the fossil record was so slow.

The Grants' observation of the evolution of beak morphology in Darwin's finches provides one example of rapid evolutionary change. The medium ground finch of Daphne

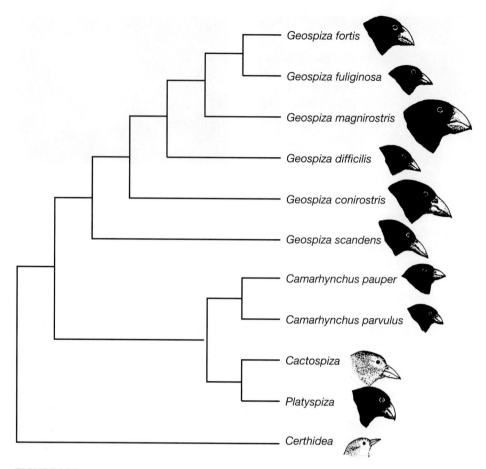

FIGURE 1.18

We can trace the relationship among various species of Darwin's finches by analyzing their protein polymorphisms. Species that are closely linked in the phylogenetic tree are more similar to one another genetically than to other species because they share a more recent common ancestor. The tree does not include 3 of the 14 species of Darwin's finches.

FIGURE 1.19

The large ground finch (*Geospiza magnirostris*) has a beak that is nearly 20% deeper than the beak of its close relative, the medium ground finch (*Geospiza fortis*). At the rate of evolution observed during the drought of 1976–1977, Peter Grant calculated that selection could transform the medium ground finch into the large ground finch in less than 46 years.

Major is one of 14 species of finches that live in the Galápagos. Evidence suggests that all 14 are descended from a single South American species that migrated to the newly emerged islands about half a million years ago (**Figure 1.18**). This doesn't seem like a very long time. Is it possible that natural selection created 14 species in only half a million years?

To start to answer the question, let's calculate how long it would take for the medium ground finch (*Geospiza fortis*) to come to resemble its closest relative, the large ground finch (*Geospiza magnirostris*), in beak size and weight (**Figure 1.19**). The large ground finch is 75% heavier than the medium ground finch, and its beak is about 20% deeper. Remember that beak size increased about 4% in two years during the 1977 drought. The Grants' data indicate that body size also increased by a similar amount. At this rate, Peter Grant calculated that it would take between 30 and 46 years for selection to increase the beak size and body weight of the medium ground finch to match those of the large ground finch. But these changes occurred in response to an extraordinary environmental crisis. The data suggest that selection doesn't generally push consistently in just one direction. Instead, in the Galápagos, evolutionary change seems to go in fits and starts, moving traits one way and then another. So let's suppose that a net change in beak size like the one that occurred during 1977 occurs only once every century. Then it would take about 2,000 years to transform the medium ground finch into the large ground finch—still a very rapid process.

CHAPTER 1: Adaptation by Natural Selection

Similar rates of evolutionary change are observed elsewhere when species invade new habitats. For example, about 100,000 years ago a population of elk (called "red deer" in Great Britain) colonized the island of Jersey, off the French coast, and then became isolated, presumably by rising sea levels. By the time the island was reconnected with the mainland approximately 6,000 years later, the red deer had shrunk to the size of a large dog. University of Michigan paleontologist Philip Gingerich compiled data on the rate of evolutionary change in 104 cases in which species invaded new habitats. These rates ranged from a low of zero (that is, no change) to a high of 22% per year, with an average of 0.1% per year.

The changes the Grants observed in the medium ground finch are relatively simple: The birds and their beaks just got bigger. More complex changes usually take longer to evolve, but several kinds of evidence suggest that selection can produce big changes in remarkably short periods.

One line of evidence comes from artificial selection. Humans have performed selection on domesticated plants and animals for thousands of years, and while for most of this period this selection was not deliberate (that is, not influenced by active human intervention), more recent deliberate selection by humans has led to rapid rates of evolution in certain species. There are many familiar examples. All domesticated dogs, for instance, are believed to be descendants of wolves. Scientists are not sure when dogs were domesticated, but 15,000 years ago is a good guess, which means that over a few thousand generations, selection changed wolves into Pekingese, beagles, greyhounds, and Saint Bernards. In reality, though, most of these breeds were created fairly recently as the products of directed breeding. Darwin's favorite example of artificial selection was the domestication of pigeons. In the nineteenth century, pigeon breeding was a popular hobby, especially among working people who competed to produce showy birds (**Figure 1.20**). Pigeon fanciers created a menagerie of wildly different forms, all

(a)

(b)

(c)

(d)

FIGURE 1.20

In Darwin's day, pigeon fanciers created many new breeds of pigeons, including (a) pouters, (b) fantails, and (c) carriers, all from (d) the common rock pigeon.

FIGURE 1.21

Fish in the genus *Poeciliopsis* include small minnows such as *Poeciliopsis occidentalis,* shown here.

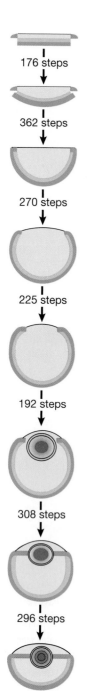

176 steps

362 steps

270 steps

225 steps

192 steps

308 steps

296 steps

descended from the rather plain-looking rock pigeon. Darwin pointed out that these breeds were often so different that biologists would surely have classified them as members of different species if they had been discovered in nature. Yet they had been produced by artificial selection within a few hundred years.

Rapid evolution of a complex feature has also been documented in a recent study of a group of very closely related species of fish from the genus *Poeciliopsis* (**Figure 1.21**). These small minnows can be found in tropical lowland streams, high-altitude lakes, and desert springs and streams in Mexico and Central America. All the species in this genus bear live young, but the sequence of events between fertilization, the initial union of the egg and sperm cells, and birth varies. In most species, females endow the eggs with nutrients before fertilization. As the young develop, they consume this endowment. In a few species, however, females continue to provide nutrients to their unborn offspring throughout development by using tissues that are analogous to mammalian placentas. When these offspring are born, they can be more than 100 times the mass of the egg at fertilization. Biologist David Reznick of the University of California, Riverside, and his colleagues have shown that these placental tissues evolved independently in three groups of species within the genus *Poeciliopsis*. Genetic data indicate that one of these species groups diverged from ancestors lacking placental tissue only 0.75 Ma, and the other two diverged less than 2.4 Ma. These time estimates actually represent the time since these species shared a common ancestor, and they set an upper bound on the amount of time required for the placenta to evolve. The generation time for these fish ranges from six months to a year, so this complex adaptation evolved in fewer than a million generations.

A third line of evidence comes from theoretical studies of the evolution of complex characters. Dan-Eric Nilsson and Susanne Pelger of Lund University in Sweden have built a mathematical model of the evolution of the eye in an aquatic organism. They start with a population of organisms, each with a simple eyespot, a flat patch of light-sensitive tissue sandwiched between a transparent protective layer and a layer of dark pigment. They then consider how every possible small (1%) deformation of the shape of the eyespot affects the resolving power of the eye. They determine which 1% change has the greatest positive effect on the eye's resolving power and then repeat the process again and again, deforming the new structure by 1% in every possible way at each step. The results are shown in **Figure 1.22**. After 538 changes of 1% each, a simple concave eye cup evolves; after 1,033 changes of 1%, crude pinhole eyes emerge; after 1,225 changes of 1%, an eye with an elliptical lens is created; and after 1,829 steps, the process finally comes to a halt because no small changes increase resolving power. The result is an eye with a spherical gradient lens just like those in fish and other aquatic organisms. As Nilsson and Pelger point out, 1,829 changes of 1% add up to a substantial amount of change. For instance, 1,829 changes of 1% would lengthen a 10-cm (4-in.) human finger to 8,000 km (5,500 miles)—about the distance from Los Angeles to New York and back. Nonetheless, making very conservative assumptions about the strength of selection, Nilsson and Pelger calculate that this would take only about 364,000 generations. For organisms with short generations, the complete structure of the eye can evolve from a simple eyespot in less than a million years, a brief moment in evolutionary time.

By comparison, most changes observed in the fossil record are much slower. Human brain size has roughly doubled in the last 2 million years—a rate of change of 0.00005% per year. This is 10,000 times slower than the rate of change that the Grants observed

FIGURE 1.22

A computer simulation of the evolution of the eye generates this sequence of forms. Between each pair of forms is the number of 1% changes (steps) necessary to transform the upper form into the lower one. The eye begins as a flat patch of light-sensitive tissue (*red*) that lies between a transparent layer (*light blue*) and a layer of dark pigmented tissue (*black*). After 176 steps, each of which increases resolving power, a shallow eye cup is formed. After 362 additional steps, the eye cup deepens. Eventually, a spherical gradient lens evolves, leading to a camera-type eye. The entire process involves about 1,800 changes of 1%.

CHAPTER 1: Adaptation by Natural Selection

in the Galápagos. Moreover, such slow rates of change typify what can be observed from the fossil record. As we will see, however, the fossil record is incomplete. It is quite likely that some evolutionary changes in the past were rapid, but the sparseness of the fossil record prevents us from detecting them.

Darwin's Difficulties Explaining Variation

Darwin's *On the Origin of Species*, published in 1859, was a best seller during his day, but his proposal that new species and other major evolutionary changes arise by the accumulation of small variations through natural selection was not widely embraced. Most educated people accepted the idea that new species arise through the transformation of existing species, and many scientists accepted the idea that natural selection is the most important cause of organic change (although by the turn of the twentieth century even this consensus had broken down, particularly in the United States). But only a minority endorsed Darwin's view that major changes occur through the accumulation of small variations.

Darwin couldn't convince his contemporaries that evolution occurred through the accumulation of small variations because he couldn't explain how variation is maintained.

Darwin's critics raised a telling objection to his theory: The actions of blending inheritance (described in the next paragraph) and selection would both inevitably deplete variation in populations and make it impossible for natural selection to continue. These were potent objections that Darwin was unable to resolve in his lifetime because he and his contemporaries did not yet understand the mechanics of inheritance.

Everyone could readily observe that many of the characteristics of offspring are an average of the characteristics of their parents. Most people, including Darwin, believed this phenomenon to be caused by the action of **blending inheritance**, a model of inheritance that assumes the mother and father each contribute a hereditary substance that mixes, or "blends," to determine the characteristics of the offspring. Shortly after publication of *On the Origin of Species*, a Scottish engineer named Fleeming Jenkin published a paper in which he clearly showed that, with blending inheritance, there could be little or no variation available for selection to act on. The following example shows why Jenkin's argument was so compelling. Suppose a population of one species of Darwin's finches displays two forms: tall and short. Further suppose that a biologist controls mating so that every mating is between a tall individual and a short individual. Then, with blending inheritance, all of the offspring will be the same intermediate height, and their offspring will be the same height as they are. All of the variation for height in the population will disappear in a single generation. With random mating, the same result will occur, though it will take longer. If inheritance were purely a matter of blending parental traits, then Jenkin would have been right about its effect on variation. However, as we will see in Chapter 3, genetics can account for the fact that offspring are intermediate between their parents without assuming any kind of blending.

Another problem arose because selection works by removing variants from populations. For example, if finches with small beaks are more likely to die than finches with large beaks, over many generations only birds with large beaks will be left. There will be no variation for beak size, and Darwin's second postulate holds that without variation there can be no evolution by natural selection. For example, suppose the environment changes so that individuals with small beaks are less likely to die than those with large beaks. The average beak size in the population will not decrease because there are no small-beaked individuals. Natural selection destroys the variation required to create adaptations.

(a)

(b)

(c)

FIGURE 1.23

(a) The wolf is the ancestor of all domestic dogs, including (b) the poodle and (c) the Saint Bernard. These transformations were accomplished in several thousand generations of artificial selection.

Even worse, as Jenkin also pointed out, there was no explanation of how a population might evolve beyond its original range of variation. The cumulative evolution of complex adaptations requires populations to move far outside their original range of variation. Selection can cull away some traits from a population, but how can it lead to new types not present in the original population? This apparent contradiction was a serious impediment to explaining the logic of evolution. How could elephants, moles, bats, and whales all descend from an ancient shrewlike insectivore unless there were a mechanism for creating new variants not present at the beginning? For that matter, how could all the different breeds of dogs have descended from their one common ancestor, the wolf (**Figure 1.23**)?

Remember that Darwin and his contemporaries knew there were two kinds of variation: continuous and discontinuous. Because Darwin believed that complex adaptations could arise only through the accumulation of small variations, he thought discontinuous variants were unimportant. However, many biologists thought that the discontinuous variants, called "sports" by nineteenth-century animal breeders, were the key to evolution because they solved the problem of the blending effect. For example, suppose that a population of green birds has entered a new environment in which red birds are better adapted. How can evolution shift the population from green to red? Some of Darwin's critics believed that any new variant that emerged in the population of green birds that was only slightly red would have only a small advantage and the color change would be rapidly swamped by blending. In contrast, an all-red bird would have a large enough selective advantage to overcome the effects of blending and could increase its frequency in the population.

Darwin's letters show that these criticisms worried him greatly. Although he tried a variety of counterarguments, he never found one that was satisfactory. The solution to these problems required an understanding of genetics, which was not available for another half century. As we will see, it was not until well into the twentieth century that geneticists came to understand how variation is maintained and Darwin's theory of evolution became generally accepted.

Key Terms

adaptations (p. 3)
natural selection (p. 6)
morphology (p. 9)
equilibrium (p. 9)

stabilizing selection (p. 9)
traits (p. 10)
characters (p. 10)
species (p. 11)

stasis (p. 11)
fecundity (p. 12)
continuous variation (p. 12)
discontinuous variation (p. 12)

convergence (p. 16)
placental mammals (p. 16)
marsupials (p. 16)
blending inheritance (p. 21)

Study Questions

1. It is sometimes observed that offspring do not resemble their parents for a particular character, even though the character varies in the population. Suppose this were the case for beak depth in the medium ground finch.
   (a) What would the plot of offspring beak depth against parental beak depth look like?
   (b) Plot the mean depth in the population among (i) adults before a drought, (ii) the adults that survived a year of drought, and (iii) the offspring of the survivors.

2. Many species of animals engage in cannibalism. This practice certainly reduces the ability of the species to survive. Is it possible that cannibalism could arise by natural selection? If so, with what adaptive advantage?

3. Some insects mimic dung. Ever since Darwin, biologists have explained this behavior as a form of camouflage: Selection favors individuals who most resemble dung because they are less likely to be eaten. The late Harvard paleontologist Stephen Jay Gould objected to this explanation. He argued that although selection could perfect such mimicry once it evolved, it could not cause the resemblance to arise in the first place. "Can there be any edge," Gould asked, "to looking 5% like a turd?" (R. Dawkins, 1996, p. 81). Can you think of a reason why looking 5% like a turd would be better than not looking at all like a turd?

4. In the late 1800s an American biologist named Hermon Bumpus collected many sparrows that had been killed in a severe ice storm. He found that birds whose wings were about average in length were rare among the dead birds. What kind of selection is this? What effect would this episode of selection have on the mean wing length in the population?

5. Critics of Darwin's theory argued that it couldn't explain how variation is maintained in populations. Explain the basis for their criticism.

6. Some insect larvae look a bit like snakes, with symmetric spots that look something like eyes and a pointed end that looks something like a snake's head. The biologist who described these snakelike features hypothesized that they deter predation by birds, which are wary of attacks by snakes. But in order for this to work, birds must be fairly gullible. They must think that the larvae really are snakes, not larvae that are trying to look like snakes. Explain why natural selection might favor gullibility over skepticism in the larvae's predators.

7. Many people find it implausible that a complex organ such as the human eye can be the product of a random, undirected process such as evolution by natural selection. Explain how the metaphor Dawkins offers of the typing monkeys helps to explain how complexity can arise.

8. Explain how competition, variation, and inheritance are central to Darwin's theory of evolution by natural selection.

9. Most people think of evolution as a very slow process that requires millions of years to produce noticeable change. Explain why this view is not necessarily correct.

10. If you see no change in the mean value of a trait from one generation to another, is it reasonable to conclude that selection is not operating on that trait?

Further Reading

Browne, J. 1995. *Charles Darwin: A Biography*, vol. I: *Voyaging*. New York: Knopf.

Dawkins, R. 1996. *The Blind Watchmaker: Why the Evidence of Evolution Reveals a Universe without Design*. New York: Norton.

Dennett, D. C. 1995. *Darwin's Dangerous Idea: Evolution and the Meanings of Life*. New York: Simon & Schuster.

Ridley, M. 1996. *Evolution*. 2nd ed. Cambridge, Mass.: Blackwell Science.

Weiner, J. 1994. *The Beak of the Finch: A Story of Evolution in Our Time*. New York: Knopf.

Visit **DIGITAL.WWNORTON.COM/HOWHUMANS8** to
- **review this chapter with personalized, interactive questions via InQuizitive**
- **view videos and animations on this chapter's key topics**

2

PART TWO

PRIMATE ECOLOGY AND BEHAVIOR

5

PRIMATE DIVERSITY AND ECOLOGY

- **Two Reasons to Study Primates p. 109**
- **Features That Define the Primates p. 111**
- **Primate Biogeography p. 114**
- **A Taxonomy of Living Primates p. 115**
- **Primate Diversity p. 118**
- **Primate Ecology p. 125**
- **Primate Sociality p. 134**
- **Primate Conservation p. 135**

CHAPTER OBJECTIVES

By the end of this chapter you should be able to

A. Identify the complex of traits that defines the primate order.

B. Show where primates live in the world.

C. Describe the major characteristics that differentiate one kind of primate from another.

D. Describe how primates cope with primary ecological challenges: finding food and avoiding predation.

E. Identify what kinds of groups primates form.

F. Discuss major factors that threaten the status of wild primate populations.

Two Reasons to Study Primates

The chapters in Part Two focus on the behavior of living nonhuman primates. Studies of nonhuman primates help us understand human evolution for two complementary but distinct reasons. First, closely related species tend to be similar morphologically because, as we saw in Chapter 4, they share traits acquired through descent from a common ancestor. For example, **viviparity** (bearing live young) and lactation are traits that all placental and marsupial mammals share, and these traits distinguish mammals from other taxa, such as reptiles. The existence of such similarities means that studies of living primates often give us more insight into the behavior of our ancestors than do studies of other organisms. This approach is called "reasoning by homology." The second reason we study primates is based on the idea that natural selection favors similar adaptations in similar environments. By assessing the patterns of diversity in the behavior and morphology of organisms in relation to their environments, we can see how evolution shapes adaptation in response to different selective pressures. This approach is called "reasoning by analogy."

Primates Are Our Closest Relatives

Because humans and other primates share many characteristics, other primates provide valuable insights about early humans.

Humans are more closely related to nonhuman primates than to any other animal species. The anatomical similarities among monkeys, apes, and humans led the Swedish naturalist Carolus Linnaeus to place us in the order Primates in the first scientific taxonomy, *Systema Naturae*, published in 1735. Later, naturalists such as Georges Cuvier and Johann Blumenbach placed us in our own order because of our distinctive mental capacities and upright posture. In *The Descent of Man*, however, Charles Darwin firmly advocated reinstating humans in the order Primates; he cited the biologist Thomas Henry Huxley's essay listing the many anatomical similarities between us and apes, and he mused that "if man had not been his own classifier, he would never have thought of founding a separate order for his own reception." Modern systematics unambiguously confirms that humans are more closely related to other primates than to any other living creatures.

Because we are closely related to other primates, we share with them many aspects of morphology, physiology, and development. For example, like other primates, we have well-developed vision and grasping hands and feet. We share features of our life history with other primates as well, including an extended period of juvenile development and larger brains in relation to body size than the members of other taxonomic groups. Homologies between humans and other primates also extend to behavior because the physiological and cognitive structures that underlie human behavior are more similar to those of other primates than to members of other taxonomic groups. The existence of this extensive array of homologous traits, the product of the common evolutionary history of the primates, means that nonhuman primates provide useful models for understanding the evolutionary roots of human morphology and for unraveling the origins of human nature.

Primates Are a Diverse Order

Diversity within the primate order helps us understand how natural selection shapes behavior.

During the last 30 years, hundreds of researchers from a variety of academic disciplines have spent thousands of hours observing many species of nonhuman primates in the wild, in captive colonies, and in laboratories. All primate species have evolved adaptations that enable them to meet the basic challenges of life, such as finding food, avoiding predators, obtaining mates, rearing young, and coping with competitors. At the same time, there is great morphological, ecological, and behavioral diversity among species within the primate order. For example, primates range in size from the pygmy mouse lemur, which weighs about 30 g (about 1 oz.), to the male gorilla, which weighs about 260 times more—160 kg (350 lb.). Some species live in dense tropical forests; others are at home in open woodlands and savannas. Some subsist almost entirely on leaves; others rely on an omnivorous diet of fruits, leaves, flowers, seeds, gum, nectar, insects, and small animal prey. Some species are solitary, and others are highly gregarious.

Some are active at night (**nocturnal**); others are active during daylight hours (**diurnal**). One primate, the fat-tailed dwarf lemur, enters a torpid state and sleeps for six months each year. Some species actively defend territories from incursions by other members of their own species (**conspecifics**); others do not. In some species, only females provide care of their young; in others, males participate actively in this process.

This variety is inherently interesting. However, evidence of diversity among closely related organisms living under somewhat different ecological and social conditions also helps researchers understand how evolution shapes behavior. Animals that are closely related to one another phylogenetically tend to be very similar in morphology, physiology, life history, and behavior. Thus differences observed among closely related species are likely to represent adaptive responses to specific ecological conditions. At the same time, similarities among more distantly related creatures living under similar ecological conditions are likely to be the product of convergence.

This approach, sometimes called the "comparative method," has become an important form of analysis as researchers attempt to explain the patterns of variation in morphology and behavior observed in nature. The same principles have been borrowed to reconstruct the behavior of extinct hominins, early members of the human lineage. Because behavior leaves little trace in the fossil record, the comparative method provides one of our only objective means of testing hypotheses about the lives of our hominin ancestors. For example, the observation that substantial differences exist in male and female body size, a phenomenon called **sexual dimorphism**, in species in which males compete over access to females and form groups that contain one male and multiple females or multiple males and multiple females suggests that highly dimorphic hominins may have lived in similar groups. In Part Three, we will see how the data and theories about behavior produced by primatologists have played an important role in reshaping our ideas about human origins.

Features That Define the Primates

Members of the primate order are characterized by several shared, derived characters, but not all primates share all of these traits.

The animals pictured in **Figure 5.1** are all members of the primate order. These animals are similar in many ways: They are covered with a thick coat of hair, they have four limbs, and they have five fingers on each hand. They give birth to live young, and mothers suckle their offspring. However, they share these ancestral features with all mammals. Beyond these ancestral features, it is hard to see what the members of this group of animals have in common that makes them distinct from other mammals. What distinguishes a ring-tailed lemur from a mongoose or a raccoon? What features link the elegant leaf monkey and the bizarre aye-aye?

In fact, primates are a rather nondescript mammalian order that cannot be unambiguously characterized by a single derived feature shared by all members. In his extensive treatise on primate evolution, however, biologist Robert Martin of the Field Museum of Natural History in Chicago defines the primate order in terms of the derived features listed in **Table 5.1**.

The first three traits in Table 5.1 are related to the flexible movement of hands and feet. Primates can grasp with their hands and feet (**Figure 5.2a**), and most monkeys and apes can oppose their thumb and forefinger in a precision grip (**Figure 5.2b**). The flat nails, distinct from the claws of many animals, and the tactile pads on the tips of primate fingers and toes further enhance their dexterity (**Figure 5.2c**). These traits enable primates to use their hands and feet differently from the ways most other animals do. Primates can grasp fruit, squirming insects, and other small items in their hands and feet, and they can grip branches with their fingers and toes. During grooming sessions,

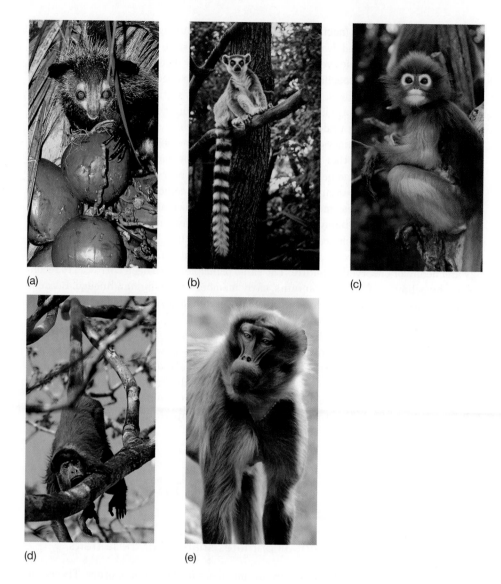

FIGURE 5.1

All of these animals are primates: (a) aye-aye, (b) ring-tailed lemur, (c) leaf monkey, (d) howler, (e) gelada monkey. Primates are a diverse order and do not possess a suite of traits that unambiguously distinguishes them from other animals.

(a) (b) (c)
(d) (e)

they delicately part their partner's hair and use their thumb and forefinger to remove small bits of debris from the skin.

Traits 4 and 5 in Table 5.1 are related to a shift in emphasis among the sense organs. Most primates are characterized by a greater reliance on visual stimuli and less reliance on olfactory stimuli than other mammals. Many primate species can perceive color, and their eyes are set forward in the head, providing them with binocular, stereoscopic vision (**Figure 5.3**). **Binocular vision** means that the fields of vision of the two eyes overlap so that both eyes perceive the same image. **Stereoscopic vision** means that each eye sends a signal of the visual image to both hemispheres in the brain to create an image with depth. These trends are not uniformly expressed within the primate order; for example, olfactory cues play a more important role in the lives of **strepsirrhine** primates than in the lives of **haplorrhine** primates. As we will explain shortly, the strepsirrhine primates include the lorises and lemurs, and the haplorrhine primates include tarsiers, monkeys, and apes.

Features 6 and 7 in Table 5.1 result from the distinctive life history of primates. As a group, primates have longer pregnancies, mature at later ages, live longer, and have larger brains than other animals of similar body size. These features reflect a progressive trend toward increased dependence on complex behavior, learning, and behavioral flexibility within the primate order. As the noted primatologist Alison Jolly points out, "If there is an essence of being a primate, it is the progressive evolution of

CHAPTER 5: Primate Diversity and Ecology

TABLE 5.1

1. The big toe on the foot is **opposable**, and hands are **prehensile**. This means that primates can use their feet and hands for grasping. The opposable big toe has been lost in humans.

2. There are flat nails on the hands and feet in most species, instead of claws, and there are sensitive tactile pads with "fingerprints" on the fingers and toes.

3. Locomotion is **hind-limb dominated**, meaning that the hind limbs do most of the work, and the center of gravity is nearer the hind limbs than the forelimbs.

4. There is an unspecialized **olfactory** (smelling) apparatus that is reduced in diurnal primates.

5. The visual sense is highly developed. The eyes are large and moved forward in the head, providing stereoscopic vision.

6. Females have small litters, and gestation and juvenile periods are longer than in other mammals of similar size.

7. The brain is larger than the brains of similarly sized mammals, and it has several unique anatomical features.

8. The **molars** are relatively unspecialized, and there is a maximum of two **incisors**, one **canine**, three **premolars**, and three molars on each half of the upper and lower jaw.

9. There are several other subtle anatomical characteristics that are useful to systematists but are hard to interpret functionally.

Definition of the primate order. See the text for more complete descriptions of these features.

(a)

(b)

(c)

FIGURE 5.2

(a) Primates have grasping feet, which they use to climb, cling to branches, hold food, and scratch themselves. (b) Primates can oppose the thumb and forefinger in a precision grip—a feature that enables them to hold food in one hand while they are feeding, to pick small ticks and bits of debris from their hair while grooming, and (in some species) to use tools. (c) Most primates, like this squirrel monkey, have flat nails on their hands and sensitive tactile pads on the tips of their fingers.

FIGURE 5.3

In most primates, the eyes are moved forward in the head. The field of vision of the two eyes overlaps, creating binocular, stereoscopic vision.

FIGURE 5.4

A high degree of intelligence characterizes some animals besides primates. Dolphins, for example, have very large brains in relation to their body size, and their behavior is quite complex.

FIGURE 5.5

The distribution of living and fossil nonhuman primates. Primates are now found in Central America, South America, Africa, and Asia. They are found mainly in tropical regions of the world. Primates were formerly found in southern Europe and northern Africa. There have never been indigenous populations of primates in Australia or Antarctica.

intelligence as a way of life." As we will see in the chapters that follow, these traits profoundly affect mating and parenting strategies and the patterns of social interaction within primate groups.

The eighth feature in Table 5.1 concerns primate dentition. Teeth play a very important role in the lives of primates and in our understanding of their evolution. The utility of teeth to primates themselves is straightforward: Teeth are necessary for processing food and are also used as weapons in conflicts with other animals. Teeth are also useful features for researchers who study living and fossil primates. Primatologists sometimes rely on tooth wear to gauge the age of individuals, and they use features of the teeth to assess the phylogenetic relationships among species. As we will see, paleontologists often rely on teeth, which are hard and preserve well, to identify the phylogenetic relationships of extinct creatures and to make inferences about their developmental patterns, their dietary preferences, and their social structure. **A Closer Look 5.1** describes primate dentition in greater detail.

Although these traits are generally characteristic of primates, you should keep two points in mind. First, none of the traits makes primates unique. Dolphins, for example, have large brains and extended periods of juvenile development, and their social behavior may be just as complicated and flexible as that of any nonhuman primate (**Figure 5.4**). Second, not every primate possesses all of these traits. Humans have lost the grasping big toe that characterizes other primates, some strepsirrhine primates have claws on some of their fingers and toes, and not all monkeys have color vision.

Primate Biogeography

Primates are restricted mainly to tropical regions of the world.

The continents of Asia, Africa, and South America and the islands that lie near their coasts are home to most of the world's nonhuman primates (**Figure 5.5**). A few species remain in Mexico and Central America. Nonhuman primates were once found in southern Europe, but no natural population survives there now. There are no natural populations in Australia or Antarctica, and none occupied these continents in the past.

Nonhuman primates are found mainly in tropical regions, where the fluctuations in temperature from day to night greatly exceed fluctuations in temperature during the

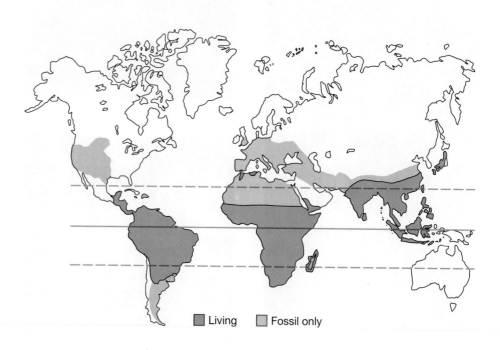

■ Living   □ Fossil only

CHAPTER 5: Primate Diversity and Ecology

year. In the tropics, the distribution of resources that primates rely on for subsistence is affected more strongly by seasonal changes in rainfall than by seasonal changes in temperature. Some species extend their ranges into temperate areas of Africa and Asia, where they manage to cope with substantial seasonal fluctuations in environmental conditions.

Within their ranges, nonhuman primates occupy an extremely diverse set of habitats, including all types of tropical forests, savanna woodlands, mangrove swamps, grasslands, high-altitude plateaus, and deserts. Almost all, however, are found in forested areas, where they travel, feed, socialize, and sleep in a largely arboreal world.

A Taxonomy of Living Primates

Scientists classify primates into two suborders: Strepsirrhini and Haplorrhini (**Table 5.2**). Many of the primates included in the suborder Strepsirrhini are nocturnal, and, like some of the earliest primates that lived 50 Ma, they have many adaptations to

TABLE 5.2 Taxonomy of the Living Primates

Suborder	Infraorder	Superfamily	Family	Subfamily	Examples
Strepsirrhini	Lemuriformes	Lemuroidea	Cheirogaleidae		Dwarf lemurs, mouse lemurs
			Daubentoniidae		Aye-ayes
			Indriidae		Indris, sifakas
			Lemuridae		Lemurs
			Lepilemuridae		Sportive lemurs
	Lorisiformes	Lorisoidea	Galagidae	Galaginae	Galagos
			Lorisidae	Lorisinae	Lorises
				Perodicticinae	Pottos
Haplorrhini	Tarsiiformes	Tarsiodea	Tarsiidae	Tarsinae	Tarsiers
	Platyrrhini	Ceboidea (New World monkeys)	Atelidae	Alouattinae	Howler monkeys
				Atelinae	Spider monkeys
			Cebidae	Aotinae	Owl monkeys
				Callitrichinae	Marmosets, tamarins
				Cebinae	Capuchins
				Saimiriinae	Squirrel monkeys
			Pitheciidae	Callicebinae	Titi monkeys
				Pitheciinae	Sakis, uakaris
	Catarrhini	Cercopithecoidea (Old World monkeys)	Cercopithecidae	Cercopithecinae	Mangabeys, macaques, vervets, baboons
				Colobinae	Langurs, colobus, leaf monkeys
		Hominoidea (apes, humans)	Hylobatidae		Gibbons, siamang
			Hominidae	Ponginae	Orangutans
				Homininae	Gorillas, chimpanzees, humans

5.1 Teeth and Guts: You Are What You Can Chew

For various reasons, biological anthropologists spend a lot of time thinking about teeth. Teeth are useful markers for taxonomic identity because various primates have different numbers of teeth. Teeth are also useful because they tell us things about what kinds of food primates eat. If we can detect a relationship between dental morphology and diet, we can apply these insights to the fossil record. This is particularly handy because teeth are the most commonly preserved parts of the body. Finally, teeth and gut morphology provide examples of how natural selection has created adaptations that enable animals to cope with their environments more effectively.

Dental Formula

To appreciate the basic features of primate dentition, you can consult **Figure 5.6**, or you can simply look in a mirror because your teeth are much like those of other primates. Teeth are rooted in the jaw. The jaw holds four kinds of teeth: In order, they are, first, the incisors at the front; then come the canines, premolars, and the molars in the rear. All primates have the same kinds of teeth, but species vary in how many of each kind of tooth they have. For convenience, these combinations are expressed in a standard format called the **dental formula**, which is commonly written in the following form:

$$\frac{2.1.3.3}{2.1.3.3}$$

Reading from left to right, the numerals tell us how many incisors, canines, premolars, and molars a particular species has (or had) on one side of its jaw. The top line of numbers represents the teeth on one side of the upper jaw (**maxilla**),

and the bottom line represents the teeth on the corresponding side of the lower jaw (**mandible**). Usually, but not always, the formula is the same for both upper and lower jaws. Like most other parts of the body, our dentition is **bilaterally symmetrical**, which means that the left side is identical to the right side. The ancestral pattern shown here has been modified in various primate taxa, as the total number of teeth has been reduced.

The dental formulas among living primates vary (**Table 5.3**). The lorises, pottos, galagos, and several lemurids have retained the primitive mammalian dental formula, but other strepsirrhine taxa have lost incisors, canines, or premolars. Tarsiers have lost one incisor on the mandible but have retained two on the maxilla. All of the New World monkeys, except the marmosets and tamarins, have retained the primitive dental formula; the marmosets and tamarins have lost one molar.

The Old World monkeys, apes, and humans have only two premolars.

Dental Morphology

Primates who rely heavily on gum for food tend to have large and prominent incisors, which they use to gouge holes in the bark of trees (**Figure 5.7**). In some strepsirrhine species, the incisors and canines are projected forward in the jaw and are used to scrape hardened gum off the surface of branches and tree trunks. Dietary specializations are also reflected in the size and shape of the molars. Primates who feed mainly on insects and leaves have molars with well-developed shearing crests that permit them to cut their food into small pieces when they chew. Insectivores tend to have higher and more pointed cusps on their molars, which are useful for puncturing and crushing the bodies of their prey. The molars of frugivores tend to have flatter, more rounded

TABLE 5.3

Primate Taxa		Dental Formula
Strepsirrhines	Lorises, pottos, galagos, dwarf lemurs, mouse lemurs, true lemurs	$\frac{2.1.3.3}{2.1.3.3}$
	Indris	$\frac{2.1.2.3}{2.0.3.3}$
	Aye-ayes	$\frac{1.0.1.3}{1.0.0.3}$
Haplorrhines	Tarsiers	$\frac{2.1.3.3}{1.1.3.3}$
	New World monkeys (most species)	$\frac{2.1.3.3}{2.1.3.3}$
	Marmosets, tamarins	$\frac{2.1.3.2}{2.1.3.2}$
	Old World monkeys, apes, humans	$\frac{2.1.2.3}{2.1.2.3}$

Primates vary in the numbers of each type of tooth that they have. The dental formulas listed here give the number of incisors, canines, premolars, and molars on each side of the upper jaw (maxilla) and lower jaw.

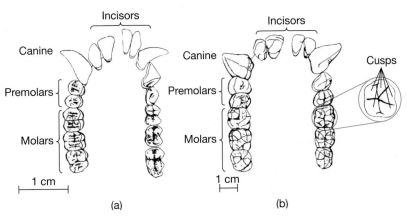

FIGURE 5.6

The upper jaw (left) and lower jaw (right) are shown here for a male colobus monkey (a) and a male gorilla (b). In Old World monkeys, the prominent anterior and posterior cusps of the lower molars form two parallel ridges. In apes, the five cusps of the lower molar form a Y-shaped pattern.

cusps, with broad and flat areas used to crush their food. Primates who rely on hard seeds and nuts have molars with very thick enamel that can withstand the heavy chewing forces needed to process these types of food.

Guts

Primates who feed principally on insects or animal prey have relatively simple digestive systems that are specialized for absorption. They generally have a simple small stomach, a small cecum (a pouch located at the upper end of the large intestine), and a small colon in relation to the rest of the small intestine. Frugivores also tend to have simple digestive systems, but frugivorous species with large bodies have capacious stomachs to hold large quantities of the leaves they consume along with the fruit in their diet. Folivores have the most specialized digestive systems because they must deal with large quantities of cellulose and secondary plant compounds. Because primates cannot digest cellulose or other structural carbohydrates directly, folivores maintain colonies of microorganisms in their digestive systems that break down these substances. In some species, these colonies of microorganisms are housed in an enlarged cecum; in other species, the colon is enlarged for this purpose. Colobines, for example, have an enlarged and complex stomach divided into several sections where microorganisms help process cellulose.

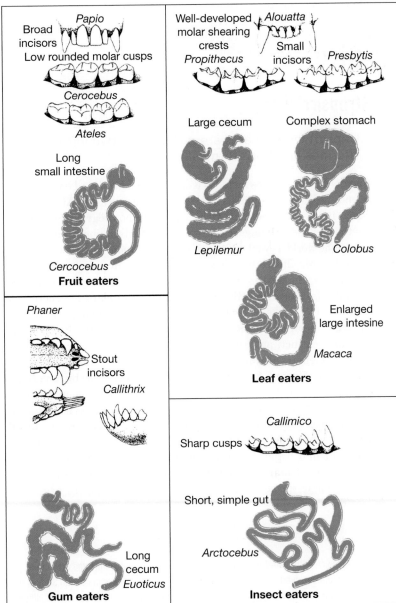

FIGURE 5.7

The dentition and digestive tracts of fruit-eating (frugivorous), leaf-eating (folivorous), gum-eating (gummivorous), and insect-eating (insectivorous) primates typically differ.

living in darkness, including a well-developed sense of smell, large eyes, and independently movable ears. By contrast, monkeys, apes, and humans, which make up the suborder Haplorrhini, evolved adaptations more suited to a diurnal lifestyle early in their evolutionary history. In the Haplorrhini, traits related to increased complexity of behavior, including large brains and longer life spans, are most fully developed. Haplorrhine monkeys are generally larger than strepsirrhines, are active during the day, are more fully dependent on vision than smell, and live in bigger and more complex social groups.

The classification of the primates that we have adopted here reflects the pattern of descent within the order. Tarsiers are included in the haplorrhines because genetic data indicate that they are more closely related to monkeys and apes than to the strepsirrhines. However, like many of the strepsirrhines, they are small-bodied and nocturnal. A cladistic classification places tarsiers within the Haplorrhini, but an evolutionary taxonomy would group tarsiers with strepsirrhines because of their overall similarity in morphology and behavior.

Primate Diversity

The Strepsirrhines

The strepsirrhine primates are divided into two infraorders: Lemuriformes and Lorisiformes.

The **infraorder** Lemuriformes includes lemurs, which are found only on Madagascar and the Comoro Islands, off the southeastern coast of Africa. These islands have been separated from Africa for 120 million years. The primitive primates that reached Madagascar evolved in total isolation from primates elsewhere in the world as well as from many of the predators and competitors that primates confront in other places. Faced with a diverse set of available ecological niches, the lemurs underwent a spectacular adaptive radiation. When humans first colonized Madagascar about 2,000 years ago, there were approximately 44 species of lemurs, some as small as mouse lemurs and others as big as gorillas. In the next few centuries, all of the larger lemur species became extinct, probably the victims of human hunters or habitat loss. The extant lemurs are mainly small- or medium-size arboreal residents of forested areas (**Figure 5.8a**). They travel quadrupedally or by jumping in an upright posture from one tree to another, a form of locomotion known as vertical clinging and leaping (**Figure 5.8b**). Activity patterns of lemurs are quite variable: About half are primarily diurnal, others are nocturnal, and some are active during both day and night. One of the most interesting aspects of lemur behavior is that females routinely dominate males. In most lemur species, females can supplant males from desirable feeding sites; and in some lemur species, females regularly defeat males in aggressive

(a)

(b)

(c)

FIGURE 5.8

(a) Ring-tailed lemurs, with their distinctive striped tails, live in social groups and are active during daylight hours. In several lemur species, females are dominant over males. (b) Sifakas use their powerful legs to jump in an upright posture, a form of locomotion known as vertical clinging and leaping. (c) Galagos are small, arboreal, nocturnal animals that can leap great distances. They are mainly solitary, though residents of neighboring territories sometimes rest together during the day.

encounters. Although such behavior may seem unremarkable in our own liberated times, female dominance is rare in other primate species.

The infraorder Lorisiformes is composed of small, nocturnal, arboreal residents of the forests of Africa and Asia. These animals include two subfamilies with different locomotion and activity patterns. Galagos are active and agile, leaping through the trees and running quickly along the tops of branches (**Figure 5.8c**). The lorises move with ponderous deliberation, and their wrists and ankles have a specialized network of blood vessels that allows them to remain immobile for long periods. These traits may be adaptations that help them avoid detection by predators. Traveling alone, the Lorisiformes generally feed on fruit, gum, and insect prey. The Lorisiformes leave their dependent offspring in nests built in the hollows of trees or hidden in masses of tangled vegetation. During the day, females sleep, nurse their young, and groom, sometimes in the company of mature offspring or familiar neighbors.

The Haplorrhines

The suborder Haplorrhini contains three infraorders: Tarsiiformes, Platyrrhini, and Catarrhini.

The infraorder Tarsiiformes includes tarsiers, which are enigmatic primates that live in the rain forests of Borneo, Sulawesi, and the Philippines (**Figure 5.9**). Like many of the strepsirrhine primates, tarsiers are small, nocturnal, and arboreal, and they move by vertical clinging and leaping. Some tarsiers live in pair-bonded family groups, but many groups have more than one breeding female. Female tarsiers give birth to infants that weigh 25% of their own weight; mothers leave their bulky infants behind in safe hiding places when they forage for insects. Tarsiers are unique among primates because they are the only primates that rely exclusively on animal matter for food, feeding on insects and small vertebrate prey.

The two infraorders Platyrrhini and Catarrhini are commonly referred to as the New World monkeys and the Old World monkeys and apes, respectively, because platyrrhine monkeys are found in South and Central America, whereas catarrhine monkeys and apes are found in Africa and Asia. This geographic dichotomy breaks down with humans, however: We are catarrhine primates, but we are spread over the globe.

The infraorder Platyrrhini (New World monkeys) is divided into three families: Atelidae, Cebidae, and Pitheciidae. Although the New World monkeys encompass considerable diversity in size, diet, and social organization, they do share some basic features. All but those in one genus are diurnal, all live in forested areas, and all are mainly arboreal. The New World monkeys range in size from the 600-g (21-oz.) squirrel monkey to the 9.5-kg (21-lb.) muriqui (**Figure 5.10**). Most New World monkeys are quadrupedal, moving along the tops of branches and jumping between adjacent trees. Some species in the family Atelidae can suspend themselves by their hands, feet, or tail and can move by swinging by their arms beneath branches. Although many people think that all monkeys can swing by their tails, prehensile tails are actually restricted to the largest species of platyrrhine monkeys.

The family Atelidae is composed of howler monkeys, spider monkeys, woolly monkeys, and muriquis. Howler monkeys are named for their long-distance roars in intergroup interactions. They live in small one-male or multimale groups, defend their home ranges, and feed mainly on leaves. Spider monkeys, woolly monkeys, and muriquis subsist mainly on fruit and leaves, and they live in multimale, multifemale groups of 15 to 25. Spider monkeys, which rely heavily on ripe fruit, typically break up into small parties for feeding (Figure 5.10b). Spider monkeys and muriquis (Figure 5.10a) are unusual among primates because females disperse from their natal (birth) groups when they reach sexual maturity, whereas males remain in their natal groups for life.

The family Cebidae includes capuchins, owl monkeys, squirrel monkeys, marmosets, and tamarins. Capuchin monkeys (Figure 5.10c) are notable, in part, because they have

FIGURE 5.9

Tarsiers are small, insectivorous primates that live in Asia. Some tarsiers form pair bonds.

(a)

(b)

(c)

(d)

FIGURE 5.10

Portraits of some New World monkeys. (a) Muriquis, or woolly spider monkeys, are large-bodied and arboreal. They are extremely peaceful creatures, rarely fighting or competing over access to resources. (b) Spider monkeys rely heavily on ripe fruit and travel in small parties. They have prehensile tails that they can use much like an extra hand or foot. (c) Capuchin monkeys have a larger brain in relation to their body size than any of the other nonhuman primates. (d) Squirrel monkeys form large multimale, multifemale groups. In the mating season, males gain weight and become "fatted" and then compete actively for access to receptive females.

very large brains in relation to their body size (see Chapter 9). They display several behavioral traits that play an important role in thinking about human origins, including tool use, social learning, and the development of behavioral traditions. Capuchins and squirrel monkeys (Figure 5.10d) live in multimale, multifemale groups of 10 to 50 individuals and forage for fruit, leaves, and insects. Owl monkeys, which form pair bonds and defend territories, are the only nocturnal haplorrhine primates.

The marmosets and tamarins, which belong to the subfamily Callitrichinae, share several morphological features that distinguish them from other haplorrhine primate species: They are extremely small, the largest weighing less than 1 kg (2.2 lb.); they have claws instead of nails; they have only two molars, whereas all other monkeys have three; and they often give birth to twins and sometimes triplets (**Figure 5.11**). Marmosets and tamarins are also notable for their domestic arrangements: In most groups there is a single breeding pair, and other group members help the parents rear the offspring.

The family Pitheciidae includes the diurnal titi monkey, which lives in pair-bonded family groups. This family also includes the uakaris and sakis, which are not yet very well studied in the wild. Whereas most primates that eat fruit swallow or spit out the seeds, which are rich in lipids, the sakis are specialized seed eaters.

The infraorder Catarrhini contains the monkeys and apes of the Old World and humans.

As a group, the catarrhine primates share several anatomical and behavioral features that distinguish them from the New World primates. For example, most Old World monkeys and apes have narrow nostrils that face downward, whereas New World monkeys have round nostrils. Old World monkeys have two premolars on each side of the upper and lower jaws; New World monkeys have three. Most Old World primates are larger than most New World species, and Old World monkeys and apes occupy a wider variety of habitats than New World species do.

The catarrhine primates are divided into two superfamilies: Cercopithecoidea (Old World monkeys) and Hominoidea (apes and humans). Cercopithecoidea contains one extant (still living) family, which is further divided into two subfamilies of monkeys: Cercopithecinae and Colobinae.

The superfamily Cercopithecoidea encompasses great diversity in social organization, ecological specializations, and biogeography.

Members of the subfamily Colobinae, which includes the colobus monkeys of Africa and the langurs and leaf monkeys of Asia, may be the most elegant of the primates (**Figure 5.12**). They have slender bodies, long legs, long tails, and often beautifully colored coats. The guereza colobus monkey, for example, has a white ring around its black face, a striking white cape on its black back, and a bushy white tail that flies out behind as it leaps from tree to tree. These monkeys are mainly leaf and seed eaters, and most species spend much of their time in trees. They have complex stomachs, almost like the chambered stomachs of cows, which allow them to maintain bacterial colonies that facilitate the digestion of cellulose. Colobines, langurs, and leaf monkeys are most often found in groups composed of one adult male and several adult females. As in many other

FIGURE 5.11

Marmosets are small-bodied South American monkeys that form pair-bonded or polyandrous social groups. Males and older offspring actively participate in the care of infants.

(a)   (b)

FIGURE 5.12

(a) African colobines, such as these guereza colobus monkeys, are arboreal and feed mainly on leaves. These animals are sometimes hunted for their spectacular coats. (b) Gray langurs, also known as Hanuman langurs, are native to India and have been the subject of extensive study during the last four decades. In some areas, gray langurs form one-male, multifemale groups, and males engage in fierce fights over membership in bisexual groups. In these groups, infanticide often follows when a new male takes over the group.

(a)

(b)

(c)

FIGURE 5.13

Some representative cercopithecines: (a) Bonnet macaques are one of several species of macaques that are found throughout Asia and North Africa. Like other macaques, bonnet macaques form multimale, multifemale groups, and females spend their entire lives in their natal (birth) groups. (b) Vervet monkeys are found throughout Africa. Like macaques and baboons, females live among their mothers, daughters, and other maternal kin. Males transfer to nonnatal groups when they reach maturity. Vervets defend their ranges against incursions by members of other groups. (c) Blue monkeys live in one-male, multifemale groups. During the mating season, however, one or more unfamiliar males may join bisexual groups and mate with females.

vertebrate taxa, the replacement of resident males in one-male groups is often accompanied by lethal attacks on infants by new males. Infanticide under such circumstances is believed to be favored by selection because it improves the relative reproductive success of infanticidal males. This issue is discussed more fully in Chapter 7.

Most cercopithecine monkeys are found in Africa, though one particularly adaptable genus (*Macaca*) is widely distributed through Asia and part of northern Africa (**Figure 5.13**). The cercopithecines occupy a wide variety of habitats and are quite variable in body size and dietary preferences. The social behavior, reproductive behavior, life history, and ecology of several cercopithecine species (particularly baboons, macaques, and vervets) have been studied extensively and will figure prominently in the discussions of mating strategies and social behavior in the next few chapters. Cercopithecines typically live in medium or large one-male or multimale groups. Females typically remain in their natal groups (the groups into which they are born) throughout their lives and establish close and enduring relationships with their maternal kin; males leave their natal groups and join new groups when they reach sexual maturity.

The superfamily Hominoidea includes two families of apes: Hylobatidae (gibbons) and Hominidae (orangutans, gorillas, chimpanzees, and humans).

The hominoids differ from the cercopithecoids in several ways. The most readily observed difference between apes and monkeys is that apes lack tails. But there are many other more subtle differences between apes and monkeys. For example, the apes share some derived traits, including broader noses, broader palates, and larger brains; and they retain some primitive traits, such as relatively unspecialized molars. In Old World monkeys the prominent anterior and posterior cusps are arranged to form two parallel ridges. In apes, the five cusps on the lower molars are arranged to form a side-turned, Y-shaped pattern of ridges.

The family Hylobatidae, sometimes called lesser apes, includes gibbons and siamangs, and its living members are now found in Asia. The family Hominidae includes the larger-bodied great apes (orangutans, gorillas, bonobos, chimpanzees, and humans). Orangutans are found in Asia, whereas chimpanzees, bonobos, and gorillas are restricted to Africa.

The lesser apes are slightly built creatures with extremely long arms in relation to their body size (**Figure 5.14**). Gibbons and siamangs are strictly arboreal, and they use their long arms to perform spectacular acrobatic feats, moving through the canopy with grace, speed, and agility. Gibbons and siamangs are the only true brachiators among the primates, propelling themselves by their arms alone, and are in free flight between handholds. (To picture this, think about swinging on monkey bars in your elementary school playground.) Gibbons and siamangs typically live in pair-bonded family groups, vigorously defend their home ranges (the areas they occupy), and feed on fruit, leaves, flowers, and insects. Siamang males play an active role in caring for young, often carrying them during the day; male gibbons are less attentive fathers. In territorial displays, mated pairs of siamangs perform coordinated vocal duets that can be heard over long distances.

Orangutans, now found only on the Southeast Asian islands of Sumatra and Borneo, are among the largest and most solitary species of primates (**Figure 5.15**). Orangutans have been studied extensively by Birutē Galdikas in Tanjung Puting, Borneo, for more than 30 years. Long-term studies of orangutans have also been conducted at Cabang Panti in Borneo and at Ketambe and Suaq Balimbing in Sumatra. Orangutans feed primarily on fruit, but they also eat some leaves and bark. Adult females associate mainly with their own infants and immature offspring and do not often meet or interact with other orangutans. Adult males spend most of their time alone. A single adult male may defend a home range that encompasses the home ranges of several adult females; other males wander over larger areas and mate opportunistically with receptive females. When resident males encounter these nomads, fierce and noisy encounters may take place.

Gorillas, the largest of the apes, existed in splendid isolation from Western science until the middle of the nineteenth century (**Figure 5.16a** and **b**). Today, our knowledge of the behavior and ecology of gorillas is based mainly on detailed long-term studies of one subspecies, the mountain gorilla, at the Karisoke Research Center in Rwanda, which was founded by the late Dian Fossey. Mountain gorillas live in small groups that

(a)

(b)

FIGURE 5.14

(a) Gibbons and (b) siamangs live in pair-bonded groups and actively defend their territories against intruders. They have extremely long arms, which they use to propel themselves from one branch to another as they swing hand over hand through the canopy, a form of locomotion called brachiation. Siamangs and gibbons are confined to the tropical forests of Asia. As with other residents of tropical forests, their survival is threatened by the rapid destruction of tropical forests.

(a)

(b)

FIGURE 5.15

(a) Orangutans are large, ponderous, and mostly solitary creatures. Male orangutans often descend to the ground to travel; lighter females often move through the tree canopy. (b) Today, orangutans are found only on the islands of Borneo and Sumatra, in tropical forests like this one.

FIGURE 5.16

(a) Gorillas are the largest of the primates. Mountain gorillas usually live in one-male, multifemale groups, but some groups contain more than one adult male. (b) Most behavioral information about gorillas comes from observations of mountain gorillas living in the Virunga Mountains of central Africa, pictured here. The harsh montane habitat may influence the nature of social organization and social behavior in these animals, and the behavior of gorillas living at lower elevations may differ.

(a)

(b)

contain one or two adult males and several adult females and their young. Each day, mountain gorillas ingest great quantities of various herbs, vines, shrubs, and bamboo. They eat little fruit because fruiting plants are scarce in their mountainous habitat. Called silverbacks because the hair on their backs and shoulders turns a striking silver-gray when they mature, adult male mountain gorillas play a central role in the structure and cohesion of their social groups. Males sometimes remain in their natal groups to breed, but most males leave their natal groups and acquire females by drawing them away from other males during intergroup encounters. The silverback largely determines the timing of group activity and the direction of travel. As data from newly established field studies of lowland gorilla populations become available, we are revising some elements of this view of gorilla social organization. For example, lowland gorillas seem to eat substantial amounts of fruit, spend more of their time in trees, and form larger and less cohesive social groups than mountain gorillas do.

As humankind's closest living relatives, chimpanzees (**Figure 5.17a**) have played a uniquely important role in the study of human evolution. Whether reasoning by homology or by analogy, researchers have found observations about chimpanzees to be important bases for hypotheses about the behavior of early hominins.

Detailed knowledge of chimpanzee behavior and ecology comes from several long-term studies conducted at sites across Africa. In the 1960s, Jane Goodall began her well-known study of chimpanzees at the Gombe Stream National Park on the shores of Lake Tanganyika in Tanzania (**Figure 5.17b**). About the same time, a second study was initiated by the late Toshisada Nishida at a site in the Mahale Mountains not far from Gombe. These studies are now moving into their sixth decade. Other important study sites have been established at Bossou, Guinea; in the Taï Forest of Ivory Coast; and at two sites in the Kibale Forest of Uganda: Kanyawara and Ngogo.

Bonobos (**Figure 5.17c**), another member of the genus *Pan*, live in inaccessible places and are much less well studied than common chimpanzees. Important field studies on bonobos have been conducted at two sites in the Democratic Republic of the Congo (formerly Zaire): Wamba and Lomako. Field studies of bonobos have been disrupted by civil conflicts that have ravaged central Africa over the last decades.

Chimpanzees and bonobos form large multimale, multifemale communities. These communities differ from the social groups formed by most other species of primates in two important ways. First, female chimpanzees usually disperse from their natal groups when they reach sexual maturity, whereas males remain in their natal groups throughout their lives. Second, the members of chimpanzee communities are rarely found together in a unified group. Instead, they split up into smaller parties that vary in size and composition from day to day. In chimpanzees, the strongest social bonds among adults are formed among males, whereas bonobo females form stronger bonds

(a)

(b)

(c)

with one another and with their adult sons than males do. Chimpanzees modify natural objects for use as tools in the wild. At several sites, chimpanzees strip twigs and poke them into termite mounds and ant nests to extract insects, a much-prized delicacy. In the Taï Forest, chimpanzees crack hard-shelled nuts by using one stone as a hammer and a heavy, flat stone or a protruding root as an anvil. At Gombe, chimpanzees wad leaves in their mouths and then dip these "sponges" into crevices to soak up water. New data also reveal tool use by wild orangutans, but chimpanzee tool use is more diverse and better studied.

Primate Ecology

Much of the day-to-day life of primates is driven by two concerns: getting enough to eat and avoiding being eaten. Food is essential for growth, survival, and reproduction, and it should not be surprising that primates spend much of every day finding, processing, consuming, and digesting a wide variety of foods (**Figure 5.18**). At the same time, primates must always be on guard against predators such as lions, pythons, and eagles that hunt them by day and leopards that stalk them by night. As we will see in the chapters that follow, both the distribution of food and the threat of predation influence the extent of sociality among primates and shape the patterns of social interactions within and between primate groups.

In this section, we describe the basic features of primate ecology. Later we will draw on this information to explore the relationships among ecological factors, social organization, and primate behavior. It is important to understand the nature of these relationships because the same ecological factors are likely to have influenced the social organization and behavior of our earliest ancestors.

The Distribution of Food

Food provides energy that is essential for growth, survival, and reproduction.

Like all other animals, primates need energy to maintain normal metabolic processes; to regulate essential body functions; and to sustain growth, development, and reproduction. The total amount of energy that an animal requires depends on four components:

FIGURE 5.17

(a) Chimpanzees live in multimale, multifemale social groups. In this species, males form the core of the social group and remain in their natal groups for life. Many researchers believe that chimpanzees and bonobos are our closest living relatives. (b) Like other apes, chimpanzees are found mainly in forests such as this area on the shores of Lake Tanganyika in Tanzania. However, chimpanzees sometimes range into more open areas as well. (c) Bonobos are members of the same genus as chimpanzees and are similar in many ways. Bonobos are sometimes called "pygmy chimpanzees," but this is a misnomer because bonobos and chimpanzees are about the same size. This infant bonobo is sitting in a patch of terrestrial herbaceous vegetation, one of the staples of the bonobo's diet.

FIGURE 5.18

A female baboon feeds on corms in Amboseli, Kenya.

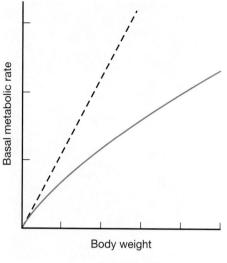

FIGURE 5.19

Average basal metabolism is affected by body size. The dashed line represents a direct linear relationship between body weight and basal metabolic rate. The solid line represents the actual relationship between body weight and basal metabolic rate. The fact that the curve bends means that larger animals use relatively less energy per unit of body weight.

1. *Basal metabolism.* **Basal metabolic rate** is the rate at which an animal expends energy to maintain life when at rest. As **Figure 5.19** shows, large animals have higher basal metabolic rates than small animals have. However, large animals require relatively fewer calories *per unit* of body weight.

2. *Active metabolism.* When animals become active, their energy needs rise above baseline levels. The number of additional calories required depends on how much energy the animal expends. The amount of energy expended, in turn, depends on the size of the animal and how fast it moves. In general, to sustain a normal range of activities, an average-size primate like a baboon or macaque requires enough energy per day to maintain a rate about twice its basal metabolic rate.

3. *Growth rate.* Growth imposes further energetic demands on organisms. Infants and juveniles, which are gaining weight and growing in stature, require more energy than would be expected from their body weight and activity levels alone.

4. *Reproductive effort.* For female primates, the energetic costs of reproduction are substantial. During the latter stages of their pregnancies, for example, primate females require about 25% more calories than usual and, during lactation, about 50% more calories than usual.

A primate's diet must satisfy the animal's energy requirements, provide specific types of nutrients, and minimize exposure to dangerous toxins.

The food that primates eat provides them with energy and essential nutrients, such as amino acids and minerals, that they cannot synthesize themselves. Proteins are essential for virtually every aspect of growth and reproduction and to regulate many body functions. As we saw in Chapter 2, proteins are composed of long chains of amino acids. Primates cannot synthesize amino acids from simpler molecules, so to build many essential proteins, they must ingest foods that contain sufficient amounts of several amino acids. Fats and oils are important sources of energy for animals and provide about twice as much energy as equivalent volumes of **carbohydrates**. Vitamins, minerals, and trace amounts of certain elements play an essential role in regulating many of the body's metabolic functions. Although specific vitamins, minerals, and trace elements are needed in only small amounts, deficiencies of these nutrients can significantly impair normal body function. For example, trace amounts of iron and copper are important to synthesize hemoglobin, vitamin C is essential for growth and healing of wounds, and sodium regulates the quantity and distribution of body fluids. Primates cannot synthesize any of these compounds and must acquire them from the foods they eat. Further, water is the major constituent of the bodies of all animals and most plants. For survival, most animals must balance their water intake with their water loss; moderate dehydration can be debilitating, and significant dehydration can be fatal.

At the same time that primates obtain nourishment from food, they must also take care to avoid **toxins**, substances in the environment that are harmful to them. Many plants produce toxins called **secondary compounds** to protect themselves from being eaten. Thousands of these secondary compounds have been identified: Caffeine and morphine are among the secondary compounds most familiar to us. Some secondary compounds, such as **alkaloids**, are toxic to consumers because they pass through the stomach into various types of cells, where they disrupt normal metabolic functions. Common alkaloids include capsaicin (the compound that brings tears to your eyes when you eat red peppers) and chocolate. Other secondary compounds, such as tannins (the bitter-tasting compound in tea), act in the consumer's gut to reduce the digestibility of plant material. Secondary compounds are particularly common among tropical plant species and are often concentrated in mature leaves and seeds. Young leaves, fruit,

TABLE 5.4

Source	Protein	Carbohydrates	Fats and Oils	Vitamins	Minerals	Water
Animals	×	(×)	×	×	×	×
Fruit		×				×
Seeds	×		×	×		
Flowers		×				×
Young leaves	×			×	×	×
Mature leaves	(×)					
Woody stems	×					
Sap		×			×	×
Gum	×	(×)			×	
Underground parts	×	×				×

Sources of nutrients for primates. (x) indicates that the nutrient content is generally accessible only to animals that have specific digestive adaptations.

and flowers tend to have lower concentrations of secondary compounds, making them relatively more palatable to primates.

Primates obtain nutrients from many sources.

Primates obtain energy and essential nutrients from a variety of sources (**Table 5.4**). Carbohydrates are obtained mainly from the simple sugars in fruit, but animal prey, such as insects, also provides a good source of fats and oils. **Gum**, a substance that plants produce in response to physical injury, is an important source of carbohydrates for some primates, particularly galagos, marmosets, and tamarins. Primates get most of their protein from insect prey or from young leaves. Some species have special adaptations that facilitate the breakdown of cellulose, enabling them to digest more of the protein contained in the cells of mature leaves. Although seeds provide a good source of vitamins, fats, and oils, many plants package their seeds in husks or pods that shield their contents from seed predators. Many primates drink daily from streams, water holes, springs, or puddles of rainwater (**Figure 5.20**). Primates can also obtain water from fruit, flowers, young leaves, animal prey, and the underground storage parts (roots and tubers) of various plants. These sources of water are particularly important for arboreal animals that do not descend from the canopy and for terrestrial animals during times of the year when surface water is scarce. Vitamins, minerals, and trace elements are obtained in small quantities from many sources.

Although primates display considerable diversity in their diet, some generalizations are possible:

1. All primates rely on at least one type of food that is high in protein and another that is high in carbohydrates. Strepsirrhines generally obtain protein from insects and carbohydrates from gum and fruit. Monkeys and apes usually obtain protein from insects or young leaves and carbohydrates from fruit.

FIGURE 5.20

These savanna baboons are drinking from a pool of rainwater. Most primates must drink every day.

2. Most primates rely more heavily on some types of foods than on others. Chimpanzees, for example, feed mainly on ripe fruit throughout their range from Tanzania to Ivory Coast. Scientists use the terms **frugivore**, **folivore**, **insectivore**, and **gummivore** to refer to primates who rely most heavily on fruit, leaves, insects, and plant gum, respectively. A Closer Look 5.1 examines some of the morphological adaptations among primates with different diets.

3. In general, insectivores are smaller than frugivores, and frugivores are smaller than folivores (**Figure 5.21**). These differences in size are related to differences in energy requirements; small animals have relatively higher energy requirements than larger animals do, and they require relatively small amounts of high-quality foods that can be processed quickly. Larger animals are less constrained by the quality of their food than by the quantity because they can afford to process lower-quality foods more slowly.

The nature of dietary specializations and the challenge of foraging in tropical forests influence ranging patterns.

Nonhuman primates do not have the luxury of shopping in supermarkets, where abundant supplies of food are concentrated in a single location and are constantly replenished. Instead, the availability of their preferred foods varies widely in space and time, making their food sources patchy and often unpredictable. Most primate species live in tropical forests. Although such forests, with their dense greenery, seem

FIGURE 5.21

Body size and diet are related among primates. In this graph, the height of the bars indicates the number of species of a particular body weight. (Not all primate species are included in this graph.) The smallest species eat mainly insects and gum; the largest species eat leaves, seeds, and herbs. Fruit-eating species fall in between.

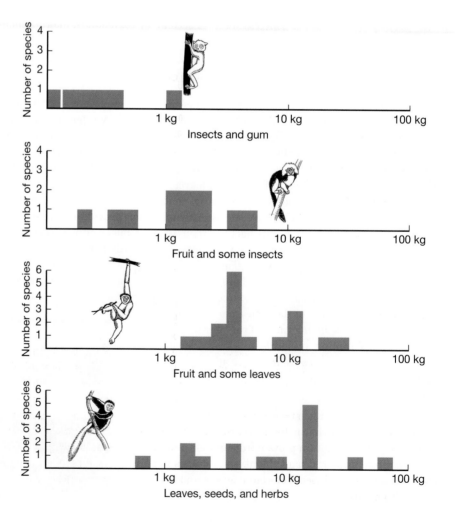

CHAPTER 5: Primate Diversity and Ecology

(a)　(b)　(c)

(d)　(e)　(f)

FIGURE 5.22

(a) Some primates feed mainly on leaves, though many leaves contain toxic secondary plant compounds. The monkey shown here is a red colobus monkey in the Kibale Forest of Uganda. (b) Some primates include a variety of insects and other animal prey in their diet. This tamarin is eating a grasshopper. (c) Mountain gorillas are mainly vegetarians. Like this male eating leaves in Volcanoes National Park in Rwanda, they consume vast quantities of plant material. (d) This vervet monkey is feeding on grass stems. (e) Although many primates feed mainly on one type of food, such as leaves or fruit, no primate relies exclusively on one type of food. For example, the main bulk of the muriqui diet comes from fruit, but muriquis also eat leaves, as shown here. (f) Langurs are folivores. Here, gray langurs in Ramnagar, Nepal, forage for water plants.

to provide abundant supplies of food for primates, appearances can be deceiving. Tropical forests contain many tree species, and individual trees of any particular species are few in number.

Primates with different dietary specializations confront different foraging challenges (**Figure 5.22**). Plants generally produce more leaves than flowers or fruit, and they bear leaves for a longer period during the year than they bear flowers and fruit. As a result, foliage is normally more abundant than fruit or flowers at a given time during the year, and mature leaves are more abundant than young leaves. Insects and other suitable prey animals occur at even lower densities than plants. This means that folivores can generally find more food in a given area than frugivores or insectivores can. However, the high concentration of toxic secondary compounds in mature leaves complicates the foraging strategies of folivores. Some leaves must be avoided altogether, and others can be eaten only in small quantities. Nonetheless, the food supplies of folivorous species are generally more uniform and predictable in space and time than the food supplies of frugivores or insectivores. Thus it is not surprising to find that folivores generally have smaller home ranges than frugivores or insectivores.

FIGURE 5.23

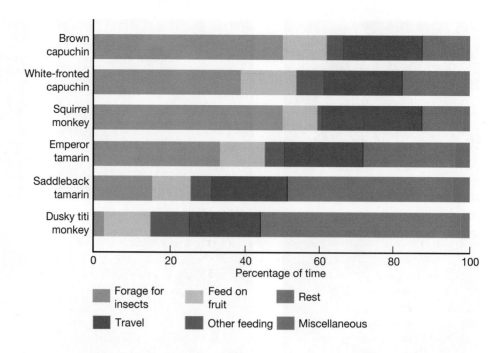

Activity Patterns

Primate activity patterns show regularity in seasonal and daily cycles.

Primates spend most of their time feeding, moving around their home ranges, and resting (**Figure 5.23**). Relatively small portions of each day are spent grooming, playing, fighting, or mating (**Figure 5.24**). The proportion of time devoted to various activities is influenced to some extent by ecological conditions. For primates living in seasonal habitats, for example, the dry season is often a time of scarce resources, and it is harder to find enough of the appropriate types of food. In some cases, this means that the proportion of time spent feeding and traveling increases during the dry season, while the proportion of time spent resting decreases.

Primate activity also shows regular patterns during the day. When primates wake up, their stomachs are empty, so one of the first tasks of the day is to visit a feeding site. Much of the morning is spent eating and moving between feeding sites. As the sun moves directly overhead and the temperature rises, most species settle down in a shady spot to rest, socialize, and digest their morning meals. Later in the afternoon they resume feeding. Before dusk they move to the night's sleeping site; some species sleep in the same trees every night; others have multiple sleeping sites within their ranges.

FIGURE 5.24

(a) All diurnal primates, like this female white-faced capuchin monkey with infant on her back, spend some part of each day resting. (b) Immature monkeys spend much of their free time playing. These vervet monkeys are play wrestling. (c) Gorillas often rest near other group members and socialize during a midday rest period.

(a)

(b)

(c)

Ranging Behavior

All primates have home ranges, but only some species are territorial—defending their home range against incursions by other members of their species.

In all primate species, groups range over a relatively fixed area, and members of a given group can be consistently found in a particular area over time. These areas are called home ranges, and they contain all of the resources that group members exploit in feeding, resting, and sleeping. However, the extent of overlap among adjacent home ranges and the nature of interactions with members of neighboring groups or strangers vary considerably among species. Some primate species, such as gibbons, maintain exclusive access to fixed areas called **territories**. Territory residents regularly advertise their presence by vocalizing, and they aggressively protect the boundaries of their territories from encroachment by outsiders (**Figure 5.25**). Although some territorial birds defend only their nest sites, primate territories contain all of the sites at which the residents feed, rest, and sleep, and the areas in which they travel. Thus, among territorial primates, the boundaries for the territory are essentially the same as for their home range, and territories do not overlap.

Nonterritorial species, such as squirrel monkeys and long-tailed macaques, establish home ranges that overlap considerably with those of neighboring groups (**Figure 5.26**). When members of neighboring nonterritorial groups meet, they may fight, avoid one

FIGURE 5.25

Siamangs and gibbons perform complex vocal duets as part of territorial defense.

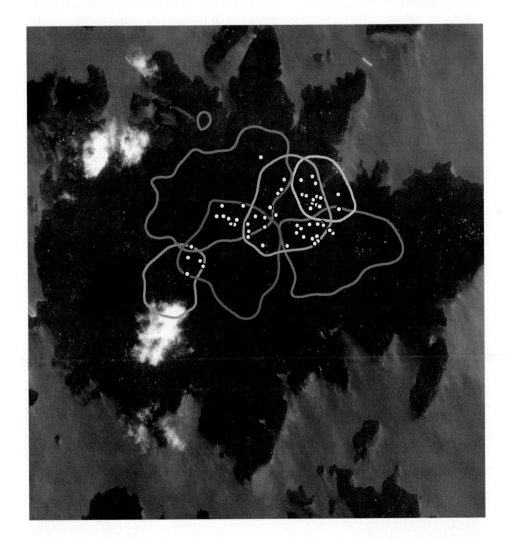

FIGURE 5.26

Overlapping home ranges of capuchin monkey groups on Barro Colorado Island, Panama. Sites of intergroup encounters are marked with a dot. (Satellite image by DigitalGlobe.)

another, or mingle peacefully. This last option is unusual, but in some species, adult females sexually solicit males from other groups, males attempt to mate with females from other groups, and juveniles from neighboring groups play together when their groups are in proximity.

The two main functions suggested for territoriality are resource defense and mate defense.

To understand why some primate species defend their home ranges from intruders and others do not, we need to think about the costs and benefits associated with defending resources from conspecifics. Costs and benefits are measured in terms of the impact on the individual's ability to survive and reproduce successfully. Territoriality is beneficial because it prevents outsiders from exploiting the limited resources within a territory. At the same time, however, territoriality is costly because the residents must be constantly vigilant against intruders, regularly advertise their presence, and be prepared to defend their ranges against encroachment. Territoriality is expected to occur only when the benefits of maintaining exclusive access to a particular piece of land outweigh the costs of protecting these benefits.

When will the benefits of territoriality exceed the costs? The answer to this question depends in part on the kinds of resources individuals need to survive and reproduce successfully and in part on the way these resources are distributed spatially and seasonally. For reasons we will discuss more fully in Chapter 6, the reproductive strategies of mammalian males and females generally differ. Usually, female reproductive success depends mainly on getting enough to eat for themselves and their dependent offspring, and males' reproductive success depends mainly on their ability to mate with females. As a consequence, females are more concerned about access to food, and males are more interested in access to females. Thus territoriality has two functions. Sometimes females defend food resources, or males defend food resources on their behalf. Other times, males defend groups of females against incursions by other males. In primates, both resource defense and mate defense seem to have influenced the evolution of territoriality.

Predation

Predation is believed to be a significant source of mortality among primates, but direct evidence of predation is difficult to obtain.

Primates are hunted by a variety of predators, including pythons, raptors, crocodiles, leopards, lions, tigers, and humans (**Figure 5.27**). In Madagascar, large lemurs are preyed upon by fossas, pumalike carnivores. Primates are also preyed on by other primates. Chimpanzees, for example, hunt red colobus monkeys, and baboons sometimes prey on vervet monkeys.

The estimated rates of predation vary from less than 1% of the population per year to more than 15%. The available data suggest that small-bodied primates are more vulnerable to predation than larger ones and immature primates are generally more susceptible to predation than adults. These data are not very solid, however, because systematic information about predation is quite hard to come by. Most predators avoid close contact with humans, and some predators, such as leopards, generally hunt at night, when most researchers are asleep. Usually predation is inferred when a healthy animal that is unlikely to have left the group abruptly vanishes (**Figure 5.28**). Such inferences are, of course, subject to error.

Another approach is to study the predators, not their prey. Crowned hawk eagles are the only large raptors that live in the tropical rain forests of Africa. They are formidable predators; although they weigh only 3 to 4 kg (6.6 to 8.8 lb.), they have powerful legs and large talons and can take prey weighing up to 20 kg (44 lb.). Crowned hawk eagles carry prey back to their nests and discard the bones. By sorting through the

(a)

(b)

(c)

(d)

(e)

FIGURE 5.27

Primates are preyed upon by a variety of predators, including the (a) python, (b) lion, (c) leopard, (d) crowned hawk eagle, and (e) crocodile.

remains under crowned hawk eagle nests, researchers can figure out what they eat. Analyses of nest remains in the Kibale Forest of Uganda and the Taï Forest in Ivory Coast indicate that crowned hawk eagles prey on all of the primates in these forests except chimpanzees. Monkeys make up 60% to 80% of the crowned hawk eagles' diets at these sites, and the eagles kill a sizable fraction (2% to 16%) of the total populations of various primate species in these forests each year.

FIGURE 5.28

Researchers can sometimes confirm predation. Here, an adult female baboon in the Okavango Delta, Botswana, was killed by a leopard. You can see (a) the depression in the sand that was made when the leopard dragged the female's body out of the sleeping tree and across a small sandy clearing, (b) the leopard's footprints beside the drag marks, and (c) the remains of the female the following morning—her jaw, bits of her skull, and clumps of hair.

(a)

(b)

(c)

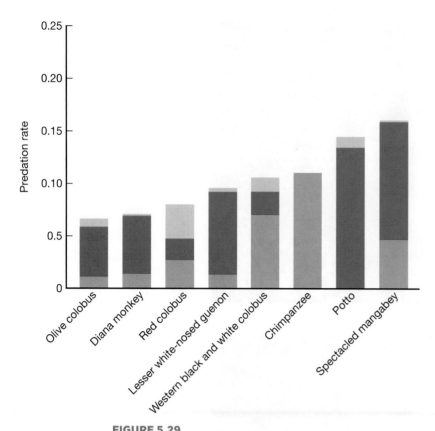

FIGURE 5.29

The rate of predation by leopards (*orange*), eagles (*green*), and chimpanzees (*blue*) in the Taï Forest on different primate species is shown here. Note that the preferred prey of chimpanzees is the red colobus monkey, and chimpanzees' only predator is the leopard.

Susanne Shultz, now at the University of Manchester, and her colleagues compared the characteristics of mammalian prey taken by crowned hawk eagles, leopards, and chimpanzees in the Taï Forest (**Figure 5.29**). In general, terrestrial species are more vulnerable than arboreal species, and species that live in small groups are more vulnerable than animals that live in large groups. Thus arboreal monkeys that live in large groups face the lowest risks. Shultz and her colleagues suggest that these results may explain some aspects of the distribution of terrestrial primates in Africa, Asia, and the neotropics. In Africa, with crowned hawk eagles and at least two large predatory felids present, terrestrial primates are large-bodied or live in large groups. In Asia, where there are no large forest raptors and few large felids, there are several semiterrestrial macaque species. And in the neotropics, where there are several species of large felids and forest raptors, there are no terrestrial monkeys at all.

Primates have evolved an array of defenses against predators.

Many primates give alarm calls when they sight potential predators, and some species have specific vocalizations for particular predators. Vervet monkeys, for example, give different calls when they are alerted to the presence of leopards, small carnivores, eagles, snakes, baboons, and unfamiliar humans. In many species, the most common response to predators is to flee or take cover. Small primates sometimes try to conceal themselves from predators; larger ones may confront potential predators. When slow-moving pottos encounter snakes, for example, they fall to the ground, move a short distance, and freeze. At some sites, adult red colobus monkeys aggressively attack chimpanzees that stalk their infants.

Another antipredator strategy that some primates adopt is to associate with members of other primate species. In the Taï Forest, several monkey species share the canopy and form regular associations with one another. For example, groups of red colobus monkeys spend approximately half their time with groups of Diana monkeys. Interspecific associations may enhance predator detection if each species occupies a different portion of the canopy and is oriented toward different predators. In addition, by associating with members of different species, monkeys may increase group size without increasing levels of competition from conspecifics that have similar dietary preferences.

Primate Sociality

Sociality has evolved in primates in response to ecological pressures. Social life has both costs and benefits.

Nearly all primates live in social groups of one kind or another. Sociality has evolved in primates because there are important benefits associated with living in groups. Primates that live in groups may be better able to acquire and control resources. Animals that live in groups can chase away lone individuals from feeding trees and can protect their own access to food and other resources against smaller numbers of intruders. As we saw earlier, grouping also offers safety from predators because groups provide the three Ds: detection, deterrence, and dilution. Animals in groups are more likely to detect predators because there are more pairs of eyes on the lookout for predators. Animals in groups are also more effective in deterring predators by actively mobbing or chasing them away. Finally, the threat of predation to any single individual is diluted when predators strike at random. If there are two animals in a group, and a predator strikes, each animal has a 50% chance of being eaten. If there are 10 individuals, the individual risk is decreased to 10%.

Although there are important benefits associated with sociality, there are equally important costs. Animals that live in groups may encounter more competition over access to food and mates, become more vulnerable to disease, and face various hazards from conspecifics (such as cannibalism, cuckoldry, inbreeding, or infanticide).

The size and composition of the groups that we see in nature are expected to reflect a compromise between the costs and benefits of sociality for individuals. The magnitude of these costs and benefits is influenced by both social and ecological factors.

Primatologists are divided over whether predation or competition for food is the primary factor favoring sociality among primates.

It is not entirely clear whether predation or competition for resources was the primary factor favoring the evolution of sociality in primates. However, many primatologists are convinced that the nature of resource competition affects the behavioral strategies of primates, particularly females, and influences the composition of primate groups (**A Closer Look 5.2**). Females come first in this scenario because their fitness depends mainly on their nutritional status: Well-nourished females grow faster, mature earlier, and have higher fertility rates than do poorly nourished females. In contrast, males' fitness depends primarily on their ability to obtain access to fertile females, not on their nutritional status. Thus ecological pressures influence the distribution of females, and males distribute themselves to maximize their access to females. (We will discuss male and female reproductive strategies more fully in Chapter 6.)

Primate Conservation

Many species of primates are in real danger of extinction in the wild.

FIGURE 5.30

Nearly all primate species are threatened with extinction (*blue*), particularly in Madagascar and Asia.

Sadly, no introduction to the primate order would be complete without noting that the prospects for the continued survival of many primate species are grim. In 2017, a group of researchers led by Alejandro Estrada of the National Autonomous University of Mexico published a comprehensive analysis of the status of wild primate populations. They concluded that approximately 60% of all primate species are now threatened in the wild (**Figure 5.30**). In Asia, 73% of all primate species are at risk of extinction. On the island of

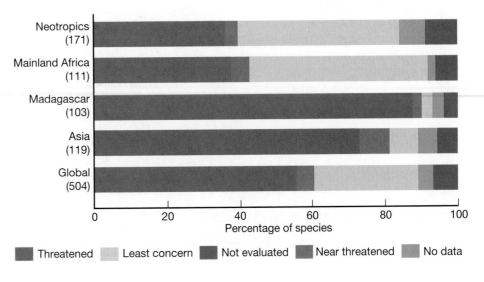

5.2 Forms of Social Groups among Primates

Most primates live in groups. A group is a social unit that is composed of animals that share a common home range or territory and interact more with one another than with other members of their species. Groups can vary in their size, age–sex composition, and degree of cohesiveness. We use the term **social organization** to describe variation along these dimensions. There are five basic types of social systems among primates (**Figure 5.31**):

Solitary: Females maintain separate home ranges or territories and associate mainly with their dependent offspring. Males establish their own territories or home ranges, which may encompass the ranges of one or more adult females. All of the **solitary** primates

are strepsirrhines, except for orangutans.

Pairs: Groups are composed of one adult male, one adult female, and immature offspring. Species that live in pairs usually defend the boundaries of their territories. Gibbons live in pairs, along with a few platyrrhine monkeys and a few strepsirrhines. In some pair-living species, males and females remain close together, but in others, they may travel independently within their territories much of the time.

Multiple males, one female: One adult female shares a territory or home range with more than one adult male and offspring. This form of social

organization is found only in marmosets and tamarins.

One male, multiple females: Groups are composed of several adult females, one resident adult male, and immature offspring. Males compete vigorously over residence in these kinds of groups, and males may band together to oust established residents. This form of social organization is characteristic of howler monkeys, some langurs, and gelada baboons.

Multiple males, multiple females: Groups are composed of several adult females, several adult males, and immatures. This form of social organization is characteristic of macaques, baboons, capuchin

FIGURE 5.31

The major types of social groups that primates form. When males and females share their home ranges, their home ranges are drawn here in brown. When the ranges of the two sexes differ, male home ranges are drawn in blue and female home ranges are drawn in red. The sizes of the male and female symbols reflect the degree of sexual dimorphism among males and females.

Solitary

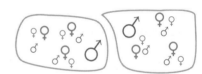
One male, multiple females (polygyny)

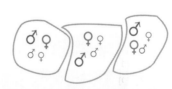
Pairs (pair bonding)

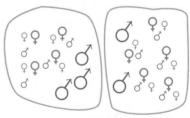
Multiple males, multiple females (polygynandry)

Multiple males, one female (polyandry)

monkeys, squirrel monkeys, and some colobines. Some species, such as chimpanzees and spider monkeys, living in these kinds of groups often divide up into smaller temporary parties (fission–fusion groups).

Primates also vary in their **mating systems**, the pattern of mating activity and reproductive outcomes. There is a close, but not perfect, relationship between social organization and mating systems. There are four main forms of mating systems in primates.

Monogamy/pair bonding: In a strictly monogamous mating system, each male and female will mate with only one member of the opposite sex. Most primates that live in pairs mate mainly with each other, but there are reports of extra-pair matings in several pair-living primate species, and extra-pair paternity has been confirmed in at least one pair-living primate, the fork-marked lemur. Thus the term **pair bonding** may be a more accurate description of the mating system of most pair-living primates than monogamy.

Polyandry: Females mate with multiple males, but each of the males mates with only one female. **Polyandry** is an uncommon mating system among mammals but may characterize some of the marmosets and tamarins. In these species, one female usually monopolizes reproduction. The breeding female may mate with all of the unrelated males in the group, but the limited available genetic data suggest that not all males are equally successful in fathering offspring.

Polygyny: Males mate with multiple females, but each female mates with a single male. This mating system characterizes most of the species that live in one-male, multifemale groups. **Polygyny** generates considerable skew in male reproductive success, as resident males largely control access to receptive females. However, in some of these species, including blue monkeys, males from outside the group sometimes enter groups and mate with females.

Polygynandry (promiscuity): Both males and females mate with more than one partner. This mating system is generally associated with species that live in multimale, multifemale groups and might also characterize some solitary species. In most species that form multimale, multifemale groups, males compete over access to mating females, and there is considerable skew in male reproductive success.

These classifications of social organization and mating systems represent idealized descriptions of residence and mating patterns. The reality is inevitably more complicated. Not all groups of a particular species may have the same social organization or mating system. For example, some groups of tarsiers are composed of a single mated pair, whereas others include additional females. Hamadryas and gelada baboons form one-male, multifemale units, but several of these units collectively belong to larger aggregations.

Madagascar, the situation is even more dire: 87% of all extant species are at risk. A smaller proportion of species in Africa and the neotropics (Central and South America) are in threatened categories, but the prospects are not encouraging. All around the world, the populations of nearly all primate species are decreasing, some very rapidly.

Species in all of the primate families are at risk (**Figure 5.32**). All of the great apes are now endangered. In West Africa, chimpanzee populations have declined drastically over the last two decades. In 1990, Ivory Coast was home to 8,000 to 12,000 chimpanzees. By 2007, that number had declined by 90%, according to a census conducted by Christophe Boesch and his colleagues. The decline is attributed to a 50% increase in the size of the human population, which created more poaching and habitat destruction and was exacerbated by civil unrest within the country. There are only 7,500 orangutans left in Sumatra, where forests are being logged or converted to oil palm plantations.

It is particularly disturbing that some of the most endangered primate species are ones that we know the least about. For example, in 2005 researchers encountered a

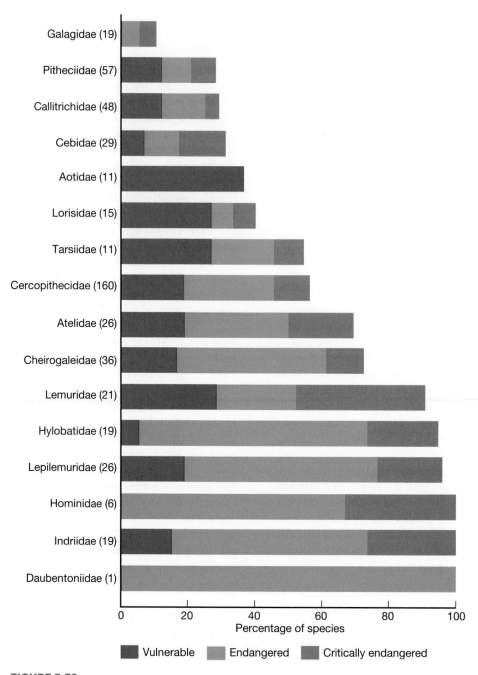

Vulnerable ■ Endangered ■ Critically endangered

FIGURE 5.32

Conservation status of primate families. Throughout the primate order, primate species are at considerable risk of extinction.

previously unknown type of monkey in the highlands of Tanzania (**Figure 5.33**). Genetic data indicate that these monkeys are different enough from other species to be placed in their own genus, *Rungwecebus*, and are most closely related to baboons. This species was restricted to two small areas of evergreen forest, 350 km (230 mi.) apart, and the total population was estimated to be only 1,100 individuals. Later surveys suggest that their numbers may be declining, and they may now be restricted to only one of the two original localities. New species continue to be found. Three new species of mouse lemurs were discovered in Madagascar in 2016, and in 2017 a new ape species was named the skywalker hoolock gibbon.

The main threat to primates in the wild is habitat loss related to agriculture, logging and wood harvesting, and livestock farming and ranching.

As arboreal residents of the tropics, most primate populations are directly affected by the rapid and widespread destruction of the world's forests. Between 1990 and 2010, agricultural enterprises claimed 1.5 square kilometers of land in areas where primates range, and 2 million square kilometers of forest were lost (**Figure 5.34**).

The destruction of tropical forests is the product of economic and demographic pressures acting on governments and local residents. Many developing countries have huge foreign debts that must be repaid. The need to raise funds to pay off these debts generates intense pressure for timber harvesting and more intensive agricultural activity. Global demand for palm oil products is linked to habitat loss and major declines of orangutan populations in Borneo and Sumatra. In Central and South America, massive areas have been cleared for large cattle ranches. In southwestern China and India, the expansion of rubber plantations has threatened several species of gibbons, one species of slow loris, and the Phayre's langur.

Rapid increases in the population of underdeveloped countries in the tropics have also created intense demand for additional agricultural land. In West Africa, Asia, and South America, for example, vast expanses of forests have been cleared to accommodate the demands of subsistence farmers trying to feed their families as well as to meet the needs of large-scale agricultural projects.

In many areas around the world, particularly South America and Africa, primates are also hunted for meat. Although systematic information about the impact of hunting on wild primate populations is scant, some case studies reveal troubling trends. In one forest in Kenya, for example, 1,200 blue monkeys and nearly 700 baboons were killed by subsistence hunters in one year. In the Brazilian Amazon, one family of rubber tappers killed 200 woolly monkeys, 100 spider monkeys, and 80 howler monkeys during an 18-month span. In addition to subsistence hunting, there is also an active market for "bushmeat" in many urban areas.

In equatorial Africa, primate populations have also been severely affected by outbreaks of epidemic disease. About 26% of one habituated chimpanzee group in the Taï Forest of Ivory Coast died of the Ebola virus during a one-month period. Later, anthrax killed more members of the same community. Several hundred gorillas, belonging to more than 100 groups, regularly foraged in a swampy clearing in Odzala-Kokoua National Park in the Congo. During a two-year period, 95% of these gorillas died from Ebola.

The capture for trade of live primates has been reduced since the Convention on International Trade in Endangered Species of Wild Fauna and Flora (CITES) was drafted in 1973. The parties to CITES, which now number 183 countries, ban commercial trade of all endangered species and monitor the trade of those that are at risk of becoming endangered. CITES has been an important weapon in protecting primate populations around the world. The United States imported more than 100,000 primates each year before ratifying CITES but had reduced this number to approximately 13,000 a decade after signing the international agreement.

Although CITES has made an important impact, some problems persist. Illegal live capture for trade remains a major threat to certain species, particularly the great apes, whose high commercial value creates strong incentives for illegal commerce. In many communities, young primates are kept as pets. For each animal taken into captivity,

FIGURE 5.33

The kapunji monkey was first discovered by scientists in 2005.

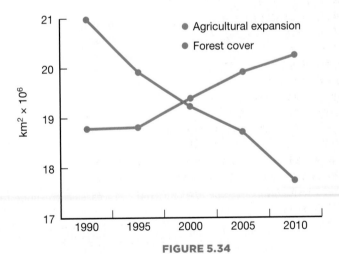

FIGURE 5.34

As agricultural land use expands, forest cover declines in the neotropics, Africa, and Southeast Asia. Because most primates live in forested areas, deforestation has serious impacts on their numbers.

many other animals are put at risk because hunters cannot obtain young primates without capturing their mothers, who are usually killed in the process. In addition, many prospective pets die from injuries suffered during capture and transport or from poor housing conditions and inappropriate diets while in captivity.

Efforts to save endangered primate populations have met with some success.

Although much remains to be done, conservation efforts have significantly improved the survival prospects of several primate species. These efforts have helped preserve muriquis and golden lion tamarins in Brazil and golden bamboo lemurs in Madagascar. But there is no room for complacency. Promising efforts to save orangutans in Indonesia and mountain gorillas in Rwanda have been severely impeded by regional political struggles and armed conflict, putting the apes' habitats and their lives in serious jeopardy. Several strategies to conserve forest habitats and preserve animal populations are on the table. These include land-for-debt swaps in which foreign debts are forgiven in exchange for commitments to conserve natural habitats, to develop ecotourism projects, and to promote sustainable development of forest resources. But as conservationists study these solutions and try to implement them, the problems facing the world's primates become more pressing. More and more forests disappear each year, and many primates are lost, perhaps forever.

Key Terms

viviparity (p. 109)
nocturnal (p. 111)
diurnal (p. 111)
conspecifics (p. 111)
sexual dimorphism (p. 111)
binocular vision (p. 112)
stereoscopic vision (p. 112)
strepsirrhine (p. 112)
haplorrhine (p. 112)
opposable (p. 113)
prehensile (p. 113)

hind-limb dominated (p. 113)
olfactory (p. 113)
molars (p. 113)
incisors (p. 113)
canine (p. 113)
premolars (p. 113)
dental formula (p. 116)
maxilla (p. 116)
mandible (p. 116)

bilaterally symmetrical (p. 116)
infraorder (p. 118)
basal metabolic rate (p. 126)
carbohydrates (p. 126)
toxins (p. 126)
secondary compounds (p. 126)
alkaloids (p. 126)
gum (p. 127)

frugivore (p. 128)
folivore (p. 128)
insectivore (p. 128)
gummivore (p. 128)
territories (p. 131)
social organization (p. 136)
solitary (p. 136)
mating systems (p. 137)
pair bonding (p. 137)
polyandry (p. 137)
polygyny (p. 137)

Study Questions

1. What is the difference between homology and analogy? What evolutionary processes correspond to these terms?

2. Suppose that a group of extraterrestrial scientists lands on Earth and enlists your help in identifying animals. How do you help them recognize members of the primate order?

3. What kinds of habitats do most primates occupy? What are the features of this kind of environment?

4. Large primates often subsist on low-quality food such as leaves; small primates specialize in high-quality foods such as fruit and insects. Why is body size associated with dietary quality in this way?

5. For folivores, tropical forests seem to provide an abundant and constant supply of food. Why is this not an accurate assessment?

6. Territorial primates do not have to share access to food, sleeping sites, mates, and other resources with

members of other groups. Given that territoriality reduces the extent of competition over resources, why are not all primates territorial?

7. Most primates specialize in one type of food, such as fruit, leaves, or insects. What benefits might such specializations have? What costs might be associated with specialization?

8. Nocturnal primates are smaller, more solitary, and more arboreal than diurnal primates. What might be the reason(s) for this pattern?

9. Sociality is a relatively uncommon feature in nature. What are the potential advantages and disadvantages of living in social groups? Why are virtually all primates social?

10. The future of primates, and other occupants of tropical forests, is precarious. What are the major hazards that primates face?

Further Reading

Campell, C. J., A. Fuentes, K. C. MacKinnon, M. Panger, and S. K. Bearder, eds. 2007. *Primates in Perspective*. New York: Oxford University Press.

Cowlishaw, G., and R. I. M. Dunbar. 2000. *Primate Conservation Biology*. Chicago: University of Chicago Press.

IUCN 2010. *IUCN Red List of Threatened Species*. Version 2010.3. www.iucnredlist.org.

Kappeler, P. M., and M. Pereira, eds. 2003. *Primate Life Histories and Socioecology*. Chicago: University of Chicago Press.

Kramer, R., C. van Schaik, and J. Johnson, eds. 1997. *Last Stand: Protected Areas and the Defense of Tropical Biodiversity*. New York: Oxford University Press.

Mitani, J., J. Call, P. Kappeler, R. Palombit, and J. B. Silk, eds. 2012. *The Evolution of Primate Societies*. Chicago: University of Chicago Press.

Strier, K. B. 2010. *Primate Behavioral Ecology*. 4th ed. Boston: Allyn & Bacon.

Visit DIGITAL.WWNORTON.COM/HOWHUMANS8 to
- **review this chapter with personalized, interactive questions via InQuizitive**
- **view videos and animations on this chapter's key topics**

6

PRIMATE MATING SYSTEMS

- **The Language of Adaptive Explanations p. 144**
- **The Evolution of Reproductive Strategies p. 145**
- **Reproductive Strategies of Females p. 147**
- **Sexual Selection and Male Mating Strategies p. 155**
- **Male Reproductive Tactics p. 159**

CHAPTER OBJECTIVES

By the end of this chapter you should be able to

A. Explain why reproduction is the central act of all living things.

B. Describe how mammalian reproductive biology influences the reproductive strategies of primate females.

C. Discuss the factors that influence female reproductive success.

D. Describe the process of sexual selection and explain why it favors traits

that would not be favored by normal natural selection.

E. Describe how competition among males over access to females influences male reproductive strategies.

F. Explain why infanticide is an adaptive strategy for male primates in some circumstances.

Reproduction is the central act in the life of every living thing. Primates perform a dizzying variety of behaviors: Gibbons fill the forest with their haunting duets, baboons threaten and posture in their struggle for dominance over other members of their group, and chimpanzees use carefully selected stone hammers to crack open tough nuts. But all of these behaviors evolved for a single ultimate purpose: to enhance reproduction. According to Darwin's theory, complex adaptations exist because they evolved step by step through natural selection. At each step, only those modifications that increased reproductive success were favored and retained in later generations of offspring. Thus each morphological feature and every behavior exist only because they were part of an adaptation that contributed to reproduction in ancestral populations. As a consequence, mating systems (the way animals find mates and care for offspring) play a crucial role in our understanding of primate societies.

Understanding the diverse reproductive strategies of nonhuman primates illuminates human evolution because we share many elements of our reproductive physiology with other species of primates.

To understand the evolution of primate mating systems, we must take into account that the reproductive strategies of living primates are influenced by their phylogenetic heritage as mammals. Mammals reproduce sexually. After conception, mammalian females carry their young internally. After they give birth, mothers suckle their young for an extended period. The mammalian male's role in the reproductive process is more variable than that of the female. In some species, males' only contribution to their offspring is a single sperm at the moment of conception. In other species, males defend territories; provide for their mates; and feed, carry, and protect their offspring.

Although mammalian physiology constrains primate reproductive strategies, there is still considerable diversity in primate mating systems and reproductive behavior. Patterns of courtship, mate choice, and parental care vary greatly within the primate order. In some species, male reproductive success is determined mainly by success in competition with other males over access to mates; in others, it is strongly influenced by female preferences. In many pair-bonded species, both males and females care for their offspring; in most non–pair-bonded species, females provide almost all care for offspring and males focus mainly on gaining access to females.

What aspects of mating do humans share with other primates? Until very recent times, all pregnant women nursed their offspring for an extended period, as do other primates. In nearly all traditional human societies, fathers contribute extensively to their children's welfare, providing resources, security, and social support. An understanding of the phylogenetic and ecological factors that shape the reproductive strategies of other primates may help us understand how evolutionary forces shaped the reproductive strategies of our hominin ancestors and give us insight about the reproductive behavior of men and women in contemporary human societies.

The Language of Adaptive Explanations

In evolutionary biology, the term *strategy* is used to refer to behavioral mechanisms that lead to particular courses of behavior in particular functional contexts, such as foraging or reproduction.

Biologists often use the term **strategy** to describe the behavior of animals. For example, folivory is characterized as a foraging strategy, and monogamy is described as a mating strategy. When evolutionary biologists use the term, they mean something very different from what we normally mean when we use *strategy* to describe, say, a general's military maneuvers or a baseball manager's tactics. In common usage, *strategy* implies a conscious plan of action. Evolutionary biologists think that other animals do not consciously decide to defend their territories, wean their offspring at a particular age, monitor their ingestion of secondary plant compounds, and so on. Instead, *strategy* refers to a set of behaviors occurring in a specific functional context, such as mating, parenting, or foraging. Strategies are the product of natural selection acting on individuals to shape the motivations, reactions, preferences, capacities, and choices that influence behavior. Strategies that led to greater reproductive success in ancestral populations have been favored by natural selection and represent adaptations.

Cost and benefit refer to how particular behavioral strategies affect reproductive success.

Different behaviors have different impacts on an animal's genetic fitness. Behaviors are said to be beneficial if they increase the genetic fitness of individuals and costly if they reduce the genetic fitness of individuals. For example, we argued in Chapter 5 that ranging behavior involves a trade-off between the benefits of exclusive access to a particular area and the costs of territorial defense. Ultimately, benefits and costs should be measured as changes in reproductive success, but this is often very difficult to do, particularly in long-lived animals such as primates. Instead, researchers rely on indirect measures, such as foraging efficiency (measured as the quantity of nutrients obtained per unit time) and assume that, all other things being equal, behavioral strategies that increase foraging efficiency also enhance genetic fitness and will be favored by natural selection. We will encounter many other examples of this type of reasoning in the chapters that follow.

The Evolution of Reproductive Strategies

Primate females always provide lots of care for their young, but males do so in only a few species.

The amount of parental care varies greatly within the animal kingdom. In most species, parents do little for their offspring. For example, most frogs lay their eggs and never see their offspring again. In such species, the nutrients that females leave in the egg are the only form of parental care. In contrast, primates—like almost all birds and mammals, and some invertebrates and fish—provide much more than just the resources included in gametes. At least one parent—and sometimes both—shelters its young from the elements, protects them from predators, and provides them with food.

The *relative* amount of parental care provided by mothers and fathers also varies within the animal kingdom. In species without parental care, females produce large, nutrient-rich gametes, and males produce small gametes and supply only genes. Among species with parental care, however, all possible arrangements occur. Primate mothers always nurse their offspring and often provide extensive care (**Figure 6.1**). The behavior of fathers is much more variable. In many species, fathers give nothing to their offspring other than the genes contained in their sperm. In a minority of species, however, males are devoted parents. In other taxa, patterns differ. For example, in most bird species, males and females form pairs and raise their young together (**Figure 6.2**).

The amount of time, energy, and resources that the males and females of a species invest in their offspring has profound consequences for the evolution of virtually every aspect of their social behavior and many aspects of their morphology. The selection pressures that affect males and females in species with equal parental investment are very different from the selection pressures that affect males and females in species in which females invest much more than males do. Thus it is important to understand why the amounts and patterns of parental investment differ among species.

Males do not care for their offspring (1) when they can easily use their resources to acquire many additional matings or (2) when caring for their offspring would not appreciably increase the offspring's fitness.

At first glance, it seems odd that most primate males fail to provide much care for their offspring. Surely, if the males helped their mates, they would increase the chances

FIGURE 6.1

In all primate species, females nurse their young. In baboons and many other species, females provide most of the direct care that infants receive.

FIGURE 6.2

In most species of birds, the male and female form a pair bond and jointly raise their young. Here, a bald eagle carries food to its hungry brood.

FIGURE 6.3

In most non–pair-bonded species, males have relatively little contact with infants. Although males such as this bonnet macaque are sometimes quite tolerant of infants, they rarely carry, groom, feed, or play with them.

FIGURE 6.4

Male sea horses carry fertilized eggs in a special pouch and provide care for their offspring as the young grow.

that their offspring would survive to adulthood. Therefore, we might expect paternal care to be favored by natural selection (**Figure 6.3**).

If time, energy, and other resources were unlimited, this reasoning would be correct. In real life, though, time, energy, and material resources are always in short supply. The effort that an individual devotes to caring for offspring (parenting effort) diverts time and energy away from mate competition (mating effort). Natural selection will favor individuals that allocate effort among these competing demands so as to maximize the number of surviving offspring they produce.

To understand the evolution of unequal parental investment, we must identify the conditions under which one sex can profitably reduce its parental effort at the expense of its partner. Consider a species in which most males help their mates feed and care for their offspring. Even in such a species, a few males will have a heritable tendency to invest less in their offspring. We will refer to these two types as "investing" and "noninvesting" fathers. Because time, energy, and resources are always limited, males that invest more in mating effort must invest less in parenting effort. On average, the offspring of such males will receive less care than will the offspring of other males, making those offspring less likely to survive and to reproduce successfully when they mature. On the other hand, because these males invest less in parenting effort, on average they will acquire more mates than will investing males. Mutations favoring the tendency to invest less in parenting effort will increase in frequency when the benefits to males (measured in terms of the increase in fitness gained from additional matings) outweigh the costs to males (measured as the decrease in offspring fitness due to a reduction in paternal care).

This reasoning suggests that unequal parental investment will be favored when one or both of the following are true:

1. Acquiring additional mates is relatively easy, so considerable gains are achieved by investing in mating effort.

2. The fitness of offspring raised by only one parent is high, so the payoff for investing in parenting effort is relatively low.

The key factors are the costs of finding additional mates and the benefits associated with incremental increases in the amount of care that offspring receive. When females are widely separated, for example, it may be difficult for males to locate them. In these cases, males may profit more from helping their current mates and investing in their offspring than from searching for additional mates. On the other hand, if females are capable of rearing their offspring alone and need little help from males, then investing males may be at a reproductive disadvantage compared with males that abandon females after mating and devote their efforts to finding eligible females.

The mammalian reproductive system commits primate females to investing in their offspring.

So far, there is nothing in our reasoning to say that if only one sex invests, it should always be the female. Why aren't there primate species in which males do all the work and females compete with each other for access to males? This is not simply a theoretical possibility: Female sea horses deposit their eggs in their mate's brood pouch and then swim away and look for a new mate (**Figure 6.4**). There are whole families of fish in which male parental care is more common than female parental care; and in several species of birds—including rheas, spotted sandpipers, and jacanas—females abandon their clutches after the eggs are laid, leaving their mates to feed and protect the young.

In primates and other mammals, selection tends to favor high female investment because females lactate and males do not. Pregnancy and lactation commit mammalian females to invest in their young and limit the benefits of male investment in offspring. Because offspring depend on their mothers for nourishment during pregnancy and after birth, mothers cannot abandon their young without greatly reducing their offspring's chances of surviving. On the other hand, males are never capable of rearing their offspring without help from females. Therefore, when only one sex invests in offspring, it is invariably the female. Sometimes males can help females by defending territories or by carrying infants so that the mother can feed more efficiently, as siamangs and owl monkeys do. Usually, however, these benefits are relatively insignificant, and selection favors males that allocate more time and energy to mating than to caring for their offspring.

You may be wondering why selection has not produced males that can lactate. This would seem like a highly desirable adaptation because it would enable males to make important contributions to offspring care and protect infants from the consequences of maternal mortality. But, as we noted in Chapter 3, most biologists believe the developmental changes that would enable males to lactate would also make them sterile. This is an example of a developmental constraint.

Reproductive Strategies of Females

Female primates invest heavily in each of their offspring.

Pregnancy and lactation are time-consuming and energetically expensive activities for all female primates, including humans. The duration of pregnancy ranges from 59 days in the tiny mouse lemur to 255 days in the hefty gorilla. In primates, as in most other animals, larger animals tend to have longer pregnancies than do smaller animals (**Figure 6.5**), but primates have considerably longer pregnancies than we would expect on the basis of their body sizes alone. The extended duration of pregnancy in primates is related to the fact that brain tissue develops very slowly. Primates have very large brains in relation to their body sizes, so extra time is needed for fetal brain growth and development during pregnancy. Primates also have an extended period of dependence after birth, further increasing the amount of care mothers must provide. Throughout this period, mothers must meet not only their own nutritional requirements but also

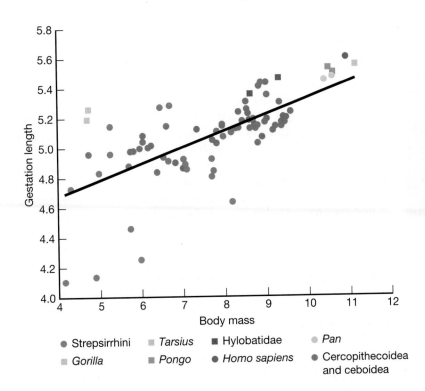

FIGURE 6.5

As in other mammalian taxa, maternal body size is correlated with gestation length. Great apes have the longest pregnancies, and small-bodied strepsirrhine primates have relatively short pregnancies.

those of their growing infants. In some species, offspring may weigh as much as 30% of their mother's body weight at the time of weaning.

The energy costs of pregnancy and lactation impose important constraints on female reproductive behavior. Because it takes so much time and energy to produce an infant, each female can rear only a relatively small number of surviving infants during her lifetime (**Figure 6.6**). For example, a female baboon that gives birth for the first time when she is about 6 or 7 years old and lives to a ripe old age of 30 would give birth to about a dozen offspring during her life. Of course, not all females will survive to old age, and nearly half of all infants will die before they reach reproductive age. Thus most baboon females produce a relatively small number of surviving infants over a lifetime, and each infant represents a substantial proportion of a female's lifetime fitness. Therefore, we would expect mothers to be strongly committed to the welfare of each of their offspring.

A female's reproductive success depends on her ability to obtain enough resources to support herself and her offspring.

In most species of primates, including humans, females must achieve a minimum nutritional level to ovulate and to conceive. For animals living in the wild, without takeout pizza or 24-hour grocery stores, getting enough to eat each day is usually a serious challenge. There is considerable evidence that female reproductive success is limited by the availability of resources within the local habitat. When females have better access to high-quality resources, they grow faster, mature earlier, and give birth at shorter intervals. At a number of sites in Japan, for example, free-ranging monkeys' natural diets were intensively supplemented with wheat, sweet potatoes, rice, and other foods by humans for many years (**Figure 6.7**). This led to rapid increases in group size (**Figure 6.8**). Comparisons of wild and provisioned primates elsewhere tell a similar story.

Sources of Variation in Female Reproductive Performance

Very young and very old females do not reproduce as successfully as middle-aged females.

Using data on births to females of known ages, researchers can compute age-specific fertility rates that provide estimates of the likelihood that a female of a given age will produce an infant. These analyses reveal that young females typically reproduce at lower rates than do middle-aged females. For example, **Figure 6.9** shows that young female baboons and gorillas have lower birth rates than do older females. First-time (**primiparous**) mountain gorilla mothers have 50% higher rates of infant mortality and 20% longer interbirth intervals after surviving births than do older females. Even among Japanese macaques, whose diets are enriched by provisioning, young mothers have longer interbirth intervals than do older females: 67% of first-time mothers skip a year before producing a second infant, whereas only 33% of experienced (**multiparous**) mothers skip years between births.

The relatively low fertility and high infant mortality of young females reflect the fact that when female monkeys and apes begin to reproduce, they are not yet fully grown. As a consequence, energetic investment in infants competes directly with energetic investment in their own skeletal growth and development. Younger females also may lack experience in handling newborn infants and may not provide appropriate care for them.

In marked contrast to humans, most primate females continue to reproduce throughout their lives. Susan Alberts of Duke University led a team of researchers who examined the survivorship and reproductive activity of females in several well-studied

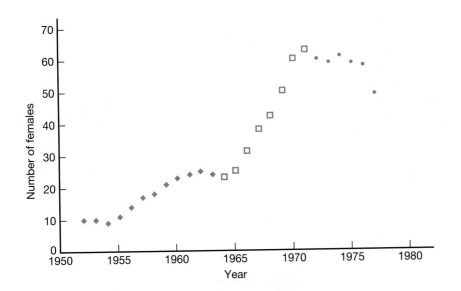

FIGURE 6.8

The size of the Koshima troop of Japanese macaques grew when provisioning was initiated (*diamonds*), and grew even more rapidly when provisioning was intensified (*squares*), and then dropped when provisioning was restricted (*circles*).

populations of primates, as varied as sifakas and gorillas. Their analyses show that the age of last reproduction is close to the age at death for most females (**Figure 6.10**). The postreproductive period represents only 1% to 6% of the life span in these species, but 43% of the life span in a representative population of human foragers, the !Kung.

Longevity is a major source of variation in female fitness.

To borrow from Woody Allen, 80% of success is showing up. This seems to be true for primate females as well. The longer females live, the more newborns they produce and the more surviving offspring they raise. Variation in longevity is a major contributor to variation in lifetime fitness among females. For example, longevity accounts for as much as 50% to 70% of the variance in lifetime reproductive success among female baboons who reach reproductive age, swamping variance from other sources. Although we have some idea of the sources of mortality among adult females, such as predation and disease, we know very little about why some females live longer than others.

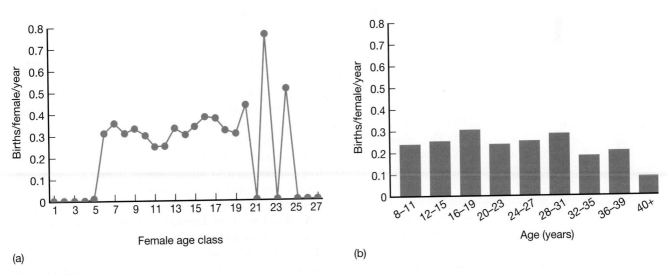

(a) (b)

FIGURE 6.9

The number of births per female is given for (a) baboons and (b) gorillas of different ages. In both species, birth rates remain fairly steady until females reach advanced ages and then decline. The variation in birth rates among old female baboons occurs partly because most females die before they reach such advanced ages, so samples are small.

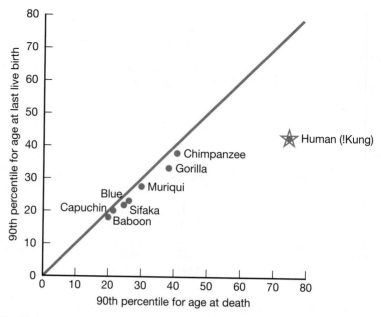

FIGURE 6.10

Female longevity is plotted against the age at last birth for a variety of primates. The 90th percentile for age at death represents the age by which 90% of the females in the sample have died (in other words, 10% of the females live past this age). The 90th percentile for age at last birth represents the age at which 90% of the females in the sample produced their last infant. The close association between age at death and age at last infant means that most primate females continue to reproduce throughout their lives.

High-ranking females tend to reproduce more successfully than do low-ranking females.

As we explained in Chapter 5, females often compete for access to food resources that they need to reproduce successfully. In some situations, females form dominance hierarchies (**A Closer Look 6.1**), which regulate access to resources. High-ranking females tend to have priority of access to the best feeding sites and can keep others from food. This may enable high-ranking females to obtain more food or higher-quality food, or forage more efficiently than lower-ranking females. For example, in a study of baboons, Robert Barton and Andrew Whiten found that the daily food intake of high-ranking females was 30% higher than that of low-ranking females. But not all studies reveal such large disparities. This may be because low-ranking females compensate for their low status by feeding on the periphery of the group, where they are less likely to be interrupted. Although doing so may reduce competition for food, it may make low-ranking females and their offspring more vulnerable to predators.

If dominance rank influences access to valuable resources and access to resources influences female reproductive success, then we should expect to find a positive correlation between dominance rank and reproductive success. And, indeed, high rank does confer reproductive advantages on females in several species. In some multi-male, multifemale groups of Old World monkeys, female dominance rank is correlated with various aspects of females' reproductive performance. In Amboseli, Kenya, for example, the offspring of high-ranking female baboons grow faster and mature earlier than do the offspring of low-ranking females. In captive vervet groups, high-ranking females have shorter interbirth intervals than lower-ranking females have. In some macaque populations, the offspring of high-ranking females are more likely to survive to reproductive age than the offspring of lower-ranking females. Associations between

CHAPTER 6: Primate Mating Systems

6.1 Dominance Hierarchies

In many animal species, as varied as crickets, chickens, and chimpanzees, competitive encounters within pairs of individuals are common. The outcome of these contests may be related to the participants' relative size, strength, experience, or willingness to fight. In many species, for example, larger and heavier individuals regularly defeat smaller individuals. If there are real differences in power (based on size, weight, experience, or aggressiveness) between individuals, then we would expect the outcomes of dominance contests to be about the same from day to day. This is often the case. When dominance interactions between two individuals have predictable outcomes, we say that a **dominance** relationship has been established.

When dominance interactions have predictable outcomes, we can assign dominance rankings to individuals. Consider the four hypothetical females in **Figure 6.11a**, which we will call Blue, Turquoise, Green, and Purple. Blue always beats Turquoise, Green, and Purple. Turquoise never beats Blue but always beats Green and Purple. Green never beats Blue or Turquoise but always beats Purple. Poor Purple never beats anybody. We can summarize the outcome of these confrontations between pairs of females in a **dominance matrix** such as the one in **Figure 6.11b**, and we can use the data to assign numerical ranks to the females. In this case, Blue ranks first, Turquoise second, Green third, and Purple fourth. When females can defeat all the females ranked below them and none of the females ranked above them, dominance relationships are said to be **transitive**. When the relationships within all sets of three individuals (trios) are transitive, the hierarchy is linear.

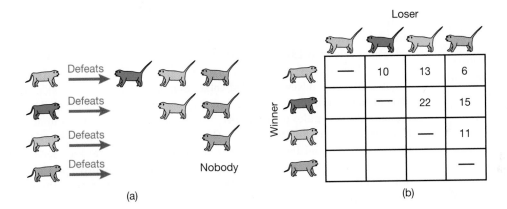

(a)

(b)

FIGURE 6.11

(a) Suppose that four hypothetical females—named Blue, Turquoise, Green, and Purple—have the following transitive dominance relationships: Blue defeats the other three in dominance contests. Turquoise cannot defeat Blue but can defeat Green and Purple. Green loses to Blue and Turquoise but can defeat Purple. Purple can't defeat anyone. (b) The results of data such as those in part a are often tabulated in a dominance matrix, with the winners listed down the left side and the losers across the top. The value in each cell of the matrix represents the number of times one female defeated the other. Here, Blue defeated Turquoise 10 times and Green defeated Purple 11 times. There are no entries below the diagonal because females were never defeated by lower-ranking females.

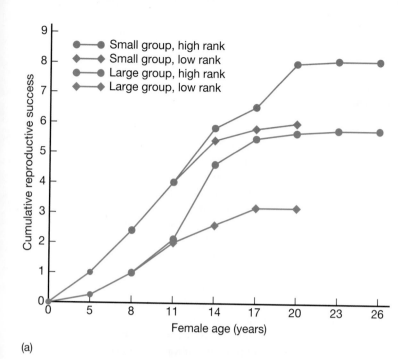

(a)

(b)

FIGURE 6.12

(a) In free-ranging groups of long-tailed macaques, both group size and dominance rank influence females' lifetime reproductive success. In general, females living in small groups reproduce more successfully than do females living in larger groups. But in both large and small groups, high-ranking females reproduce more successfully than do low-ranking females. (b) A long-tailed macaque and her nursing infant.

FIGURE 6.13

A female gray langur at Jodhpur threatens another group member.

dominance rank and reproductive success may produce variation in lifetime fitness among females, particularly if females maintain the same rank over their lives, as female macaques and baboons typically do. Thus Maria van Noordwijk and Carel van Schaik have found substantial differences in the lifetime reproductive success of high-, middle-, and low-ranking long-tailed macaques (**Figure 6.12**).

In gray langurs, female rank also influences female reproductive performance. In this species, female rank is inversely related to age, so young females typically outrank older ones (**Figure 6.13**). Long-term studies of hanuman langurs near Jodhpur, India, conducted by a group of German primatologists, including Carola Borries (at Stony Brook University in New York) and Volker Sommer (at University College London), have shown that young, high-ranking females reproduce more successfully than do older, lower-ranking females (**Figure 6.14**). Studies of gray langurs at Ramnagar in southern Nepal conducted by another group of German primatologists, including Andreas Koenig, Carola Borries, and Paul Winkler, have found that high-ranking females manage to commandeer higher-quality food patches and can consequently maintain higher levels of body fat. Females in good condition have higher fertility rates than do females in poor condition.

Anne Pusey, now at Duke University, and her colleagues have found that the offspring of high-ranking female chimpanzees are more likely to survive to the age of weaning than are the offspring of low-ranking females. In addition, their daughters grow faster and mature earlier than do the daughters of low-ranking females. These differences create substantial differences in lifetime fitness for high- and low-ranking female chimpanzees at Gombe Stream National Park, Tanzania (**Figure 6.15**). Recent analyses of long-term data on female mountain gorillas by Martha Robbins of the Max Planck Institute for Evolutionary Anthropology and her colleagues show that high-ranking females have substantially shorter interbirth intervals than low-ranking females.

Marmoset and tamarin groups in the wild often contain more than one adult female, but the dominant female is usually the only one who breeds successfully. Other group members, typically offspring from previous litters, help care for the dominant pair's offspring. Subordinate females do not cycle normally, and if they do become pregnant the dominant female is likely to kill their infants. Infanticidal attack on the offspring of subordinates is probably favored because it reduces competition for resources needed by the dominant female's infants.

The quality of social bonds may also influence female reproductive success.

In some species of primates, females spend a considerable amount of time sitting near, grooming, and interacting peacefully with other group members. Females save time for socializing, even when times are tough (**Figure 6.16**). For example, female baboons are forced to spend more time foraging and moving between feeding sites in the dry season than in the wet season. In response, they cut down on the time that they spend resting, but they preserve time for socializing. Social bonds seem to matter to females. Anne Engh, at Kalamazoo College, and colleagues from the University of Pennsylvania found that female baboons who lose close companions to predators experience substantial increases in cortisol levels, a hormonal indicator of stress. Now, you might think that females are simply stressed about living

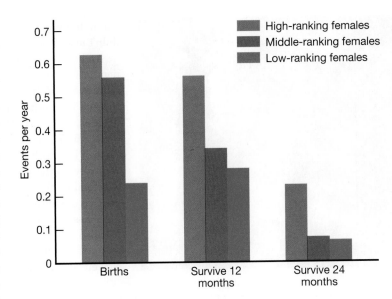

FIGURE 6.14

Female gray langurs reproduce more successfully when they are young and hold higher rank than when they are older and have lower rank. The three bars on the left represent the proportion of females of each rank category who give birth each year. The other sets of bars represent the proportion of females in each rank category who give birth each year to infants who survive to 12 months and 24 months. Dominance rank influences both the likelihood of giving birth and the likelihood that infants will survive.

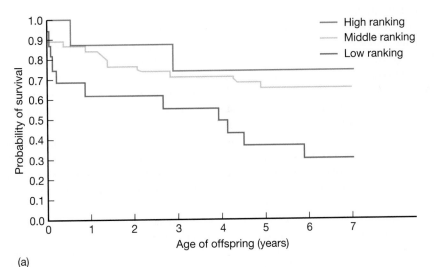

(a)

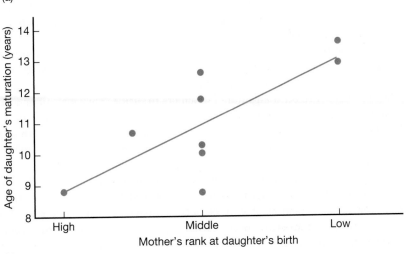

(b)

FIGURE 6.15

Among chimpanzees at Gombe Stream National Park, Tanzania, female rank influences reproductive performance. (a) The offspring of high-ranking (*red line*) and middle-ranking (*blue line*) females are more likely to survive to weaning age than are the offspring of low-ranking females (*green line*). (b) Daughters of high-ranking females mature at earlier ages than do the daughters of lower-ranking females.

FIGURE 6.16

In many primate species, females spend considerable amounts of time in the company of other group members. Here adult female langurs rest and groom.

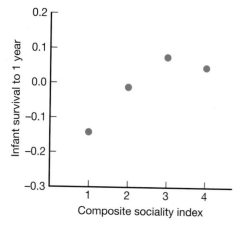

FIGURE 6.17

The sociality index is a composite measure that captures information about how much time females spend grooming and associating with other group members. High values represent more sociable females. More sociable females have higher survivorship among their offspring, and these effects are not due to differences in female rank or the size of their families.

through a predator attack, but females who were present in the group and didn't lose close associates were not affected.

Archival analyses of data derived from long-term studies of two baboon populations suggest that females who have stronger social bonds reproduce more successfully than other females. Females who spent more time grooming and near other group members had more surviving infants than other females, and these effects were independent of the females' dominance rank (**Figure 6.17**). In fact, sociality seems to insulate females from some of the costs of low rank. The most sociable low-ranking females reproduce as successfully as the most sociable high-ranking females. We do not yet know why females who spend more time interacting with others enjoy these reproductive advantages. It's possible that they derive material benefits from their associations with others, such as better protection from predators. It's also possible that social contact reduces females' levels of stress, and this stress reduction has beneficial effects on their health and the welfare of their offspring.

Reproductive Trade-offs

Females must make a trade-off between the number of offspring they produce and the quality of care they provide.

Just as both males and females must allocate limited effort to parental investment and mating, females must apportion resources among their offspring. All other things being equal, natural selection will favor individuals that can convert effort into offspring most efficiently. Because mothers have a finite amount of effort to devote to offspring, they cannot maximize both the quality and the quantity of the offspring they produce. If a mother invests great effort in one infant, she must reduce her investment in others. If a mother produces many offspring, she will be unable to invest very much in any of them.

In nature, maternal behavior reflects this trade-off when a mother modifies her investment in relation to an offspring's needs. Initially, infants spend virtually all of their time in contact with their mothers. The very young infant depends entirely on its mother for food and transportation and cannot anticipate or cope with environmental hazards. At this stage, mothers actively maintain close contact with their infants (**Figure 6.18**), retrieving them when they stray too far and scooping them up when danger arises.

As infants grow older, however, they become progressively more independent and more competent. They venture away from their mothers to play with other infants and to explore their surroundings. They begin to sample food plants, sometimes mooching scraps of their mother's food. They become aware of the dangers around them, attending to alarm calls given by other group members and reacting to disturbances within the group. Mothers use a variety of tactics to actively encourage their infants to become more independent. They may subtly resist their infants' attempts to suckle. They may also encourage their infants to travel independently. Nursing is gradually limited to brief and widely spaced bouts that may provide the infant more with psychological comfort than physical nourishment. At this stage, infants are carried only when they are ill, injured, or in great danger.

The changes in maternal behavior reflect the shifting balance between the requirements of the growing infant and the energy costs to the mother of catering to her infant's needs. As infants grow older, they become heavier to carry and require more food, imposing substantial burdens on mothers. However, as infants grow older they also become more capable of feeding themselves and of traveling independently, and this means that mothers can gradually limit investment in their older infants without jeopardizing their welfare (**Figure 6.19**). Mothers can thus conserve resources that can be allocated to infants born later. Moreover, because lactation inhibits ovulation in many primate species, a mother must wean her present infant before she can conceive another.

Sexual Selection and Male Mating Strategies

Sexual selection leads to adaptations that allow males to compete more effectively with other males for access to females.

So far, we have seen that primate females invest heavily in each of their young and produce relatively few offspring during their lives. Moreover, most primate females can raise their offspring without help from males. Female reproductive success is limited by access to food, not access to mates. Males can potentially produce progeny from many females, and as a result, males compete for access to females. Characteristics that increase male success in competition for mates will spread as a result of what Darwin called **sexual selection**.

It is important to understand the distinction between natural selection and sexual selection. Most kinds of natural selection favor phenotypes in both males and females that enhance their ability to survive and reproduce. Many of these traits are related to resource acquisition, predator avoidance, and offspring care. Sexual selection is a special category of natural selection that favors traits that increase success in competition for mates, and it will be expressed most strongly in the sex whose access to members of the opposite sex is most limited. Sexual selection may favor traits that increase the animal's attractiveness to potential mates, such as the peacock's tail, the red deer's antlers, and the hamadryas baboon's mane, even if those traits reduce the ability of

FIGURE 6.18

A female chimpanzee sits beside her youngest infant in Gombe Stream National Park in Tanzania.

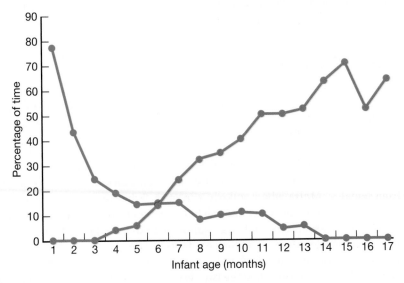

FIGURE 6.19

The y axis shows the proportion of time that free-ranging baboon infants spend suckling (*blue circles*) and feeding on their own (*red circles*). As infants get older, they spend less time suckling and more time feeding independently. These changes reflect changes in the costs and benefits of infant care for mothers.

(a)

(b)

FIGURE 6.20

Sexual selection can favor traits not favored by natural selection. (a) The peacock's tail hinders his ability to escape from predators, but it enhances his attractiveness to females. Female peahens are attracted to males that have the most eyespots in their trains. (b) Male red deer use their antlers when they fight with other males. Red deer antlers are a good example of a trait that has been favored by sexual selection.

the animal to survive or acquire resources—outcomes not usually favored by natural selection (**Figure 6.20**).

Sexual selection is often much stronger than ordinary natural selection.

In mammalian males, sexual selection can affect behavior and morphology more than other forms of natural selection because male reproductive success usually varies much more than female reproductive success. Data from long-term studies of lions conducted by Craig Packer of the University of Minnesota and Anne Pusey of Duke University show that the lifetime reproductive success of the most successful males is often much greater than that of even the most successful females (**Figure 6.21**). The same pattern is likely to hold for non–pair-bonded primates. A primate male who succeeds in competition with other males may sire many offspring; a successful female might give birth to 5 or 10 offspring. Unsuccessful males and females will fail to reproduce at all. Because the strength of selection depends on how much variation in fitness there is among individuals, sexual selection acting on male primates can be much stronger than selective forces acting on female primates. (Incidentally, in species such as sea horses, in which males invest in offspring and females do not, the entire pattern is reversed: Sexual selection acts much more strongly on females than on males.)

There are two types of sexual selection: (1) Intrasexual selection, which results from competition among males, and (2) intersexual selection, which results from female choice.

Many students of animal behavior subdivide sexual selection into two categories: intrasexual selection and intersexual selection. In species in which females cannot choose their mates, access to females will be determined by competition among males. In such species, **intrasexual selection** favors traits that enhance success in male–male competition. In species in which females can choose the partner(s) with which they mate, selection favors traits that make males more attractive to females. This is called **intersexual selection**. There is not much evidence that intersexual selection plays an important role in primates, so we will focus our attention on intrasexual selection.

Intrasexual Selection

Competition among males for access to females favors large body size, large canine teeth, and other weapons that enhance male competitive ability.

For primates and most other mammals, intrasexual competition is most intense among males. In the most basic form of male–male competition, males simply drive other males away from females. Males who regularly win such fights have higher reproductive success than those who lose. Thus intrasexual selection favors features such as large body size, horns, tusks, antlers, and large canine teeth that enable males to be effective fighters. For example, male gorillas compete fiercely over access to groups of females, and males weigh twice as much as females and have longer canine teeth.

As explained in Chapter 5, when the two sexes consistently differ in size or appearance, they are said to be sexually dimorphic (**Figure 6.22**). The body sizes of males and females represent compromises among many competing selective pressures. Larger animals are better fighters and are less vulnerable to predation, but they also need more food and take longer to mature. Intrasexual competition favors larger body size, larger teeth, and other traits that enhance fighting ability. Males compete over females;

(a)

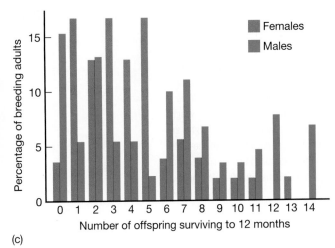

(c)

(b)

FIGURE 6.21

The reproductive success of (a) male lions is considerably more variable than that of (b) female lions. (c) In Serengeti National Park and the Ngorongoro Crater of Tanzania, few female lions fail to produce any surviving cubs, but most females produce fewer than six surviving cubs during their lives. Many males fail to produce any cubs, and a few males produce many cubs.

females compete over resources but generally do not compete over mates. The effect of intrasexual competition among males, however, is quantitatively greater than the effect of competition among females because the fitness payoff to a very successful male is greater than it is to a very successful female. Therefore, sexual selection is much more intense than ordinary natural selection. As a result, intrasexual selection leads to the evolution of sexual dimorphism.

> The fact that sexual dimorphism is greater in primate species forming one-male, multifemale groups than in pair-bonded species indicates that intrasexual selection is the likely cause of sexual dimorphism in primates.

If sexual dimorphism among primates is the product of intrasexual competition among males over access to females, then we should expect to see the most pronounced sexual dimorphism in the species in which males compete most actively over access to females. One indirect way to assess the potential extent of competition among males is to consider the ratio of males to females in social groups. In general, male competition is expected to be most intense in social groups in which males are most outnumbered by females. At first, this prediction might seem paradoxical because we might expect to have more competition when more males are present. The key to resolving this paradox is to remember that in most natural populations, there are approximately equal numbers of males and females at birth. In species that form one-male groups, there are many **bachelor males** (males who don't belong to

FIGURE 6.22

Adult male baboons are nearly twice the size of adult females. The degree of sexual dimorphism in body size is most pronounced in species with the greatest competition among males over access to females.

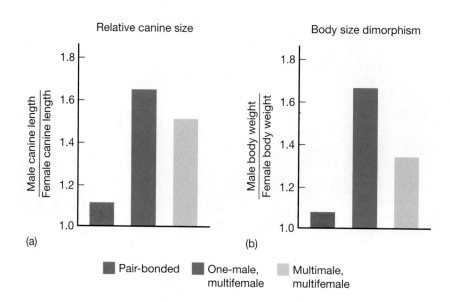

FIGURE 6.23

The degree of sexual dimorphism is a function of the ratio of males to females in social groups. (a) Relative canine size (male canine length divided by female canine length) and (b) body size dimorphism (male body weight divided by female body weight) are greater in species that form one-male, multifemale groups than in species that form multimale, multifemale groups or pair-bonded groups.

social groups) who exert constant pressure on resident males. In species that form pair bonds, each male is paired with a single female, reducing the intensity of competition among males over access to females.

Comparative analyses originally conducted by Paul Harvey of the University of Oxford and Tim Clutton-Brock of the University of Cambridge have shown that the extent of sexual dimorphism in primates indeed corresponds roughly to the composition of the groups in which the males live (**Figure 6.23**). There is little difference in body weight or canine size between males and females in species that typically form pair bonds, such as gibbons, titi monkeys, and marmosets. At the other extreme, the most pronounced dimorphism is found in species that live in one-male, multifemale groups, such as gorillas and black-and-white colobus monkeys. And in species that form multimale, multifemale groups, the extent of sexual dimorphism is generally intermediate between these extremes. Thus sexual dimorphism is most pronounced in the species in which the ratio of males to females living in bisexual (coed) groups is lowest (that is, the relative number of females is the highest).

In multimale, multifemale groups, in which females mate with several males during a given estrous period, sexual selection favors increased sperm production.

In most primate species, as with mammals in general, the female is receptive to mating mainly during the portion of her reproductive cycle when fertilization is possible. That period is called **estrus**. In primate species that live in multimale, multifemale groups, females can often mate with several males during a single estrous period. In such species, sexual selection favors increased sperm production because males who deposit the most sperm in the female reproductive tract have the greatest chance of impregnating them. Competition in the quantity of sperm is likely to be relatively unimportant in pair-bonded species because females mate mainly with their own partners. Because sperm production involves some cost to males, pair-bonded males may do better by guarding their partners when they are sexually receptive than by producing large quantities of sperm. Similarly, competition in sperm quantity probably does not play an important role in species that form one-male, multifemale groups. In these species, competition among males is over access to groups of females, which favors traits related to fighting ability. If resident males can exclude other males from associating with females in their groups, there may be little need to produce large quantities of sperm.

Social organization is associated with testis size, much as we would expect. Males with larger testes typically produce more sperm than do males with smaller testes, and males who live in multimale groups have much larger testes in relation to their body size than do males who live in either pair-bonded or one-male, multifemale groups (**Figure 6.24**).

Male Reproductive Tactics

Morphological evidence suggests that male–male competition is less intense in pair-bonded species than in species without pair bonds. As we will see in the rest of this chapter, sexual selection has shaped male mating strategies as well as male morphology.

Investing Males

Pair bonding is generally associated with relatively high levels of paternal investment.

In species that form pair bonds, males do not compete directly over access to females. In these species, males' reproductive success depends mainly on their ability to establish territories, find mates, and rear surviving offspring. In such pair-bonded species, mate guarding and offspring care are important components of males' reproductive tactics.

Mate guarding may be an important component of pair-bonded males' reproductive effort. Many genetic studies of pair-bonded birds have shown that a significant fraction of the young are not sired by the female's mate. (This is why biologists now avoid using the term *monogamy* to describe pair-bonded species.) Primatologists have known for some time that pair-bonded primates sometimes mate with individuals other than their social partners, but it has not been clear whether "extrapair" matings lead to offspring. Recent analyses of paternity in a population of white-handed gibbons that have been studied for many years by Ulrich Reichard of Southern Illinois University indicate that about 10% of offspring are the product of extrapair matings. If females occasionally participate in extrapair copulations, their partners may benefit from keeping close watch on them. Ryne Palombit of Rutgers University, who has studied the dynamics of pair bonding in gibbons, suspects that males do just that. Male gibbons are principally responsible for staying near their female partners, and most males groom their mates more than they are groomed in return (**Figure 6.25**).

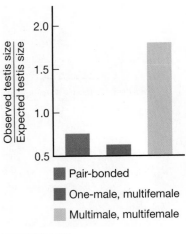

FIGURE 6.24

The average size of testes in species that typically form pair-bonded and one-male, multifemale groups is relatively smaller than the average size of testes in multimale, multifemale groups. Here, observed testis weight is divided by the expected testis weight to produce relative testis size. The expected testis weight is derived from analyses that correct for the effects of body size.

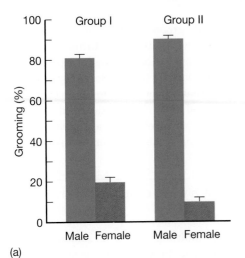

FIGURE 6.25

(a) In two white-handed gibbon groups, males groom their mates far more than they are groomed in return. The blue bar is the proportion of grooming from the male to the female, and the red bar is the proportion of grooming from the female to the male. Males' solicitous attention to females may be a form of mate guarding. (b) A pair of white-handed gibbons (*Hylobates lar*) grooms.

FIGURE 6.26

Some marmoset and tamarin groups contain more than one adult male and a single breeding female. In at least some of these groups, mating activity is limited to the group's dominant male, even though all the males participate in the care of offspring.

Pair-bonded males tend to invest heavily in their mates' offspring. In titi monkeys and owl monkeys, adult males play an active role in caring for infants. They carry them much of the time, share food with them, groom them, and protect them from predators. Male siamangs are also helpful fathers, carrying their infants for long periods every day.

In cooperatively breeding species, males invest heavily in offspring, but the reproductive benefits to males are not clear.

Groups of cooperatively breeding primates, which include marmosets and tamarins, typically consist of one dominant pair and helpers of both sexes (**Figure 6.26**). Behavioral and genetic data suggest that reproductive benefits are not divided equally among males in these species. In most species of marmosets and tamarins, the dominant male monopolizes matings with receptive females.

The presence of multiple male helpers seems to enhance female fertility. Marmosets and tamarins are unusual among primates because they usually produce twins, and females produce litters at relatively short intervals, sometimes twice a year. Males play an active role in child care, often carrying infants, grooming them, and sharing food with them. Even in the cushy conditions of captivity, infant care is costly for males. Males typically lose weight while they are caring for infants.

Data compiled by Paul Garber of the University of Illinois at Urbana-Champaign show that groups with multiple adult males reared more surviving infants than did groups with only one male (**Figure 6.27**). In contrast, groups with multiple females produced slightly fewer infants than did groups with only one female resident.

Male–Male Competition in Groups without Pair Bonds

In non–pair-bonded groups, the reproductive success of males depends on their ability to gain access to groups of unrelated females and to obtain matings with receptive females.

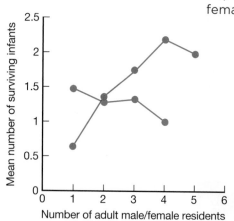

FIGURE 6.27

In tamarin groups, males clearly contribute to the reproductive success of breeding females. Tamarin groups that contain more adult males (*red circles*) produce higher numbers of surviving infants, but the effects flatten out when there are more than four males in the group. In contrast, the presence of additional females (*blue circles*) does not enhance infant survivorship.

As we explained in Chapter 5, males often live in groups that contain multiple females, and polygynous and polygynandrous mating systems characterize many primate species. Both polygyny and polygynandry are often associated with male–male competition over access to females and considerable disparities in male reproductive success. In the rest of this chapter, we will consider how males respond to competitive pressures.

In species that normally form one-male groups, males compete actively to establish residence in groups of females.

In primate species that form one-male groups, resident males face persistent pressure from nonresidents. In the highlands of Ethiopia, gelada baboons challenge resident males and attempt to take over their social groups, leading to fierce confrontations that may last for several days (**Figure 6.28**). Among gray langurs, males form all-male bands that collectively attempt to oust resident males from bisexual groups. Once they succeed in driving out the resident male, the members of the all-male band compete among themselves for sole access to the group of females. One consequence of this competition is that male tenure in one-male groups is often short.

Residence in one-male groups does not always ensure exclusive access to females.

Surprisingly, the male residents of one-male, multifemale groups sometimes face competition over access to females within their groups. In patas and blue monkeys, for

CHAPTER 6: Primate Mating Systems

example, researchers have discovered that the resident male sometimes cannot prevent other males from associating with the group and mating with sexually receptive females. Such incursions are concentrated during the mating season and may last for hours, days, or weeks and involve one or several males.

Some primate species form both one-male and multimale groups, depending on the circumstances. For example, Teresa Pope and Carolyn Crockett have found that one-male groups predominate in Venezuelan forests that are relatively sparsely populated by red howlers and where it is relatively easy to establish territories. But when the forests become more densely populated and dispersal opportunities are more limited, males adopt a different strategy: They pair up with other males and jointly defend access to groups of females. These partnerships enable males to defend larger groups of females and to maintain residence in groups for longer periods.

In gelada baboons, approximately one-third of all social units include a leader and one or more "follower" males. Follower males are sometimes former leaders who remain in the group after being deposed in a takeover. In other cases, bachelor males team up to take over social units; afterward, one male becomes the leader and one or more other males may remain in the group as followers. Noah Snyder-Mackler, now at Duke University, and his colleagues Jacinta Beehner and Thore Bergman at the University of Michigan have found that followers tend to be found in units containing larger numbers of females and that the presence of additional males increases leader males' tenure and reduces the rate of takeover attempts (**Figure 6.29**). Followers actively defend the group against challenges by groups of bachelor males. Leader males sire about 83% of the infants born within their groups, and followers sire the rest. These data suggest that leaders may tolerate the presence of followers because followers help leaders maintain their position, whereas followers may accept their subordinate positions within social units because they gain some, albeit limited, reproductive success.

FIGURE 6.28

Most gelada groups contain only one male. Males sometimes attempt to take over groups and oust the resident male; in other cases, males join groups as followers and establish co-residence. Takeovers are risky because they do not always succeed and males are sometimes badly injured.

For males in multimale groups, conflict arises over group membership and access to receptive females.

In multimale groups, there is more competition over gaining access to mating partners than over establishing group membership. Nonetheless, it is not necessarily easy to join a new group; no one puts out the welcome mat. In some macaque species, males hover near the periphery of social groups, avoid aggressive challenges by resident males, and attempt to ingratiate themselves with females. In chacma baboons, immigrant males sometimes move directly into the body of the group and engage high-ranking resident males in prolonged vocal duels and chases. Although there may be conflict when males attempt to join nonnatal groups, males spend most of their adult lives in groups that contain both males and females.

In multimale groups, males often compete directly over access to receptive females. Sometimes males attempt to drive other males away from females, to interrupt copulations, or to prevent other males from approaching or interacting with females. More often, however, male–male competition is mediated through dominance relationships that reflect male competitive abilities. These relationships are generally established in contests that can involve threats and stereotyped gestures but that can also lead to escalated conflicts in which males chase, wrestle, and bite one another (**Figure 6.30**). Male fighting ability and dominance rank are generally closely linked to physical condition:

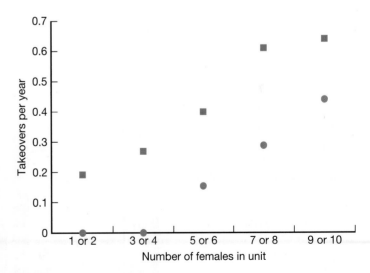

FIGURE 6.29

The rate of takeover attempts rises as the number of females in social units increases. However, units with more than one male (*circles*) experience fewer takeover attempts than units with only one male (*squares*).

FIGURE 6.30

Male baboons compete over access to an estrous female.

Prime-age males in good physical condition can usually dominate others (**Figure 6.31**).

It seems logical that male dominance rank would correlate with male reproductive success in multimale groups, but this conclusion has been energetically debated. The issue has been difficult to resolve because it is difficult to infer paternity from behavioral observations of mating. However, genetic techniques now make it possible to assess paternity with a much higher degree of precision.

As more and more genetic information about paternity has become available, the links between male dominance rank and reproductive success have become stronger. For example, Susan Alberts and her colleagues have compiled information about the reproductive performance of more than 100 adult males who lived in seven baboon social groups over a 13-year period. High-ranking males sired substantially more offspring than other males (**Figure 6.32**). In addition, the highest-ranking males were more likely to mate-guard females during estrous cycles in which those females actually conceived than during cycles in which they did not conceive. Among chimpanzees in the Taï Forest, Christophe Boesch and his colleagues at the Max Planck Institute for Evolutionary Anthropology have found that the highest-ranking male sires nearly half of all the infants born in the group (**Figure 6.33**). Another team led by Susan Perry of the University of California, Los Angeles, showed that the top-ranking male sired 38% to 70% of all infants born in three multimale groups of white-faced capuchins. Genetic analyses of paternity in multimale groups of hanuman langurs, long-tailed macaques, howler monkeys, patas monkeys, and chimpanzees also show that high-ranking males reproduce more successfully than do other males.

These genetic analyses also reveal that dominance rank is not the only factor that influences males' reproductive performance. Among both baboons and chimpanzees, the highest-ranking male can monopolize access to receptive females most effectively when there are relatively few other males present in the group and when there are relatively few estrous females present at the same time. In most species, males disperse from groups before their own daughters become sexually mature, thus reducing the likelihood of father–daughter matings. However, in white-faced capuchins, Perry's group found that some high-ranking males remain in groups long enough to potentially mate with their own daughters. Nonetheless, father–daughter matings are largely avoided. The

FIGURE 6.31

In baboons, male rank (*black dots*) is closely linked to male age and physical condition. Males reach their highest ranks, on average, when they are about 8 years old and then gradually fall in rank as they age. Male reproductive success (*green bars*) closely corresponds to male age and male rank.

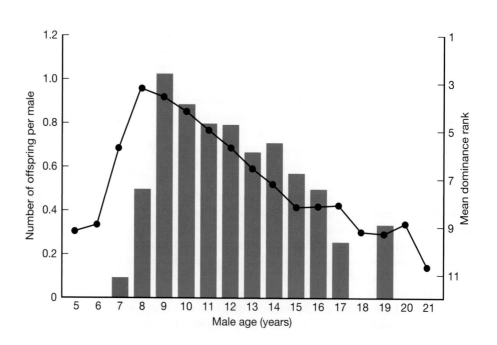

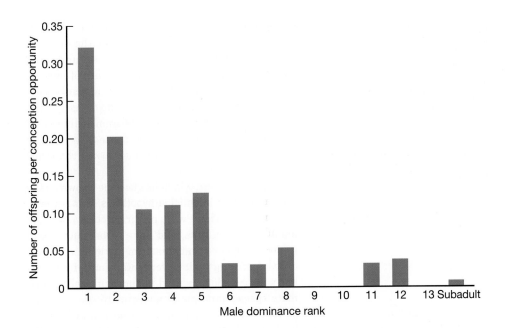

FIGURE 6.32

In baboons, male reproductive success is closely related to dominance rank. The highest-ranking male obtains the highest proportion of conceptions but does not monopolize conceptions entirely.

alpha males sired 79% of the offspring produced by unrelated females but only 6% of their own daughters' offspring.

Infanticide

Infanticide is a sexually selected male reproductive strategy.

We have seen that high-ranking males can monopolize access to receptive females, and this generates fierce competition over residence in one-male groups and competition for high-ranking positions within multimale groups. Sarah Blaffer Hrdy, now retired from the University of California, Davis, was the first to see that these circumstances might favor the evolution of infanticide as a male reproductive tactic. Her reasoning was based on the following logic: When a female monkey gives birth to an infant, she nurses it

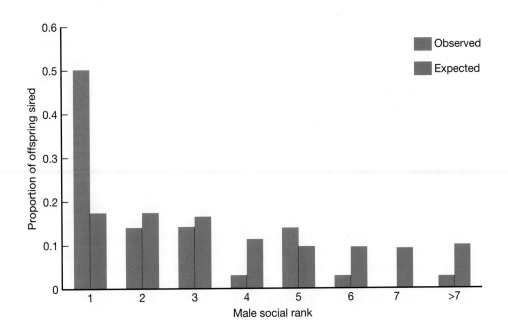

FIGURE 6.33

Among chimpanzees in the Taï Forest, high-ranking males monopolize conceptions. The highest-ranking male obtained many more conceptions than expected based on the number of males present in the group.

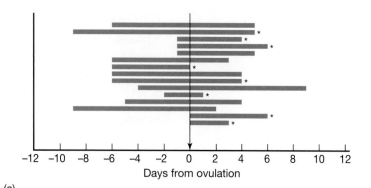

(a)

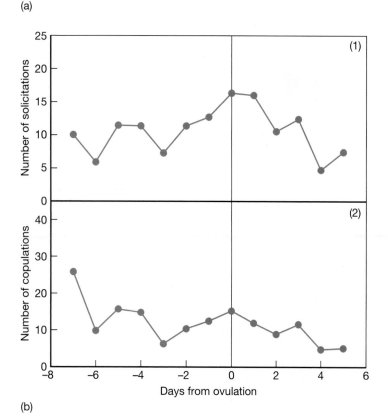

(b)

FIGURE 6.34

In some species, females have evolved counterstrategies to infanticide. Gray langurs seem to obscure information about the timing of ovulation. (a) Females are sexually receptive for about nine days, and ovulation can occur anytime within that period. Asterisks indicate receptive periods in which conceptions occurred. (b) Sexual activity is not concentrated around the time of ovulation. Females solicit males, and males copulate with females at fairly consistent rates throughout the receptive period.

for several months and does not become pregnant again for a considerable time. After the death of an infant, however, lactation ends abruptly and females resume cycling. Thus the death of nursing infants hastens the resumption of maternal receptivity. A male who takes over a group or rises to the top-ranking position may benefit from killing nursing infants because their deaths cause their mothers to become sexually receptive much sooner than they would otherwise.

This hypothesis, which has become known as the **sexual selection infanticide hypothesis**, was initially controversial. There were no direct observations of males killing infants, and some researchers found it hard to believe that this form of violence was an evolved strategy. However, infanticide by males has now been documented in approximately 40 primate species (and many nonprimate species, such as lions). Researchers have witnessed at least 60 infanticidal attacks in the wild and have recorded many nonlethal attacks on infants by adult males. There are many more instances in which healthy infants have disappeared after takeovers or changes in male rank. Infanticide occurs in species that typically form one-male groups, and in multimale groups of savanna baboons, langurs, capuchins, and Japanese macaques.

This body of data enables researchers to test several predictions derived from Hrdy's hypothesis. If infanticide is a male reproductive strategy, then we would expect that (1) infanticide would be associated with changes in male residence or status; (2) males should kill infants whose deaths hasten their mothers' resumption of cycling; (3) males should kill other males' infants, not their own; and (4) infanticidal males should achieve reproductive benefits.

All of these predictions have been supported. Carel van Schaik compiled information about 55 infanticides in free-ranging groups that were actually witnessed by observers. He found that nearly all infanticides (85%) followed changes in male residence or dominance rank. He also found that most infanticides involve unweaned infants, whose deaths will have the greatest impact on female sexual receptivity. Males largely avoid killing related infants. Only 7% of infanticides were committed by males who were sexually active in the group at the time the infants were conceived. Finally, in at least 45%—and possibly as much as 70%—of these cases, the infanticidal male later mated with the mother of the infant that he killed.

Infanticide is sometimes a substantial source of mortality for infants.

Among mountain gorillas in the Virunga Mountains of Rwanda, savanna baboons in the Moremi Game Reserve in Botswana, gray langurs in Ramnagar in Nepal, and red howlers in Venezuela, approximately one-third of all infant deaths are due to infanticide. Among the gelada baboons of the Simien Mountains in Ethiopia, approximately 40% of infants are killed after takeovers.

Females have evolved a battery of responses to infanticidal threats.

Although infanticide may enhance male reproductive success, it can have a disastrous effect on females who lose their infants. Thus we should expect females to evolve counterstrategies to infanticidal threats. The most obvious counterstrategy would be for females to try to prevent males from harming their infants. However, females' efforts to defend their infants are unlikely to be effective. Remember that males are generally larger than females in species without pair bonds, and the extent of sexual dimorphism is most pronounced in species that form one-male groups.

Females may try to confuse males about paternity. As we have seen already, males seem to kill infants when there is no ambiguity about their paternity; if females can increase uncertainty about paternity, they may reduce the risk of infanticide. Females might confuse males about paternity by obscuring information about their reproductive state, by mating with multiple males when they are sexually receptive, and by mating with males at times when they are not likely to conceive. All of these strategies have been documented among primates. A group of researchers led by Michael Heistermann of the German Primate Center has examined the patterns of sexual behavior and ovulatory status among female gray langurs in multimale groups. They found that females are sexually receptive for about nine days, on average, and they can ovulate anytime within that period (**Figure 6.34a**). Females sexually solicit males throughout this period, and male mating behavior is not concentrated around the day of ovulation (**Figure 6.34b**), suggesting that males can't tell when females are likely to conceive. Female langurs also mate with multiple males and sometimes solicit males after takeovers when they are already pregnant.

Gelada females have adopted a different strategy to reduce the impact of infanticide. Eila Roberts, at Arizona State University, and her colleagues used hormonal data to monitor the reproductive status of females before and after takeovers. They discovered that females terminate pregnancies in the days that follow takeovers (**Figure 6.35**). Although this may seem like a very costly strategy for females, it may actually provide a net benefit. Females whose pregnancies were terminated after takeovers had shorter interbirth intervals than females who carried their pregnancies to term and then lost their infants before they were weaned. It may be advantageous for females to terminate their investment in an infant that is very likely to be killed by the new leader male and to reallocate maternal effort to another reproductive attempt. It is important to understand that pregnancy termination reflects an adaptive, evolved response to male takeovers and is not based on conscious decisions made by individual female monkeys.

The threat of infanticide seems to influence the nature of male–female relationships in baboons.

Researchers have long known that mothers of newborn infant baboons sometimes form close relationships ("friendships") with one or sometimes two adult males (**Figure 6.36**). Females are primarily responsible for staying near their male associates

FIGURE 6.35

Gelada females terminate pregnancies immediately after takeovers. Levels of estrogen fall precipitously after takeovers, indicating that pregnancies have ended. Before takeovers, the hormone levels of females who terminated their pregnancies cannot be distinguished from the hormone levels of females who carry pregnancies to term.

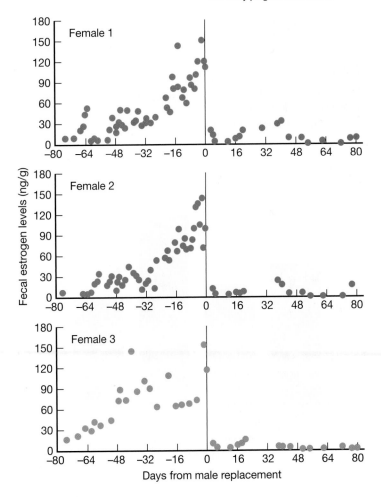

and grooming them. Males defend their female associates when the females are threatened. Males also hold, carry, and groom their female associates' infants, and they sometimes intervene on behalf of immatures who become involved in aggressive encounters.

A growing body of evidence suggests that these relationships protect infants from infanticidal attacks. In Moremi, Botswana, where male–female relationships are prominent and infanticide is common, female baboons are extremely agitated in the presence of new males. Jacinta Beehner and her colleagues have found that females' cortisol levels, which provide a physiological index of stress, rise sharply when immigrant males enter the group (**Figure 6.37**). The presence of a male "friend," however, reduces new mothers' agitation. Ryne Palombit has found that males are acutely sensitive to the distress of their female associates, but how males respond is directly tied to the infant's presence. If the infant dies, males stop responding.

FIGURE 6.36

After they give birth, many females begin to associate closely with one or two adult males. Here, a high-ranking female and her infant sit with the mother's male associate.

If the data on infanticide are so consistent, why is the idea so controversial?

When Hrdy first proposed the idea that infanticide is an evolved male reproductive strategy, there was plenty of room for skepticism and dispute. Now, however, we have good evidence that the patterning of infanticidal attacks fits predictions derived from the sexual selection infanticide hypothesis. But controversy still lingers. Volker Sommer, whose own work on infanticide in gray langurs has been attacked by critics of Hrdy's hypothesis, believes that the criticism comes from a tendency to commit what is called the "naturalistic fallacy," the tendency to assume that what we see in nature is somehow right, just, and inevitable. Critics are concerned that if we accept the idea that infanticide is an adaptive strategy for langurs or baboons, it will justify similar behavior in humans. However, to try to extract moral meaning from the behavior of other animals is misguided. As we will discuss in Chapter 16, human societies rely on culturally evolved moral norms, which is what makes the naturalistic fallacy an erroneous form of reasoning.

FIGURE 6.37

(a) The cortisol levels of female baboons increased when a new male immigrated into the group and took over the alpha position. (b) This effect was most pronounced for females who did not have a close male associate.

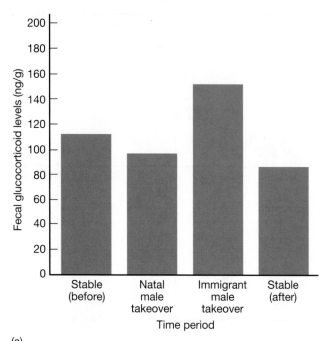

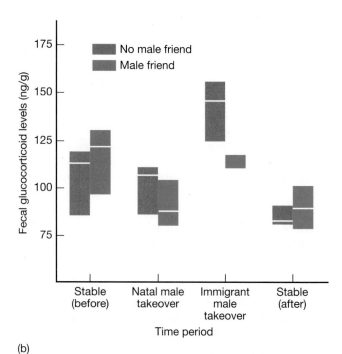

Key Terms

strategy (p. 144)
primiparous (p. 148)
multiparous (p. 148)
dominance (p. 151)

dominance matrix (p. 151)
transitive (p. 151)
sexual selection (p. 155)

intrasexual selection (p. 156)
intersexual selection (p. 156)

bachelor males (p. 157)
estrus (p. 158)
sexual selection infanticide hypothesis (p. 164)

Study Questions

1. Explain why reproductive success is a critical element of evolution by natural selection. When biologists use the terms *cost* and *benefit*, what currency are they trying to measure?

2. What is the difference between polygyny and polyandry? It seems likely that females might prefer polyandry over polygyny, while males would favor polygyny. Explain why males and females might prefer different mating systems. If this conflict of interest occurs, why is polygyny more common than polyandry?

3. In many primate species, reproduction is highly seasonal. Some researchers have suggested that reproductive seasonality has evolved as a means for females to manipulate their reproductive options. How would reproductive seasonality alter females' options? Why do you think this strategy might be advantageous for females?

4. Imagine that you came upon a species in which males and females were the same size, but males had very large testes in relation to their body size. What would you infer about their social organization? Now suppose you found another species in which males were much larger than females but had relatively small testes. What would

you deduce about their social system? Why do these relationships hold?

5. Among mammalian species, male fitness is typically more variable than female fitness. Explain why this is often the case. What implications does this have for evolution acting on males and females?

6. What factors influence the reproductive success of females? How do these factors contribute to variance in female reproductive success?

7. Biologists use the term *investment* to describe parental care. What elements of the selective forces acting on parental strategies does this term capture?

8. Explain the logic underlying the sexual selection infanticide hypothesis. What predictions follow from this hypothesis? List the predictions, and explain why they follow from the hypothesis.

9. In general, infanticide seems to be more common in species that form one-male groups than in species that form multimale, multifemale groups or pair-bonded groups. Explain why this might be the case.

10. Why is the naturalistic fallacy considered a problematic way to think about the behavior of other animals?

Further Reading

Altmann, J. 2001. *Baboon Mothers and Infants*. Chicago: University of Chicago Press.

Kappeler, P. M., and C. P. van Schaik, eds. 2004. *Sexual Selection in Primates: New and Comparative Perspectives*. New York: Cambridge University Press.

Mitani, J., J. Call, P. Kappeler, R. Palombit, and J. B. Silk, eds. 2012. *The Evolution of Primate Societies*. Chicago: University of Chicago Press.

Van Schaik, C. P., and C. H. Janson, eds. 2000. *Infanticide by Males and Its Implications*. New York: Cambridge University Press.

Westneat, D. F., and C. W. Fox, eds. 2010. *Evolutionary Behavioral Ecology*. Section V. Oxford: Oxford University Press.

Visit DIGITAL.WWNORTON.COM/HOWHUMANS8 to
- review this chapter with personalized, interactive questions via InQuizitive
- view videos and animations on this chapter's key topics

7

THE EVOLUTION OF COOPERATION

- **Altruism: A Puzzle** p. 169
- **Mutualism** p. 170
- **The Problem with Group-Level Explanations** p. 171
- **Kin Selection** p. 172
- **Reciprocal Altruism** p. 184

CHAPTER OBJECTIVES

By the end of this chapter you should be able to

A. Explain why altruism is unlikely to evolve in most circumstances.

B. Describe how evolution can favor altruism through the processes of kin selection and reciprocal altruism.

C. Discuss the mechanisms that allow primates to recognize their relatives.

D. Explain how kinship influences the distribution of altruism in primate groups.

E. Evaluate arguments about the importance of reciprocal altruism in primate groups.

Altruism: A Puzzle

So far, we have explained the evolution of morphology and behavior in terms of individual reproductive success. Natural selection favored deeper beaks in Darwin's finches during the drought because deeper beaks allowed individuals to crack tougher seeds. It favors infanticide by male langurs and lions because it allows them to sire offspring with the dead infants' mothers. However, primates (and many other creatures) also perform **altruistic behaviors** that benefit others but at a personal cost. For example, virtually all social primates groom other group members, removing parasites, cleaning scabs, and picking debris from their hair (**Figure 7.1**). Grooming other individuals consumes time that could be spent looking for food, courting prospective mates, caring

FIGURE 7.1

Gray langurs groom one another. Grooming is usually considered altruistic because the groomer expends time and energy when it grooms another animal, and the recipient benefits from having ticks removed from its skin, wounds cleaned, and debris removed from its hair.

for offspring, or scanning for predators. The recipient, meanwhile, gets a thorough cleaning of parts of her body that she might find difficult to reach and may enjoy a period of pleasant relaxation. And grooming isn't the only altruistic behavior; primates warn others about the presence of predators, even though doing so makes them more conspicuous. They risk injury to help others in dominance contests, and in some species, individuals share food. If natural selection favors individually advantageous traits, how can we explain the evolution of such altruistic behaviors?

The answer to this question is one of the triumphs of evolutionary biology. Beginning in the 1960s and 1970s with the work of William D. Hamilton and Robert Trivers, biologists have developed a rich theory that explains why selection sometimes favors altruistic behavior and why it often does not. This theory has transformed our understanding of the evolution of social behavior. In this chapter, we show how natural selection can favor the evolution of altruistic behavior and describe how it explains the form and pattern of cooperation in primate groups. Cooperation plays an important role in the lives of other primates and plays an even more important role in human societies. In Chapter 16 you will see that the same kinds of processes that shape cooperation in monkeys and apes also influence human cooperation, but human cooperation also extends beyond the patterns that we see in other primates.

Mutualism

Sometimes helping others benefits the actor as well as the recipient. Such behaviors are mutualistic.

FIGURE 7.2

The pyramid will collapse if anyone slacks off.

Mutualistic interactions provide benefits to both participants. This seems like a win–win proposition, and you might think these kinds of interactions would be very common in nature. But there is a catch. To see what it is, think back to those group projects you worked on in grade school. The problem with group projects is that if someone doesn't do his share, the rest of the group has to take up the slack. You could punish the slacker, but that just compounds the problem because doing so is a lot of trouble. So you grumble and finish the project yourself. The general lesson here is that mutualistic cooperation is fragile when slacking is profitable for individuals. Mutualism is most likely to work in situations in which slacking off isn't profitable for any of the participants. Imagine that you are entering a human-pyramid contest (**Figure 7.2**). The group that can construct the largest pyramid wins a big prize. If someone doesn't hold up his or her end, the pyramid collapses, and everyone loses. So no one is motivated to slack off.

Coalitions among male baboons may be an example of mutualism. In East Africa, male baboons guard receptive females. The highest-ranking male usually attempts to monopolize access to females on the days when females are most likely to conceive. Two males may jointly challenge a mate-guarding male and try to gain control of the female (**Figure 7.3**). These interactions can escalate to energetically costly chases and physical confrontations. The challengers often succeed in driving the male away, and one of them begins to mate-guard the female. Males that hold middle-ranking positions are most likely to form coalitions. These males have very little chance of gaining access to receptive females on their own, but two middle-ranking males are a formidable force when they work together. As long as each male has some probability of ending up with the female, it may be profitable for both to participate in the coalition. There is no incentive to slack off because slacking off guarantees failure.

Like male baboons, chimpanzees also mate-guard receptive females. In the Kibale Forest, some pairs of high-ranking males jointly defend access to females. Cooperation

FIGURE 7.3

Two male baboons (on the right) jointly challenge a third male over access to a receptive female.

allows males to fend off other males' approaches and keep close tabs on females at the same time. Coalition partners share matings with the female they are guarding. Males switch from mate guarding alone to joint mate guarding when they are in large parties with many potential competitors. Again, this strategy may pay off for males if they are able to obtain more matings when they cooperate with other males than when they attempt to monopolize females on their own.

The Problem with Group-Level Explanations

Altruistic behaviors cannot be favored by selection just because they are beneficial to the group as a whole.

You might think that if the average effect of an act on all members of the group is positive, then it would be beneficial for all individuals to perform it. For example, suppose that when one monkey gives an alarm call, the other members of the group benefit, and the total benefits to all group members exceed the cost of giving the call. Then, if every individual gave the call when a predator was sighted, all members of the group would be better off than if no warning calls were ever given. You might think that alarm calling would be favored because every individual in the group benefits.

This inference is wrong because it confuses the effect on the group with the effect on the actor. In most circumstances, the fact that alarm calls are beneficial to those hearing them doesn't affect whether the trait of alarm-calling evolves; all that matters is how giving the alarm call affects the caller. To see why this is true, imagine a hypothetical monkey species in which some individuals give alarm calls when they are the first to spot a predator. Monkeys who hear the call have a chance to flee. Suppose that one-fourth of the population ("callers") give the call when they spot predators, and three-fourths of the individuals ("noncallers") do not give an alarm call in the same circumstance. (These proportions are arbitrary; we chose them because it's easier to follow the reasoning in examples with concrete numbers.) Let's suppose that in this species the tendency to give alarm calls is genetically inherited.

Now we compare the fitness of callers and noncallers. Because everyone in the group can hear the alarm calls and take appropriate action, alarm calls benefit everyone in

(a) Altruist gives alarm call to group.

(b) Nonaltruist doesn't give alarm call to group.

FIGURE 7.4

Two groups of monkeys are approached by a predator. (a) In one group, one individual (*pink*) has a gene that makes her call in this context. Giving the call lowers the caller's fitness but increases the fitness of every other individual in the group. Like the rest of the population, one out of four of these beneficiaries also carries the genes for calling. (b) In the second group, the female who detects the predator does not carry the gene for calling and remains silent. This lowers the fitness of all members of the group a certain amount because they are more likely to be caught unaware by the predator. Once again, one out of four is a caller. Although members of the caller's group are better off on average than members of the noncaller's group, the gene for calling is not favored, because callers and noncallers in the caller's group both benefit from the caller's behavior but callers incur some costs. Callers are at a disadvantage in comparison with noncallers. Thus calling is not favored, even though the group as a whole benefits.

the group to the same extent (**Figure 7.4**). Calling does not affect the *relative* fitness of callers and noncallers because, on average, one-fourth of the beneficiaries will be callers and three-fourths of the beneficiaries will be noncallers—the same proportions we find in the population as a whole. Calling reduces the risk of mortality for everyone who hears the call, but it does not change the frequency of callers and noncallers in the population because everyone gains the same benefits. However, callers are conspicuous when they call, so they are more vulnerable to predators. Although all individuals benefit from hearing alarm calls, callers are the only ones who suffer the costs from calling. This means that, on average, noncallers will have a higher fitness than callers. Thus, genes that cause alarm calling will not be favored by selection, even if the cost of giving alarm calls is small and the benefit to the rest of the group is large. Instead, selection will favor genes that suppress alarm calling because noncallers have a higher fitness than callers. (See **A Closer Look 7.1** for more about the role of group selection in nature.)

Kin Selection

Natural selection can favor altruistic behavior if altruistic individuals are more likely to interact with each other than chance alone would dictate.

If altruistic behaviors can't evolve by ordinary natural selection or by group selection, then how do they evolve? A clear answer to this question did not come until 1964, when a young biologist named William D. Hamilton published a landmark paper. This paper was the first of a series of fundamental contributions that Hamilton made to our understanding of the evolution of behavior.

The argument made in the previous section contains a hidden assumption: Altruists and nonaltruists are equally likely to interact with one another. We supposed that

A CLOSER LOOK

7.1 Group Selection

Group selection was once thought to be the mechanism for the evolution of altruistic interactions. In the early 1960s, the British ornithologist V. C. Wynne-Edwards contended that altruistic behaviors such as those we have been considering here evolved because they enhanced the survival of whole groups of organisms. Thus individuals gave alarm calls, despite the costs of becoming more conspicuous to predators, because calling protected the group as a whole from attacks. Wynne-Edwards reasoned that groups containing a larger number of altruistic individuals would be more likely to survive and prosper than groups containing fewer altruists, and the frequency of the genes leading to altruism would increase.

Wynne-Edwards's argument is logical because Darwin's postulates logically apply to groups as well as individuals. However, group selection is not an important force in nature because there is generally not enough genetic variation among groups for selection to act on. Group selection can occur if groups vary in their ability to survive and to reproduce and if that variation is heritable. Then group selection may increase the frequency of genes that increase group survival and reproductive success. The strength of selection among groups depends on the amount of genetic variation among groups, just as the strength of selection among individuals depends on the amount of genetic variation among individuals. However, when individual selection and group selection are opposed and group selection favors altruistic behavior while individual selection favors selfish alternatives, individual selection has a tremendous advantage. This is because the amount of variation among groups is much smaller than the amount of variation among individuals, unless groups are very small or there is very little migration among them. Thus individual selection favoring selfish behavior will generally prevail over group selection, making group selection an unlikely source of altruism in nature.

callers give alarm calls when they hear a predator, no matter who is nearby. Hamilton's insight was to see that any process that causes altruists to be more likely to interact with other altruists than they would by chance could facilitate the evolution of altruism.

To see why this is such an important insight, let's modify the previous example by assuming that our hypothetical species lives in groups composed of full siblings, offspring of the same mother and father. The frequencies of the calling and noncalling genes don't change, but their distribution will be affected by the fact that siblings live together (**Figure 7.5**). If an individual is a caller, then, by the rules of Mendelian genetics, there is a 50% chance that the individual's siblings will share the genes that cause calling behavior. This means that the frequency of the genes for calling will be higher in groups that contain callers than in the population as a whole and, therefore, more than one-fourth of the beneficiaries will be callers themselves. When a caller gives an alarm call, the audience will contain a higher fraction of callers than the population at large does. Thus, the caller raises the average fitness of callers with respect to noncallers. Similarly, because the siblings of noncallers are more likely to be noncallers than chance alone would dictate, callers are less likely to be present in such groups than in the population at large. Therefore, the absence of a warning call lowers the fitness of noncallers more significantly relative to callers.

When individuals interact selectively with relatives, callers are more likely to benefit than noncallers and, all other things being equal, the benefits of calling will favor

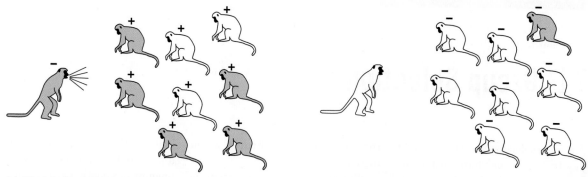

(a) Altruist gives alarm call to siblings.   (b) Nonaltruist doesn't give alarm call to siblings.

FIGURE 7.5

Two groups of monkeys are approached by a predator. Each group is composed of nine sisters. (a) In one group there is a caller (*pink*), an individual with a gene that makes her call in this context. Her call lowers her own fitness but increases the fitness of her sisters. (b) In the second group, the female who detects the predator is not a caller and does not call when she spots the predator. As in Figure 7.4, calling benefits the other group members but imposes costs on the caller. However, there is an important difference between the situations portrayed here and in Figure 7.4. Here the groups are made up of sisters, so five of the eight recipients of the call also carry the calling gene. In any pair of siblings, half of the genes are identical because the siblings inherited the same gene from one of their parents. Thus, on average, half of the caller's siblings also carry the calling allele because they inherited it from their mother or father. The remaining four siblings carry genes inherited from the other parent; and, like the population as a whole, one out of four of them is a caller. The same reasoning shows that in the group with the noncaller, there is only one caller among the beneficiaries of the call. Half are identical to their sister because they inherited the same noncalling gene from one of their parents; one of the remaining four is a caller. In this situation, callers are more likely to benefit from calling than noncallers, and so calling alters the relative fitness of callers and noncallers. Whether the calling behavior actually evolves depends on whether these benefits are big enough to compensate for the reduction in the caller's fitness.

the genes for calling. However, we must remember that calling is costly, and this will tend to reduce the fitness of callers. Calling will be favored by natural selection only if its benefits are sufficiently greater than its costs. The exact nature of this trade-off is specified by what we call Hamilton's rule.

Hamilton's Rule

Hamilton's rule predicts that altruistic behaviors will be favored by selection if the costs of performing the behavior are less than the benefits discounted by the coefficient of relatedness between actor and recipient.

Hamilton's theory of **kin selection** is based on the idea that selection could favor altruistic alleles if animals interacted selectively with their genetic relatives. Hamilton's theory also specifies the quantity and distribution of help among individuals. According to **Hamilton's rule**, an act will be favored by selection if

$$rb > c$$

where

r = the average coefficient of relatedness between the actor and the recipients
b = the sum of the fitness benefits to all individuals affected by the behavior
c = the fitness cost to the individual performing the behavior

The **coefficient of relatedness**, *r*, measures the genetic relationship between interacting individuals. More precisely, r is the probability that two individuals will acquire the same allele through descent from a common ancestor. **Figure 7.6** shows how these probabilities are derived in a simple genealogy. Female A obtains one allele at a given locus from her mother and one from her father. Her half sister, female B, also obtains one allele at the same locus from each of her parents. We obtain the probability that both females receive the same allele from their mother by multiplying the probability that female A obtains the allele (0.5) by the probability that female B obtains the same allele (0.5); the result is 0.25. Thus half sisters have, on average, a 25% chance of obtaining the same allele from their mothers. Now consider the relatedness between female B and her brother, male C. In this case, note that female B and male C are full siblings: They have the same mother and the same father. The probability that both siblings will acquire the same allele from their mother is still 0.25, but female B and male C might also share an allele from their father. The probability of this event is also 0.25. Thus, the probability that female B and male C share an allele is equal to the sum of 0.25 and 0.25, or 0.5. This basic reasoning can be extended to calculate the degrees of relatedness among various categories of kin (**Table 7.1**).

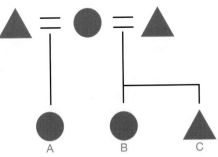

FIGURE 7.6

This genealogy shows how the value of r is computed. Triangles represent males, circles represent females, and the equals sign represents mating. The relationships between individuals labeled in the genealogy are described in the text.

Hamilton's rule leads to two important insights: (1) Altruism is limited to kin and (2) closer kinship facilitates more costly altruism.

If you reflect on Hamilton's rule for a while, you will see that it produces two predictions about the conditions that favor the evolution of altruistic behaviors. First, altruism is not expected to be directed toward nonkin because the coefficient of relatedness, r, between nonkin is 0. The condition for the evolution of altruistic traits will be satisfied only for interactions between kin when $r > 0$. Thus, altruists are expected to be nepotistic, showing favoritism toward kin.

Second, close kinship is expected to facilitate altruism. If an act is particularly costly, it is most likely to be restricted to close kin. **Figure 7.7** shows how the benefit:cost ratio scales with the degree of relatedness among individuals. Compare what happens when $r = 1/16$ (or 0.0625) and when $r = 1/2$ (or 0.5). When $r = 1/16$, the benefits must be more than 16 times as great as the costs for Hamilton's inequality $rb > c$ to be satisfied. When $r = 1/2$, the benefit needs to be just over twice as large as the costs. All other things being equal, Hamilton's rule will be easier to satisfy for close kin than for distant kin, and altruism will be more common among close relatives than among distant ones.

TABLE 7.1

Relationship	*r*
Parent and offspring	0.5
Full siblings	0.5
Half siblings	0.25
Grandparent and grandchild	0.25
First cousins	0.125 or 0.0625
Unrelated individuals	0

The value of r for selected categories of relatives. (When cousins are offspring of full siblings, they are related by 0.125, but when they are the offspring of half siblings they are related by 0.0625.)

FIGURE 7.7

As the degree of relatedness (r) between two individuals declines, the value of the ratio of benefits to costs ($b:c$) required to satisfy Hamilton's rule for the evolution of altruism rises rapidly.

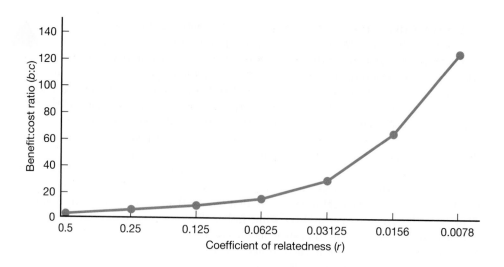

Kin Recognition

Primates may use contextual cues to recognize maternal relatives.

In order for kin selection to provide an effective mechanism for the evolution of cooperative behavior, animals must be able to distinguish relatives from nonrelatives and close relatives from distant ones. Some organisms can recognize their kin by their smell or likeness to themselves. This is called **phenotypic matching**. Others learn to recognize relatives by using contextual cues—such as familiarity and proximity—that predict kinship (**Figure 7.8**). In the past, primatologists assumed that primates relied solely on contextual cues to identify their relatives, but new data suggest that phenotypic matching may also play a role in primate kin recognition.

Mothers seem to make use of contextual cues to recognize their own infants. After they give birth, females repeatedly sniff and inspect their newborns. By the time their infants are a few weeks old, mothers can clearly recognize them. After this, females of most species nurse only their own infants and respond selectively to their own infants' distress calls. Primate mothers don't really need innate means of recognizing their young because young infants spend virtually all of their time

FIGURE 7.8

(a) Even mothers must learn to recognize their own infants. Here, a female bonnet macaque peers into her infant's face. (b) Primates apparently learn who their relatives are by observing patterns of association among group members. Here, a female inspects another female's infant.

(a)

(b)

in physical contact with their mothers. Thus, mothers are unlikely to confuse their own newborn with another.

Monkeys and apes may learn to recognize other maternal kin through contact with their mothers. Offspring continue to spend considerable amounts of time with their mothers even after their younger siblings are born. Thus, they have many opportunities to watch their mothers interact with their new brothers and sisters. Similarly, the newborn infant's most common companions are its mother and siblings (**Figure 7.9**). Because adult females continue to associate with their mothers, infants also become familiar with their grandmothers, aunts, and cousins.

(a)

(b)

Contextual cues may play some role in paternal kin recognition as well.

Primatologists were once quite confident that most primates could not recognize their paternal kin. This conclusion was based on the following reasoning: First, pair bonds are uncommon in most primate species, so patterns of association between males and females do not provide accurate cues of paternal kinship. Second, females may mate with several males near the time of conception, creating confusion about paternity. Even in pair-bonded species, such as gibbons and titi monkeys, females sometimes mate with males from outside their groups.

New evidence from field studies on macaques and baboons suggests that monkeys use contextual cues to assess paternal kinship. Jeanne Altmann of Princeton University pointed out that age may provide a good proxy measure of paternal kinship in species in which a single male typically dominates mating activity within the group. When this happens, all infants born at about the same time are likely to have the same father. Recent studies suggest that Altmann's logic is correct—monkeys do use age to identify paternal kin. Female baboons in the population that Altmann studied distinguish between paternal half sisters and unrelated females, and they seem to rely on closeness in age to make these discriminations. Anja Widdig of the Max Planck Institute for Evolutionary Anthropology in Leipzig, Germany, and her colleagues have also found that females show strong affinities for paternal half sisters (**Figure 7.10**). Their affinities for paternal kin seem to be based partly on strong preferences for interacting with age-mates. However, females also distinguished *among* their age-mates, preferring paternal half sisters over unrelated females of the same age.

It is not entirely clear what cues females use to distinguish their paternal half sisters from other age-mates. However, new research suggests that facial resemblances among relatives might play some role. In one study, researchers measured multiple features of rhesus macaque faces and compared the similarity of the faces of kin and nonkin. Not surprisingly, kin tend to resemble one another. In a second study, humans were asked to rate the similarity between an adult face and the faces of two immature macaques of the same age and sex. One of the immatures

FIGURE 7.9

Monkey and ape infants grow up surrounded by various relatives. (a) These adult baboon females are mother and daughter. Both have young infants. (b) An adolescent female bonnet macaque carries her younger brother while her mother recovers from a serious illness.

FIGURE 7.10

Female macaques can identify paternal siblings. Females groom far more often with maternal half siblings (*blue bar*) than with paternal siblings, but they groom more often with paternal siblings than with nonkin. Age similarity seems to provide a cue for paternal kinship: Females groom more often with paternal half-sibling peers (*red hatched bar*) than with paternal half siblings that are not close in age (*solid red bar*). But note that females also distinguish among peers, preferring half-sibling peers over unrelated peers (*purple hatched bar*). Similar patterns are found for spatial associations.

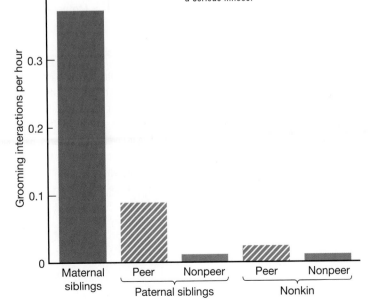

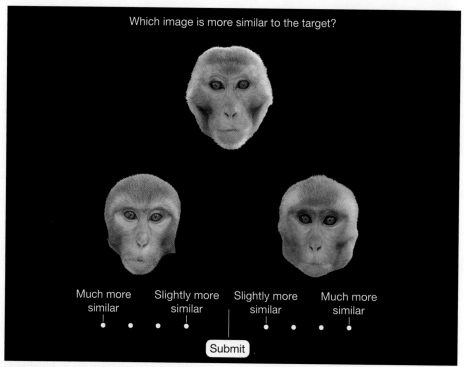

(a)

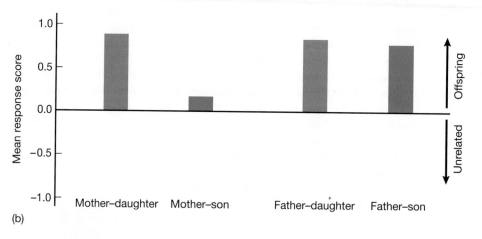

(b)

FIGURE 7.11

Kin recognition may be based in part on facial resemblances among relatives. (a) In a recent study, human subjects were asked to rate the facial resemblances between an adult rhesus macaque and two immatures matched for age and sex. One of the immatures was the adult's offspring, and the other was unrelated. You can try this yourself. (b) The human subjects perceived adults to be significantly more similar to their offspring than to unrelated immatures. Bars that extend above the x axis mean that subjects were more likely to choose the adult's own offspring than the unrelated immature. A value of zero indicates no difference in similarity to offspring and unrelated immatures.

*The offspring is on the right side.

(a)

(b)

(c)

(d)

FIGURE 7.12

Some of the many species of primates that groom are (a) capuchin monkeys, (b) blue monkeys, (c) baboons, and (d) gorillas.

was the adult's offspring and the other was unrelated (**Figure 7.11a**). Human raters, even those with no previous experience working with macaques, were significantly more accurate than expected by chance (**Figure 7.11b**). Taken together, these studies suggest that facial resemblances among kin may provide cues about kinship.

Kin Biases in Behavior

A considerable body of evidence suggests that the patterns of many forms of altruistic interactions among primates are largely consistent with predictions derived from Hamilton's rule. Here we consider several examples.

Grooming is more common among kin than nonkin.

Social **grooming** plays an important role in the lives of most gregarious primates (**Figure 7.12**). Grooming is likely to be beneficial to the participants in at least two ways: First, grooming serves hygienic functions because bits of dead skin, debris, and parasites are removed and wounds are kept clean and open. Second, grooming may provide a means for individuals to establish relaxed, **affiliative** (friendly) contact and to reinforce social relationships with other group members (**A Closer Look 7.2**). Grooming is costly because the actor expends both time and energy in performing these services. Moreover, Marina Cords of Columbia University has shown that blue monkeys are less vigilant when they are grooming, perhaps exposing themselves to some risk of being captured by predators.

Grooming is more common among kin, particularly mothers and their offspring, than among nonkin. For example, Ellen Kapsalis and Carol Berman of the University at Buffalo have documented the effect of maternal relatedness among rhesus macaques on Cayo Santiago. In this population, females groom close kin at higher rates than nonkin, and close kin are groomed more often than distant kin (**Figure 7.13**). As relatedness declined, the differences in the proportions of time spent

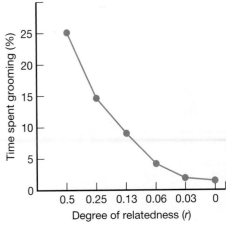

FIGURE 7.13

Rhesus monkeys on Cayo Santiago groom close relatives more often than they groom distant relatives or nonkin.

7.2 How Relationships Are Maintained

onflict and competition are fundamental features of social life for many primates: Females launch unprovoked attacks on unsuspecting victims, males battle over access to receptive females, subordinates are supplanted from choice feeding sites, and dominance relationships are clearly defined and frequently reinforced. Although violence and aggression are not prevalent in all primates (muriquis, for example, are so peaceful that dominance hierarchies cannot be detected), many primates can be charitably characterized as contentious. This raises an intriguing question: How is social life sustained in the face of such relentless conflict? After all, it seems inevitable that aggression and conflict will drive animals apart, disrupt social bonds, and reduce the cohesiveness of social groups.

Social relationships matter to primates. They spend a considerable portion of every day grooming other group members. Grooming

is typically focused on a relatively small number of partners and is often reciprocated. Robin Dunbar of the University of Oxford contends that in Old World monkeys, grooming has transcended its original hygienic function and now serves as a means to cultivate and maintain social bonds. Social bonds may have real adaptive value to individuals. For example, grooming is sometimes exchanged for support in coalitions, and grooming partners may be allowed to share access to scarce resources.

When tensions do erupt into violence, certain behavioral mechanisms may reduce the disruptive effects of conflict on social relationships. After conflicts end, victims often flee from their attackers— an understandable response. In some cases, however, former opponents make peaceful contact in the minutes that follow conflicts. For example, chimpanzees sometimes kiss their former opponents, female baboons grunt quietly to

their former victims, and golden monkeys may embrace or groom their former adversaries. The swift transformation from aggression to affiliation prompted Frans de Waal of Emory University to suggest that these peaceful postconflict interactions are a form of reconciliation, a way to mend relationships that were damaged by conflict. Inspired by de Waal's work, several researchers have documented reconciliatory behavior in a variety of primate species.

Peaceful postconflict interactions seem to have a calming effect on former opponents. When monkeys are nervous and anxious, rates of certain self-directed behaviors, such as scratching, increase. Thus self-directed behaviors are a good behavioral index of stress. Filippo Aureli of Liverpool John Moores University and his colleagues at Utrecht University and Emory University have studied how fighting and reconciliation affect the rate of self-directed behaviors. They found

FIGURE 7.14

Two baboons form an alliance against an adult female.

grooming kin and nonkin were essentially eliminated. This may mean that monkeys cannot recognize more distant kin or that the conditions of Hamilton's rule ($rb > c$) are rarely satisfied for distant kin.

Primates most often form coalitions with close kin.

Most disputes in primate groups involve two individuals. Sometimes, however, several individuals jointly attack another individual, or one individual comes to the support of another individual involved in an ongoing dispute (**Figure 7.14**). We call these kinds of interactions **coalitions** or **alliances**. Support is likely to be beneficial to the individual who receives aid because support alters the balance of power among the original contestants. The beneficiary may be more likely to win the contest or less likely to be injured in the confrontation. At the same time, however, intervention may be costly to

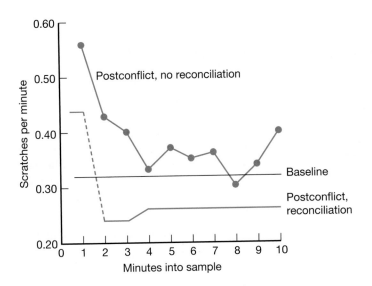

FIGURE 7.15

Rates of scratching, an observable index of stress, by victims of aggression are elevated over normal levels in the minutes that follow aggressive encounters. If some form of affiliative contact (reconciliation) between former opponents occurs during the postconflict period, however, rates of scratching drop rapidly below baseline levels. If there is no reconciliatory contact during the first few minutes of the postconflict period, rates of scratching remain elevated above baseline levels for several minutes. These data suggest that affiliative contact between former opponents has a calming effect. Similar effects on aggressors have also been detected.

that levels of self-directed behavior, and presumably stress, rise sharply above baseline levels after conflicts. Both victims and aggressors seem to feel the stressful effects of conflicts. If former opponents interact peacefully in the minutes that follow conflicts, rates of self-directed behavior fall rapidly to baseline levels (**Figure 7.15**). If adversaries do not reconcile, rates of self-directed behavior remain elevated above baseline levels for several minutes longer. If reconciliation provides a means to preserve social bonds, then we would expect primates to reconcile selectively with their closest associates. In several groups, former opponents who have strong social bonds are most likely to reconcile. Kin also reconcile at high rates in some groups, even though some researchers have argued that kin have little need to reconcile because their relationships are unlikely to be frayed by conflict.

Reconciliation may also play a role in resolving conflicts among individuals who do not have strong social bonds. Like many other primates, female baboons are strongly attracted to newborn infants and make persistent efforts to handle them. Mothers reluctantly tolerate infant handling, but they do not welcome the attention. Female baboons reconcile at particularly high rates with the mothers of young infants, even when they do not have close relationships with them. Reconciliation greatly enhances the likelihood that aggressors will be able to handle their former victims' infants in the minutes that follow conflicts. Thus, in this case, reconciliation seems to be a means to an immediate end but not a means to preserve long-term relationships.

the supporter, who expends time and energy and risks defeat or injury by becoming involved. Hamilton's rule predicts that support will be preferentially directed toward kin and that the greatest costs will be expended on behalf of close relatives.

Many studies have shown that support is selectively directed toward close kin. Female macaques and baboons defend their offspring and close kin more often than they defend distant relatives or unrelated individuals (**Figure 7.16**). Females run some risk when they participate in coalitions, particularly when they are allied against higher-ranking individuals. Coalitions against high-ranking individuals are more likely to result in retaliatory attacks against the supporter than are coalitions against lower-ranking individuals. Female macaques are much more likely to intervene against higher-ranking females on behalf of their own offspring than on behalf of unrelated females or juveniles. Thus, macaque females take the greatest risks on behalf of their closest kin.

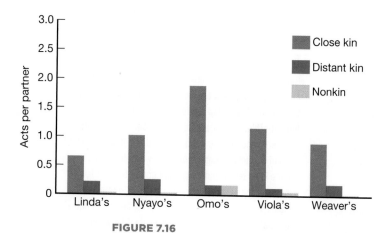

FIGURE 7.16

In five groups of wild baboons, rates of coalitionary support provided by close kin (mothers, daughters, and sisters), more distant maternal kin, and all others are shown. In all five groups, support is biased toward close kin.

Kin-based support in conflicts affects the social structure of macaque, vervet, and baboon groups.

Maternal support in macaques, vervets, and baboons influences the outcome of aggressive interactions and dominance contests. Initially, an immature monkey can defeat older and larger juveniles only when its mother is nearby. Eventually, regardless of their age or size, juveniles can defeat everyone their mothers can defeat, even when the mother is some distance away. Maternal support contributes directly to several remarkable properties of dominance hierarchies within these species:

- Maternal rank is transferred with great fidelity to offspring, particularly daughters. In a group of baboons at Gilgil, Kenya, for example, maternal rank is an almost perfect predictor of the daughter's rank (**Figure 7.17**).

- Maternal kin occupy adjacent ranks in the dominance hierarchy, and all the members of one **matrilineage** (maternal kin group) rank above or below all members of other matrilineages.

- Ranking within matrilineages is often quite predictable. Usually, mothers outrank their daughters, and younger sisters outrank their older sisters.

- Female dominance relationships are amazingly stable, often remaining the same over months and sometimes over years. The stability of dominance relationships among females may be a result of the tendency to form alliances in support of kin.

Kin-biased support plays an important role in the reproductive strategies of red howler males.

Behavioral and genetic studies of red howlers in Venezuela conducted by Teresa Pope have shown that kinship influences howler males' behavior in important ways.

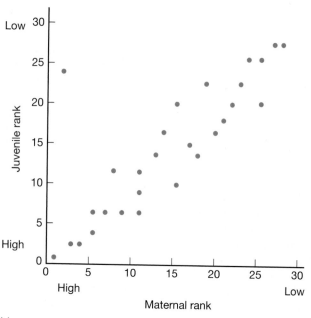

(a)

(b)

FIGURE 7.17

Juvenile female baboons acquire ranks very similar to their mother's rank. (a) The anomalous point at maternal rank 2 belongs to a female whose mother died when she was an infant. (b) Here, the dominant female of a baboon group is flanked by her two daughters, ranked 2 and 3.

Red howlers live in groups that contain two to four females and one or two males. Males sometimes join up with migrant females and help them establish new territories. Once such groups have been established, resident males must defend their position and their progeny from infanticidal attacks by alien males. When habitats are crowded, males can gain access to breeding females only by taking over established groups and evicting male residents. This is a risky endeavor because males are often injured in takeover attempts. Moreover, as habitats become more saturated and dispersal opportunities become more limited, males tend to remain in their groups longer. Maturing males help their fathers defend their groups against takeover attempts. Collective defense is crucial to males' success because single males cannot defend their group against incursions by rival males.

This situation leads to a kind of arms race because migrating males also form coalitions and cooperate in efforts to evict residents. After they have established residence, males collectively defend the group against incursions by extragroup males. Cooperation among males is beneficial because it helps deter rivals. But it also involves clear fitness costs because, as behavioral and genetic data have demonstrated, only one male succeeds in siring offspring within the group. Not surprisingly, kinship influences the duration and stability of male coalitions. Coalitions that are made up of related males last nearly four times as long as coalitions composed of unrelated males. Coalitions composed of related males are also less likely to experience rank reversals. In this case, the costs of cooperation may be balanced by gains in inclusive fitness.

Kin selection plays an important role in cooperatively breeding primate groups.

In marmosets and tamarins, reproduction is usually monopolized by a single breeding pair, and all group members help care for offspring. This raises an obvious question: Why do helpers help? The answer seems to be linked to kin selection. When infants mature, they often remain in their natal groups for several years and help rear their younger siblings. At some point, older offspring disperse with same-sex siblings and form new groups when they meet appropriate members of the opposite sex. Then one of the siblings becomes the dominant breeder, and the others become helpers. Again, helpers are closely related to the infants that they care for.

Kinship seems to reduce the extent of competition among females to some degree. Recall from Chapter 6 that there is competition among females over reproductive opportunities. When subordinate females produce infants, the dominant female often kills them. However, in golden lion tamarins (**Figure 7.18**), there are some groups in which females share reproduction with subordinate females for one or two years. Females are most likely to share breeding with their own daughters, less commonly with sisters, and rarely with unrelated females.

Sometimes biology is even stranger than fiction. Genetic **chimeras** are organisms that carry more than one genetically distinct population of cells derived from more than one zygote. Chimerism is generally rare in mammals but occurs in marmosets, which commonly produce fraternal twins. The twins share a common placenta and **chorion**, the membrane that surrounds the embryo in the uterus, and stem cells are passed between them. The twins are genetic chimeras with tissues derived from both their own and their siblings' cell lines. Although this phenomenon has been known for some time, it was thought that chimeric tissues were limited to tissues that produce blood cells. However, Corinna Ross and her colleagues from the University of Nebraska have discovered that chimerism extends to all bodily tissues, including the gametes. This means that individuals sometimes pass along their siblings' genes, not their own genes, to their offspring. This would raise the relatedness between nonbreeding helpers and infants and might be one of the factors that favor such high levels of cooperation in these species.

FIGURE 7.18

Golden lion tamarins are cooperative breeders, but conflict sometimes arises over breeding opportunities.

Parent–Offspring Conflict

Kin selection helps to explain why there is conflict between parents and offspring as well as among siblings.

As we explained in the last chapter, mothers must wean their infants so that they can conserve energy for infants born later. As mothers begin to curtail investment, their infants often resist, sometimes vigorously. Chimpanzee infants throw full-fledged tantrums when their mothers rebuff their efforts to nurse, and baboons whimper piteously when their mothers refuse to carry them. These weaning conflicts arise from a fundamental asymmetry in the genetic interests of mothers and their offspring. Mothers are equally related to all of their offspring ($r = 0.5$), but offspring are more closely related to themselves ($r = 1.0$) than to their siblings ($r = 0.5$ or 0.25). This phenomenon was labeled **parent–offspring conflict** by Rutgers biologist Robert Trivers, who was the first to recognize the evolutionary rationale underlying the conflict between parents and their offspring.

To understand why there is parent–offspring conflict, imagine a mutation that increases the amount of maternal investment in the current infant by a small amount, thereby reducing investment in future infants by the same amount. According to Hamilton's rule, selection will favor the expression of this gene in mothers if

$$0.5 \times \text{(increase in fitness of current infant)}$$
$$> 0.5 \times \text{(decrease in fitness of future offspring)}$$

Because the mother shares half of her genes with each of her offspring, 0.5 appears on both sides of the inequality. The inequality tells us that selection will increase investment in the current offspring until the benefits to the current offspring are equal to the costs to future offspring. The result is quite different if the genes expressed in the current infant control the amount of maternal investment. This time, consider a gene expressed in the current infant that increases the investment the infant receives by a small amount. Once again, we use Hamilton's rule, this time from the perspective of the current infant:

$$1.0 \times \text{(increase in fitness of current fetus)}$$
$$> 0.5 \times \text{(decrease in fitness of future offspring)}$$

In this case, the infant is related to itself by 1.0 and to its full sibling by 0.5. Now selection will increase the amount of maternal investment until the incremental benefit of another unit of investment in the current infant is twice the cost to future brothers and sisters of the fetus (and four times for half siblings). Thus, genetic asymmetries lead to a conflict of interest between mothers and their offspring. Selection will favor mothers who provide less investment than their infants desire, and selection will favor offspring who demand more investment than their mothers are willing to give. This conflict of interest plays out in weaning tantrums and sibling rivalries.

Reciprocal Altruism

Altruism can also evolve if altruistic acts are reciprocated.

The theory of **reciprocal altruism** relies on the basic idea that altruism among individuals can evolve if altruistic behavior is balanced between partners (pairs of interacting individuals) over time. In reciprocal relationships, individuals take turns being actor and recipient—giving and receiving the benefits of altruism (**Figure 7.19**). Reciprocal altruism is favored because over time the participants in reciprocal acts obtain benefits that outweigh the costs of their actions. This theory was first formulated by Robert Trivers and later amplified and formalized by others.

Three conditions occurring together favor the development of reciprocal altruism: Individuals must (1) have an opportunity to interact often, (2) be able to keep track of support given and received, and (3) provide support only to those who help them. The first condition is necessary so that individuals will have the opportunity for their own altruism to be reciprocated. The second condition allows individuals to balance altruism given to and received from particular partners. The third condition produces the nonrandom interaction necessary for the evolution of altruism. If individuals are unrelated, initial interactions will be randomly distributed to altruists and nonaltruists. However, reciprocators will quickly stop helping those who do not help in return, while continuing to help those who do. Thus, as with kin selection, reciprocal altruism can be favored by natural selection because altruists receive a disproportionate share of the benefits of altruistic acts. Note that altruistic acts need not be exchanged in kind; it is possible for one form of altruism (such as grooming) to be exchanged for another form of altruism (such as coalitionary support).

FIGURE 7.19

Two old male chimpanzees groom each other. Reciprocity can involve taking turns or interacting simultaneously. Male chimpanzees remain in their natal communities throughout their lives and develop close bonds with one another.

In primates, the conditions for the evolution of reciprocal altruism probably are satisfied often, and there is some evidence that it occurs.

Most primates live in social groups that are fairly stable, and they can recognize all of the members of their groups. We do not know whether primates have the cognitive capacity to keep track of support given and received from various partners, but we do know that they are very intelligent and can solve complex problems. Thus, primates provide a good place to look for examples of contingent forms of reciprocity.

In several species of macaques, baboons, vervet monkeys, and chimpanzees, individuals tend to spend the most time grooming those who spend the most time grooming them, and they most often support those from whom they most often receive support. In some cases, monkeys seem to exchange grooming for support. Sometimes monkeys switch roles during grooming bouts so that the amount of grooming given and received during each grooming bout is balanced; sometimes grooming is balanced across bouts.

Among male chimpanzees, social bonds seem to be based on reciprocal exchanges in many currencies (Figure 7.19). For example, John Mitani of the University of Michigan and David Watts of Yale University have found that male chimpanzees at Ngogo, a site in the Kibale Forest of Uganda, share meat selectively with males who share meat with them and with males who regularly support them in agonistic interactions. Males who hunt together also tend to groom one another selectively, support one another, and participate in border patrols together. Interestingly, close associates are often not maternal or paternal kin, suggesting that males' relationships are based on reciprocity, not kinship.

These correlational findings are consistent with predictions derived from the theory of reciprocal altruism, but they do not demonstrate that altruism is contingent on reciprocation.

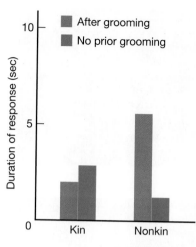

FIGURE 7.20

Vervet monkeys responded more strongly to recruitment calls played from a hidden speaker if the nonkin caller had previously groomed them than if the caller had not.

A few studies suggest that primates keep track of these contingencies, at least over short periods.

Robert Seyfarth and Dorothy Cheney conducted the first study to examine the contingent nature of altruistic exchanges. Like most other monkeys, vervets spend much of their free time grooming. Vervets also form coalitions and use specific vocalizations to recruit support. In this experiment, Seyfarth and Cheney played tape-recorded recruitment calls to individuals in two situations. Vervet A's recruitment call was played to vervet B from a hidden speaker (1) after A had groomed B and (2) after a fixed time during which A and B had not groomed. It was hypothesized that if grooming were associated with support in the future, then B should respond more strongly to A's recruitment call after being groomed. And that's just what the vervets did when they had interacted with nonrelatives. In contrast, when the vervets interacted with their relatives, their responses were not consistently affected by prior grooming (**Figure 7.20**). Seyfarth and Cheney have replicated these results with baboons, adding several controls that help rule out alternative explanations for the subjects' responses to the playbacks.

Although several naturalistic experiments suggest that primates respond to previous help in a contingent way, more controlled experiments conducted in the laboratory have been largely unsuccessful. For example, Alicia Melis, now at the University of Warwick, and her colleagues conducted an experiment in which one chimpanzee needed help from a second chimpanzee to get into a locked room. Each subject was paired with two helpers, one who provided help and another who did not provide help. Then the roles were reversed, and the individual who had needed help was able to provide help to the previously helpful and unhelpful partners. The chimpanzees were as likely to help the unhelpful partner as they were to help the helpful partner.

At this point it is not entirely clear how to interpret the data. Some researchers think that primates selectively help those from whom they have previously received help. Such researchers focus on the correlational evidence and the naturalistic experiments. Others emphasize the shortcomings of correlational studies, such as the lack of evidence from carefully controlled studies in the laboratory, and speculate that primates may not have the cognitive ability to keep track of help given and received from multiple partners over extended periods. However, most researchers would agree on one point: Kin selection plays a more important role in regulating the distribution of altruism in primate groups than does reciprocity.

Key Terms

altruistic behaviors (p. 169)
kin selection (p. 174)
Hamilton's rule (p. 174)
coefficient of relatedness (*r*) (p. 175)

phenotypic matching (p. 176)
grooming (p. 179)
affiliative (p. 179)

coalitions (p. 180)
alliances (p. 180)
matrilineage (p. 182)
chimeras (p. 183)

chorion (p. 183)
parent–offspring conflict (p. 184)
reciprocal altruism (p. 184)

Study Questions

1. Consider the accompanying kinship diagram. What is the kinship relationship (for example, mother, aunt, or cousin) and degree of relatedness (such as 0.5 or 0.25) for each pair of individuals?

CHAPTER 7: The Evolution of Cooperation

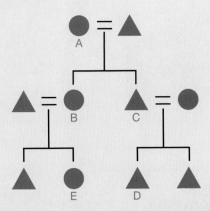

2. In biological terms, explain the difference between the following situations: (a) A male monkey sitting high in a tree gives alarm calls when he sees a lion at a distance. (b) A female monkey abandons a desirable food patch when she is approached by another female.

3. In documentaries about animal behavior, animals are often said to do things "for the good of the species." For example, when low-ranking animals do not reproduce, they are said to give up reproducing to prevent the population from becoming too numerous and exhausting its resource base. What is wrong with this line of reasoning?

4. Why is some sort of nonrandom interaction among altruists necessary for altruism to be maintained?

5. Suppose that primates cannot recognize paternal kin, as many primatologists have assumed. What would that tell you about how natural selection produces adaptations?

6. Data from several studies indicate that primates are more likely to behave altruistically toward kin than toward nonkin. However, many of the same studies show that rates of aggression toward kin and nonkin are basically the same. How does this fit with what you have learned about kin selection? Why are monkeys as likely to fight with kin as with nonkin?

7. There are relatively few good examples of reciprocal altruism in nature. Why is reciprocal altruism uncommon? Why might we expect reciprocal altruism to be more common among primates than among other kinds of animals?

8. Seyfarth and Cheney found that vervet monkeys tended to respond more strongly to the calls of the animals who had groomed them earlier in the day than to the calls of animals who had not groomed them. However, this effect held only for unrelated animals, not for kin. The vervets responded as strongly to the calls of grooming relatives as to those of nongrooming relatives. How might we explain kinship's influence on these results?

9. In addition to kin selection and reciprocal altruism, a third mechanism leading to nonrandom interaction of altruists has been suggested. Suppose altruists had an easily detected phenotypic trait, perhaps a green beard. Then they could use the following rule: "Do altruistic acts only for individuals who have green beards." Once the allele became common, most individuals carrying green beards would not be related to one another, so this would not be a form of kin selection. However, there is a subtle flaw in this reasoning. Assuming that the genes controlling beard color are at different genetic loci from the genes controlling altruistic behavior, explain why green beards would not evolve.

10. Explain why punishment does not provide a ready solution to the problem of cheating in mutualistic interactions.

Further Reading

Chapais, B., and C. M. Berman, eds. 2004. *Kinship and Behavior in Primates*. New York: Oxford University Press.

Dugatkin, L. A. 1997. *Cooperation among Animals: An Evolutionary Perspective*. New York: Oxford University Press.

Kappeler, P. M., and C. P. van Schaik, eds. 2006. *Cooperation in Primates and Humans: Mechanisms and Evolution*. New York: Springer.

Mitani, J., J. Call, P. Kappeler, R. Palombit, and J. B. Silk, eds. 2012. *The Evolution of Primate Societies*. Chicago: University of Chicago Press.

Westneat, D. F., and C. W. Fox, eds. 2010. *Evolutionary Behavioral Ecology*. Oxford: Oxford University Press.

 Visit DIGITAL.WWNORTON.COM/HOWHUMANS8 to
- review this chapter with personalized, interactive questions via InQuizitive
- view videos and animations on this chapter's key topics

8

- **Big Brains and Long Lives** p. 189
- **Life History Theory** p. 190
- **Selective Pressures Favoring Large Brains in Monkeys and Apes** p. 193
- **What Do Monkeys Know about One Another?** p. 197
- **The Value of Studying Primate Behavior** p. 202

PRIMATE LIFE HISTORIES AND THE EVOLUTION OF INTELLIGENCE

CHAPTER OBJECTIVES

By the end of this chapter you should be able to

A. Explain how life history theory helps us understand why certain features, such as fertility and longevity, are correlated.

B. Assess how the evolution of big brains has shaped primate life history strategies.

C. Explain why primatologists think natural selection has favored large brains in monkeys and apes.

D. Describe what primates know about their physical environment.

E. Describe what primates know about their social world.

Big Brains and Long Lives

Large brains and long life spans are two of the features that define the primate order (**Figure 8.1**). Compared with most other animals, primates rely more heavily on learning to acquire the knowledge and skills that they need to survive and reproduce successfully. The complex behavioral strategies that we have explored in the last few chapters depend on primates' ability to respond flexibly in novel situations. Primates also have long periods of development and long life spans. Cognitive complexity and longevity have become even more exaggerated among modern humans, who live longer than any other primates and have relatively

189

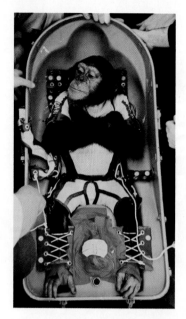

FIGURE 8.1

Primates are intelligent and long-lived. The first ape in space was a 4-year-old chimpanzee named Ham, who was trained to perform a variety of tasks while hurtling into space. In May 1961, three months after Ham's flight, Alan Shepard followed the chimp into space. Ham was one of several dozen chimpanzees that NASA used to test the safety of space travel for humans. Although Ham died at the age of 27, several of his fellow "astrochimps" are still alive in their 40s. The survivors and some of their descendants are now living in sanctuaries in New Mexico and southern Florida.

larger brains than any other creatures on the planet. It is not a coincidence that primates have both big brains and long lives; these traits are correlated across mammalian species. As we complete our discussion of the behavior and ecology of contemporary primates and turn our attention to the history of the human lineage, it is important to consider the forces that have shaped the evolution of large brains and long life spans in the primate order.

Selection for larger brains generates selection for long lives.

Correlations tell us that two traits are related but not why this relationship exists. In this case, we have some reason to think that the causal arrow goes from brain size to life span, not vice versa. We come to this conclusion because brains are expensive organs to maintain. Our brains account for just 2% of our total body weight, but they consume about 20% of our metabolic energy.

Natural selection does not maintain costly features such as the brain unless they confer important adaptive advantages. Moreover, the extent of investment that organisms make in a particular feature will be linked to the benefit that is derived from the investment. This is the same reason that you are usually willing to spend more for something that you will use for a long time than for something you will use only once. Animals that live for a long time will derive a greater benefit from the energy they expend on building and maintaining their brains than will animals that live for only a short time.

Life History Theory

Life history theory focuses on the evolutionary forces that shape trade-offs between the quantity and quality of offspring and between current and future reproduction.

Birth and death mark the beginning and end of every individual's life cycle. Between these two end points, individuals grow, reach sexual maturity, and begin to reproduce. Natural selection has generated considerable variation around this basic scheme. For example, Pacific salmon are hatched in freshwater but spend their adult lives in the open ocean. After years in the sea, they return to the streams where they were hatched to lay or fertilize their eggs; they die soon after they complete this journey. Opossums, the only North American marsupial, produce their first litter at the age of 1 year. Females have one to two litters per year and live less than 3 years (**Figure 8.2**). Lion females produce litters of up to six cubs at 2-year intervals. Elephants conceive for the first time at 10 years of age, have 22-month pregnancies, and give birth to single infants at 4- to 9-year intervals.

If natural selection favors increased reproductive success, why doesn't it extend the opossum's life span, reduce the lion's interbirth interval, or increase the elephant's litter size? The answer is that all organisms face trade-offs that constrain their reproductive options. As we explained in Chapter 6, investment in one infant limits investment in other offspring, so parents must make trade-offs between the quality and quantity of offspring they produce. Organisms also face trade-offs between current and future reproduction. All other things being equal, fast maturation and early reproduction are advantageous because they increase the length of the reproductive life span and reduce generation time. However, energy devoted to current reproduction diverts energy from growth and maintenance. If growth enhances reproductive success, then it may be advantageous to grow large before beginning to reproduce. Thus many kinds of organisms have a juvenile phase in which they do not reproduce at all. They do not become sexually mature until they reach a size at which the payoffs of allocating energy to current reproduction exceed the payoffs of continued growth. The same kind of argument applies to maintenance. Energy that is diverted from current reproduction to maintenance enables individuals to survive and reproduce successfully in the future.

Aging and death result from trade-offs between reproduction at different ages and survivorship.

Like humans, other primates age; as they get older, their physical abilities deteriorate. They don't run as fast, jump as high, or react as quickly (**Figure 8.3**). Their teeth wear down, making it harder for them to chew their food, and their joints deteriorate. Although humans are the only primates to experience menopause, the fertility of female primates of all species declines when they reach old age. Males seem to reach peak physical condition in early adulthood and then decline.

At first glance, aging and death seem to be the inevitable effects of wear and tear on bodies. Organisms are complicated machines, like cars or computers. A machine has many components that must function together for it to work. It seems logical that the components in animals' bodies simply wear out and break down, like a worn clutch or faulty hard disk. But this explanation of aging is flawed because the analogy between organisms and machines is not really apt. Every cell in an organism contains all of the genetic information necessary to build a complete, new body, and this genetic information can be used to repair damage. Wounds heal and bones mend, and some organisms, such as frogs, can regenerate entire limbs. Some organisms that reproduce asexually by budding or fission do not experience senescence at all.

If senescence is not inevitable, why doesn't natural selection do away with it? The answer has to do with the relative magnitude of the benefits that animals can derive from current reproduction or from living longer. Organisms could last longer if they were built better. A Lexus is of higher quality than a Subaru and is thus not expected to break down as often, but it also costs much more to build. The same trade-off applies to organisms. Our teeth would last longer if they were protected by a thicker covering of enamel, but building stronger teeth would require more nutrients, particularly calcium. Building higher-quality organisms consumes time and resources, thus reducing the organism's growth rate and early fertility.

The trade-off between survival and reproduction is strongly biased against characteristics that prolong life at the expense of early survival or reproduction.

Senescence is at least partly the consequence of genes that increase fitness at early ages and decrease it at later ages. Aging is favored by selection because traits that increase fertility at young ages are favored at the expense of traits that increase longevity.

The key to understanding this idea is to realize that selective pressures are much weaker on traits that affect only the old. To see why, think about the fate of two mutant alleles. One allele kills individuals before they reach adulthood, and the other kills individuals late in their lives. Carriers of the allele that kills infants and juveniles have a fitness of zero because none survives long enough to transmit the gene to their descendants. Therefore, there will be strong selection against alleles with deleterious effects on the young. In contrast, selection will have much less impact on a mutant allele that kills animals late in their lives. Carriers of a gene that kills them late in life will have already produced offspring before the effects of the gene are felt. Thus a mutation that affects the old will have limited effects on reproductive performance, and there will be little or no selection against it. This means that genes with pleiotropic effects that enhance early fertility but reduce fitness at later ages may be favored by natural selection because they increase individual fitness.

FIGURE 8.2

The Virginia opossum, *Didelphis virginiana*, is the only marsupial mammal in North America. Females produce many tiny fetuses, which make their way into the mother's pouch, attach themselves to a nipple, and nurse for 2 to 3 months. Then they emerge from the pouch and cling to their mother's back.

FIGURE 8.3

Virtually all organisms experience senescence (aging). When this photograph was taken, this old male chimpanzee, named Hugo, was missing a lot of hair on his shoulders and back, he had lost a considerable amount of weight, and his teeth had been worn down to the gums.

FIGURE 8.4

Elephants are an example of a species at the slow/long end of the life history continuum. They are very large (approximately 6,000 kg, or 13,200 lb.) and can live up to 60 years in the wild. Females mature at about 10 years of age, have a 22-month gestation period, and give birth to single offspring at 4- to 9-year intervals.

The trade-offs between current and future reproduction and between the quantity and quality of offspring generate constellations of interrelated traits.

Animals that begin to reproduce early also tend to have small body sizes, small brains, short gestation times, large litters, high rates of mortality, and short life spans. Animals that begin to reproduce at later ages tend to have larger body sizes, larger brains, longer gestation times, smaller litters, lower rates of mortality, and longer life spans (**Figure 8.4**). Life history traits are clustered together in this way because of the inherent trade-offs between current and future reproduction and between the quantity and quality of offspring. Animals that begin to reproduce early divert energy from growth and remain small. Animals that have small litters can invest more in maintenance and extend their life spans. These clusters of correlated traits create a continuum of life history strategies that runs from fast to slow or from short to long. Opossums fall somewhere along the fast/short end of the continuum; elephants lie at the slow/long end.

The trade-off between current and future reproduction depends on ecological factors that influence survival rates.

It makes little sense to divert energy to future reproduction if the prospects for surviving into the future are slim. For example, selection is likely to favor fast/short life histories in species that experience intense predation pressure. If predators are abundant and the prospects of surviving from one day to another are low, it makes little sense to postpone reproducing. In this situation, individuals that mature quickly and begin reproducing at early ages are likely to produce more surviving offspring than those that mature more slowly, so selection will favor faster/shorter life history strategies. Other kinds of ecological factors may favor slower/longer life histories. Suppose that there is severe competition for access to the resources that animals need to reproduce successfully and that larger animals are more successful in competitive encounters than are small animals. In this situation, small animals will be at a competitive disadvantage, and it may be profitable to invest more energy in growth, even if such an investment delays maturation. The life history strategies that characterize organisms reflect the net effects of these kinds of ecological pressures.

Natural selection shifts life history traits in response to changes in environmental conditions.

Natural selection adjusts life history traits in response to changes in prevailing conditions. Because life history traits are tightly clustered together (**Figure 8.5**), selection pressures acting on one trait often influence the value of other traits as well. For example, Steven Austad, a biologist at the University of Texas, compared the effect of predation on the life histories of two populations of opossums. One population lived on the mainland and was vulnerable to a variety of predators. Another population lived on an island that had very few predators for several thousand years. Opossums on the island aged more slowly, lived longer, and had smaller litters than opossums on the mainland. In this case, reduction of predation pressure favored a decelerated life history.

In some cases, organisms adjust their life histories in relation to current ecological conditions. Recall from Chapter 6 that female monkeys mature more quickly and reproduce at shorter intervals when food is abundant. This is not simply an inevitable response to the availability of food; it is an evolved capacity to adjust development in response to local conditions.

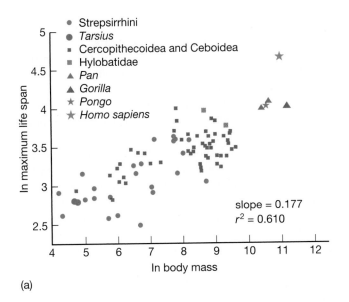

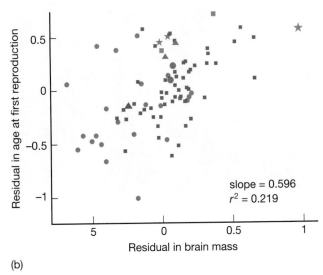

(a)

(b)

FIGURE 8.5

(a) Body weight is plotted against maximum life span for various primate species. In general, larger-bodied species live longer than smaller-bodied species. Note that humans live considerably longer than expected for their body size. (b) Brain size (corrected for body size) is plotted against age at first reproduction (corrected for body size). Species that have relatively large brains for their body size mature more slowly and reproduce for the first time at older ages than species that have smaller brains for their body size. Humans produce their first infant at about the age expected based on brain size.

Primates fall toward the slow/long end of the life history continuum.

As a group, primates tend to delay reproduction and grow to relatively large sizes, and they also have relatively long gestation times, small litters, low rates of mortality, long life spans, and large brains in relation to their body size (Figure 8.5). However, there is also variation within the primate order: Monkeys have relatively larger brains and slower life histories than strepsirrhines, and great apes have larger brains and slower life histories than monkeys.

As in other taxa, there is some evidence that ecological conditions influence life history variables in primates. Orangutans live in tropical rain forests on the islands of Borneo and Sumatra. Soil quality is higher in Sumatra than Borneo, and Sumatran forests have more fruit than Bornean forests. In addition, there is less temporal variation in fruit availability in Sumatra than in Borneo. Sumatran orangutans feed mainly on fruit throughout the year, whereas orangutans living in the relatively unproductive forests of eastern and northeastern Borneo experience long periods in which fruit is scarce and they must rely on lower-quality foods, such as bark (**Figure 8.6**). Andrea Taylor of Duke University and Carel van Schaik of the University of Zürich suggest that these conditions have favored the evolution of relatively smaller brains and substantially shorter interbirth intervals in Bornean orangutans than in Sumatran orangutans.

Selective Pressures Favoring Large Brains in Monkeys and Apes

Social or ecological pressures may have favored cognitive evolution in monkeys and apes.

Most primatologists now believe that the enlargement and reorganization of the brain in monkeys and apes is linked to the competitive pressures produced by sociality. In social groups, animals compete for food, mates, grooming partners, and other valuable resources. They also form social bonds that influence their participation in coalitions, exchange networks, access to resources, and so on (**Figure 8.7**). The larger a group becomes, the more difficult it gets to sustain social bonds and keep track of relationships

FIGURE 8.6

Variation in the availability of fruit may influence the life history strategies of orangutans in Borneo and Sumatra.

FIGURE 8.7

Many primates live in complex social groups. Geladas form one-male units, which combine to form large bands composed of hundreds of individuals.

within the group. The ability to operate effectively in this complicated social world may reward greater flexibility in behavior and favor expansion of the parts of the brain that are linked to learning and planning. This idea is called the **social intelligence hypothesis**.

An alternative set of hypotheses links increased brain size to ecological challenges, behavioral flexibility, innovation, and social learning capacities. Simon Reader of Utrecht University and Kevin Laland of the University of St. Andrews propose that natural selection has favored changes in the primate brain that enhance behavioral flexibility and enable animals to invent appropriate solutions to novel problems and to learn new behaviors from conspecifics (**Figure 8.8**). The benefits derived from innovation and social learning generated selective pressures that favored expansion and development of the parts of the brain linked to learning, planning, and behavioral flexibility. The ability to innovate and learn from others might enhance animals' ability to cope with ecological challenges. Monkeys feed mainly on plants and include many plant species in their diets. They must evaluate the ripeness, nutritional content, and toxicity of food items. Moreover, some primates rely heavily on **extracted foods** that require complex processing techniques. For example, chimpanzees and capuchin monkeys eat hard-shelled nuts that must be cracked open with stones or smashed against a tree trunk; baboons dig up roots and tubers; aye-ayes extract insect larvae from underneath tree bark (**Figure 8.9**). Extracted foods are valuable elements in primate diets because they tend to be rich sources of protein and energy. However, they require complicated, carefully coordinated techniques to process.

Comparative analyses provide some support for both types of hypotheses about cognitive evolution in primates.

These models of the evolution of cognitive complexity generate specific predictions about the pattern of variation in the brains and cognitive abilities of living primates. For example, the social intelligence hypothesis predicts a link between social complexity and cognitive complexity, and the behavioral flexibility hypothesis predicts that innovations and social learning will be linked to brain size.

To test these hypotheses, we need a reliable measure of cognitive ability. Unfortunately, it is very difficult to assess cognitive ability in other species. Instead, most work in this area has relied on measurements of the size or organization of particular parts of the brain. Researchers focus on the development of the forebrain, particularly the **neocortex**, because this is the site of the most substantial evolutionary changes in size and complexity (**Figure 8.10**). Moreover, the neocortex seems to be the part of the brain most closely associated with problem solving and behavioral flexibility. Neocortex size alone is not a very useful measure because larger animals generally have larger brains (and larger neocortexes) than smaller animals. Thus researchers make use of measures that control for these effects. Robin Dunbar, for example, measures the **neocortex ratio**, the ratio between the volume of the neocortex and the volume of the rest of the brain. Dunbar's analyses indicate that animals living in larger groups have larger neocortex ratios than animals living in smaller groups.

FIGURE 8.8

Wolfgang Köhler was one of the first scientists to systematically study cognitive abilities in captive chimpanzees. He hung a bunch of bananas out of the chimpanzees' reach and put several wooden crates in the room. Eventually, one individual, named Sultan, managed to stack the crates, clamber onto the precarious tower, and grab the bananas.

(a)

(b)

FIGURE 8.9

Primates sometimes exploit foods that are difficult to extract. Here (a) a male chimpanzee pokes a long twig into a hole in a termite mound and extracts termites, and (b) a green monkey punctures an eggshell and extracts the contents.

There is also evidence that behavioral flexibility and social learning are linked to brain evolution. Reader and Laland surveyed the primate literature for information about three measures of behavioral flexibility: (1) reports of behavioral innovation, which they defined as novel solutions to ecological or social problems; (2) examples of social learning, the acquisition of skills and information from others; and (3)

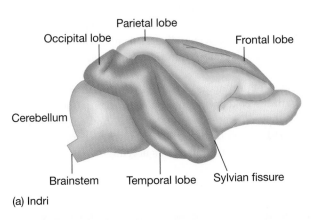
(a) Indri

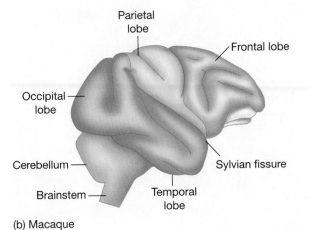
(b) Macaque

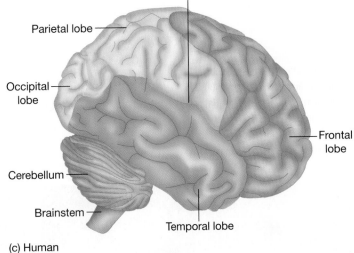
(c) Human

FIGURE 8.10

The brains of (a) an indri, a large strepsirrhine; (b) a macaque; and (c) a human. There are three main components of the brain: the hindbrain, which contains the cerebellum and medulla (part of the brainstem); the midbrain, which contains the optic lobe (not visible here); and the forebrain, which contains the cerebrum. The cerebrum is divided into four main lobes: occipital, parietal, frontal, and temporal. The forebrain is greatly expanded in primates and other mammals, and much of the gray matter (which is made up of cell bodies and synapses) is located on the outside of the cerebrum in a layer called the cerebral cortex. The neocortex is a component of the cerebral cortex, and in mammals the neocortex covers the surface of virtually the entire forebrain.

observations of tool use. They demonstrated that these measures of behavioral flexibility are closely linked to the executive brain ratio (the size of the executive brain in relation to the brainstem). Primates with relatively large executive brains are more likely to innovate, learn from others, and use tools than primates with relatively small executive brains. In addition, primates seem to be more flexible in their foraging behavior than in their social behavior. In the long list of examples of innovations and socially learned behaviors that Reader and Laland compiled, foraging innovations predominate. In these comparative analyses, there is no consistent relationship between social learning and group size.

Thus, it is not entirely clear whether social or ecological challenges were primary factors favoring the evolution of big brains in primates. And these two hypotheses are not mutually exclusive. Primates may have derived benefits both from being able to cope more effectively with social challenges and from being able to master ecological challenges. Alternatively, cognitive abilities that evolved for one purpose may be applied in other contexts.

Great apes do not fit the social intelligence hypothesis very well.

Great apes have larger brains in relation to their body size than monkeys do, but they live in smaller groups than many monkeys. Although chimpanzees and bonobos may live in communities that include as many as 50 individuals, gorillas live in much smaller groups, and orangutans are largely solitary. This obviously poses a problem for the social intelligence hypothesis.

Richard Byrne points out that great apes make use of more complicated foraging techniques than other primates, enabling them to feed on some foods that other primates cannot process. For example, virtually all plant foods that mountain gorillas rely on are well defended by spines, hard shells, hooks, and stingers. Consuming each of their food items requires a particular routine—a complicated sequence of steps structured in a particular way. Many of the foods that orangutans feed on are also difficult to process.

Great apes sometimes use tools to obtain access to certain foods that are not otherwise available to them. Chimpanzees poke twigs into holes of termite mounds and anthills, use leaves as sponges to mop up water from deep holes, and employ stones as hammers to break open hard-shelled nuts (**Figure 8.11**). Sumatran orangutans use sticks to probe for insects and to pry seeds out of the husks of fruit.

FIGURE 8.11

Chimpanzees use tools to help them obtain certain kinds of foods. (a) This chimpanzee at Gombe Stream National Park in Tanzania is using a long stick to dip for ants. (b) Here a chimpanzee uses a large stone to hammer open hard-shelled nuts.

(a)

(b)

CHAPTER 8: Primate Life Histories and the Evolution of Intelligence

What Do Monkeys Know about One Another?

Although the selective forces that favored the evolution of large brains and slow life histories among primates are not fully understood, it is clear that primates know a lot about the other members of their groups. One of the most striking things about primates is the interest they take in one another. Newborns are greeted and inspected with interest (**Figure 8.12**). Adult females are sniffed and visually inspected regularly during their estrous cycles. When a fight breaks out, other members of the group watch attentively. As we have seen in previous chapters, monkeys know a considerable amount about their own relationships to other group members. A growing body of evidence suggests that monkeys also have some knowledge of the nature of relationships among other individuals, or **third-party relationships**. Monkeys' knowledge of social relationships may enable them to form effective coalitions, compete effectively, and manipulate other group members to their own advantage.

FIGURE 8.12

In many primate species, all group members take an active interest in infants. Here, a female baboon greets a newborn infant. Evidence from playback experiments, laboratory experiments, and naturalistic observations suggests that monkeys know something about the relationships among group members.

Monkeys and apes know something about kinship relationships among other members of their groups.

One of the first indications that monkeys understand the nature of other individuals' kinship relationships came from a playback experiment on vervet monkeys conducted by Dorothy Cheney and Robert Seyfarth in Kenya's Amboseli National Park. Several female vervets heard a tape-recorded scream of a juvenile vervet piped from a hidden speaker. When the call was played, the mother of the juvenile stared in the direction of the speaker longer than other females did. This response suggests that mothers recognized the call of their own offspring. Even before the mother reacted, however, other females in the vicinity looked directly at the juvenile's mother. This response suggests that other females understood which monkey the juvenile belonged to and that they were aware that a special relationship existed between the mother and her offspring.

Monkeys may also have broader knowledge of kinship relationships (**Figure 8.13**). The evidence for this claim also comes from Cheney and Seyfarth's work on vervet monkeys. When monkeys are threatened or attacked, they often respond by threatening or attacking a lower-ranking individual who was not involved in the original incident—a

FIGURE 8.13

Living in complex social groups may have been the selective factor favoring large brains and intelligence among primates.

phenomenon we call **redirected aggression**. Vervets selectively redirect aggression toward the maternal kin of the original aggressor. So, if female A threatens female B, then B threatens AA, a close relative of A. If monkeys were simply blowing off steam or venting their aggression, they would choose a target at random. Thus the monkeys seem to know that certain individuals are somehow related.

Monkeys probably understand rank relationships among other individuals.

Because kinship and dominance rank are major organizing principles in most primate groups, it makes sense to ask whether monkeys also understand third-party rank relationships. The most direct evidence that monkeys understand third-party rank relationships comes from two playback experiments conducted in the Okavango Delta of Botswana on a group of baboons that has been studied for the last 15 years by Seyfarth, Cheney, and their colleagues. In this group, dominance relationships were stable, and females never responded submissively toward lower-ranking females.

In one experiment that Seyfarth and Cheney designed, females listened to a recording of a female's grunt followed by another female's submissive fear barks. Female baboons responded more strongly when they heard a higher-ranking female responding submissively to a lower-ranking female's grunt than when they heard a lower-ranking female responding submissively to a higher-ranking female's grunt. Thus females were more attentive when they heard a sequence of calls that did not correspond to their knowledge of dominance rank relationships among other females. Control experiments excluded the possibility that females were reacting simply to the fact that they had not heard a particular sequence of calls before. The pattern of responses suggests that females knew the relative ranks of other females in their group and were particularly interested in the anomalous sequence of calls.

In a second experiment, Thore Bergman and Jacinta Beehner collaborated with Seyfarth and Cheney to probe the baboons' knowledge of the hierarchical nature of rank relationships in groups with matrilineal dominance ranks. Using the same basic experimental paradigm, researchers played sequences of vocalizations that simulated rank reversals within lineages and rank reversals between lineages. As young female baboons mature, they often rise in rank above their older sisters and other female kin. Thus changes in the relative rank of females in the same lineage are part of the normal course of rank acquisition. However, changes in the relative ranks of unrelated females are much less common. The baboons reacted much more strongly to simulated rank reversals between lineages than to simulated rank reversals within lineages. Again, the researchers were careful to control for confounding variables, such as rank distance and novelty. This result suggests that the females understood the relative ranks of other females and that they understood that changes in rank relationships within lineages are not the same as changes in rank relationships between lineages.

Participation in coalitions probably draws on sophisticated cognitive abilities.

Even the simplest coalition is a complex interaction. When coalitions are formed, at least three individuals are involved, and several kinds of interactions are going on simultaneously (**Figure 8.14**). Consider the case in which one monkey (the aggressor) attacks another monkey (the victim). The victim then solicits support from a third party (the ally), and the ally intervenes on behalf of the victim against the aggressor. The ally behaves altruistically toward the victim, giving support to the victim at some potential cost to itself. At the same time, however, the ally behaves aggressively toward the aggressor, imposing harm or energy costs

FIGURE 8.14

Complex fitness calculations may be involved in decisions about whether to join a coalition. By helping the victim against the aggressor, the ally increases the fitness of the victim and decreases the fitness of the aggressor.

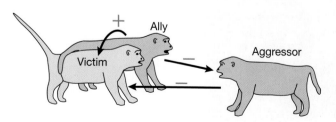

(a)

(b)

FIGURE 8.15

Primates form coalitions that are more complicated than the coalitions of most other animals. (a) In a captive bonnet macaque group, members of opposing factions confront one another. (b) Three capuchin monkeys are in defense mode.

on the aggressor. Thus the ally simultaneously has a positive effect on the victim and a negative effect on the aggressor. Under these circumstances, decisions about whether to intervene in a particular dispute may be quite complicated. Consider a female who witnesses a dispute between two of her offspring. Should she intervene? If so, which of her offspring should she support? When a male bonnet macaque is solicited by a higher-ranking male against a male who frequently supports him, how should he respond? In each case, the ally must balance the benefits to the victim, the costs to the opponent, and the costs to itself (**Figure 8.15**).

Given the complexity of even simple coalitions, knowledge of third-party relationships may be valuable because it enables individuals to predict how others will behave. Thus animals who understand the nature of third-party relationships may have a good idea about who will support them and who will intervene against them in confrontations with particular opponents, and they may also be able to tell which of their potential allies are likely to be most effective in coalitions against their opponents.

Susan Perry and her colleagues at the University of California, Los Angeles, have studied capuchin monkeys' use of third-party information in coalitions. Their analysis reveals that capuchins follow three basic rules when they form coalitions: (1) support females against males, (2) support dominants against subordinates, and (3) support close associates against others. If capuchins understand these rules, particularly the last one, they are not expected to recruit support against dominant opponents or from males who have closer relationships with their opponents than with themselves. And, indeed, the evidence shows that they do not recruit in these ways. Their ability to adhere to these rules suggests that they understand the nature of relationships among other group members.

We are beginning to gain insight into what monkeys and apes know about others' minds.

Monkeys and apes seem to be very good at predicting what other animals will do in particular situations. For example, we have seen that vervets groom monkeys who support them in coalitions, female langurs with newborn infants are fearful of new resident males, baboons express surprise when low-ranking animals elicit signs of submission from higher-ranking animals, and capuchins don't try to recruit support from monkeys who have closer bonds to their opponents than to themselves. These examples indicate that monkeys can predict what others will do and adjust their behavior accordingly.

Monkeys' ability to predict what other individuals will do may not seem very remarkable. After all, we know that many animals are very good at learning to make associations between one event and another. In the laboratory, rats, pigeons, monkeys, and many other animals can learn to pull a lever, push a button, or peck a key to obtain food. These are examples of associative learning, the ability to track contingencies between

FIGURE 8.16

In Menzel's experiments, a researcher showed a young chimpanzee where food was hidden in the chimp's enclosure, as pictured here. Then the chimpanzee was reunited with the other members of the group, and the group was released inside the enclosure. The young chimpanzee often led the group back to the hidden food, but it also learned to divert the group so that it could get bits of food before others found the cache.

one event and another. Monkeys' ability to predict what others will do in particular situations might be based on sophisticated associative learning capacities, prodigious memory of past events, and perhaps some understanding of conceptual categories such as kinship and dominance. On the other hand, it is also possible that monkeys' ability to predict what others will do is based on their knowledge of the mental states of others—what psychologists call a **theory of mind**.

It may seem relatively unimportant whether monkeys and apes rely on associative learning to predict what others will do or whether they have a well-developed theory of mind. However, there may be some things that animals cannot do unless they understand what is going on in other animals' minds. For example, some researchers think that effective deception requires the ability to manipulate or take advantage of others' beliefs about the world. In the 1960s, the late Emil Menzel conducted a landmark set of experiments about chimpanzees' ability to find and communicate about the location of hidden objects (**Figure 8.16**). In a set of experiments, Menzel showed one chimpanzee where a food item was hidden and then released the knowledgeable chimpanzee and his companions into their enclosure. The group quickly learned to follow their knowledgeable companion; but he just as quickly learned that when he led others to the hidden food, he would not get a very big share of it. Menzel noticed that the knowledgeable chimpanzee sometimes led his companions in the wrong direction and then dashed off and grabbed the hidden treasure. How did the knowledgeable chimpanzee work out this tactic? He might have understood that his knowledge differed from the knowledge of other group members and then have come up with a way to take advantage of this discrepancy effectively. If this is what he did, then we would conclude that he had a well-developed theory of mind.

Although some researchers suggest that deception does not rely on a theory of mind, it seems clear that a theory of mind would allow for more complicated and successful deceptions. Similarly, the ability to pretend, empathize, take another's perspective, read minds, console, imitate, and teach relies on knowing what others know or how they feel. Humans do all of these things, but it is not clear whether other primates do.

It is difficult to be sure what nonhuman primates know about the minds of other individuals. However, primatologists have begun to make some progress in this area.

Bryan Hare, now at Duke University, and Josep Call and Michael Tomasello of the Max Planck Institute for Evolutionary Anthropology in Leipzig, Germany, developed a protocol that evaluates individuals' ability to take advantage of discrepancies between their own knowledge and other individuals' knowledge in a competitive situation. In their experiments, they paired subordinate and dominant chimpanzees in the configuration illustrated in **Figure 8.17**. The experiments take advantage of the fact that subordinates cannot obtain food when dominants are present. Here, two pieces of food are visible to the subordinate, but the dominant can see only one; the other is hidden behind a barrier. Hare and his colleagues predicted that if the subordinate *knew* what the dominant could see, the subordinate would head for the piece of food that the dominant could not see, hoping to consume the hidden food item while the dominant was occupied with the other piece. This is exactly what the subordinate chimpanzees did. So the chimpanzees seemed to understand what other chimpanzees know.

Laurie Santos of Yale University and her colleagues applied the same reasoning in designing experiments with free-ranging rhesus macaques on Cayo Santiago. In these experiments, monkeys were given the chance to "steal" food from two human experimenters. In one experiment, one experimenter was facing toward the monkey, and the other was facing away. The monkeys were more likely to approach the experimenter who was facing away than the experimenter who was facing forward. In other experiments, the monkeys selectively approached experimenters whose faces were pointed away and experimenters whose eyes were averted (**Figure 8.18**). In another set of experiments,

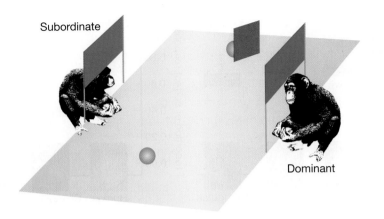

Subordinate

Dominant

FIGURE 8.17

In this experiment, one food item was hidden behind a barrier so that it could be seen by only the subordinate animal, and one food item was in plain sight of the dominant. Subordinates are unlikely to obtain food rewards when dominant animals are present. So if the subordinate knew what the dominant could see, the subordinate was expected to head for the item that was hidden from the dominant. This is what the chimpanzees did most of the time.

Santos placed food rewards in two transparent boxes covered with bells. In one box, the ringers on the bells were removed, creating one noisy box and one quiet box. The experimenter baited the boxes, shook the boxes to display their auditory qualities, and then walked away and hid his face. The monkeys showed strong preferences for the quiet container, suggesting that they knew what the experimenter could hear. Santos and her colleagues argue that rhesus monkeys can accurately perceive what others see and hear in these competitive situations.

Human social cognition is more sophisticated than that of apes.

Although apes and monkeys can solve many complex cognitive tasks, there are still substantial differences between the cognitive skills of humans and other primates. These differences are most pronounced in tasks that involve social learning, communication, and knowledge of others' minds. In a comprehensive comparative study of ape cognition, Esther Herrmann and her colleagues from the Max Planck Institute for Evolutionary Anthropology evaluated the performance of 105 two-year-old humans on a battery of cognitive tasks and compared this with the performance of 106 chimpanzees and 32 orangutans of all ages on the same tasks. Some tasks focused on cognition about the physical world, such as tracking a reward after it has been moved or using a

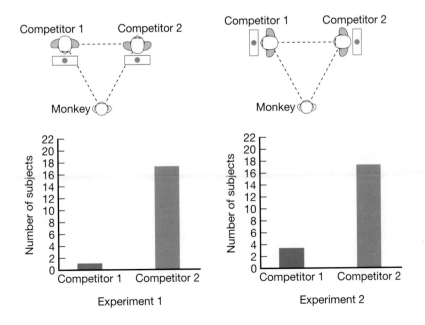

Experiment 1 | Experiment 2

FIGURE 8.18

In this set of experiments, monkeys were presented with two human competitors who had food that the monkeys could potentially steal. The graphs show that monkeys were much more likely to approach the person who was looking away from them than the person who was facing them, and they were more likely to approach the person who was looking away from the food than the person who was looking toward the food. This suggests that monkeys know what others can and cannot see.

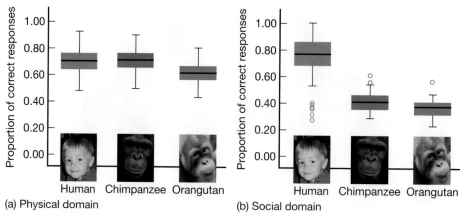

(a) Physical domain   (b) Social domain

FIGURE 8.19

Children and apes were presented with an identical set of tasks that examined their physical and social cognition. (a) Children and apes showed no differences in tasks based on physical cognition. (b) But children were considerably more successful than apes on tasks that were based on social cognition. In this graph, the median value is indicated by the line that runs through each box and the box spans the interquartile range that includes 50% of the values. The lines outside the boxes (sometimes called "whiskers") represent maximum and minimum values, excluding outliers (*circles*), which are values that lie at least 1.5 times above or below the interquartile range.

tool to retrieve a reward that is out of reach. Other tasks focused on social cognition, such as solving a novel problem after observing the demonstration of a solution or following a gaze to a target. There was little difference in the performance of children and apes on tasks that involved physical cognition (**Figure 8.19**). However, there were greater differences in the social domain. The human children were significantly more successful than the chimpanzees and orangutans on tasks that required social learning, communication, and knowledge of others' minds. Herrmann and her colleagues hypothesize that humans have "evolved some specialized socio-cognitive skills (beyond those of primates in general) for living and exchanging knowledge in cultural groups: communicating with others, learning from others, and 'reading the mind' of others in especially complex ways." We will come back to this idea in Part Four, when we discuss the evolution of the human capacity for culture.

The Value of Studying Primate Behavior

As we come to the end of Part Two, it may be useful to remind you why information about primate behavior and ecology plays an integral role in the story of human evolution. First, humans are primates, and the first members of the human species were probably more similar to living nonhuman primates than to any other animals on Earth. Thus, by studying living primates we can learn something about the lives of our ancestors. Second, humans are closely related to primates and similar to them in many ways. If we understand how evolution has shaped the behavior of animals that are so much like us, we may have greater insights about the way evolution has shaped our own behavior and the behavior of our ancestors. Both of these kinds of reasoning will be apparent in Part Three, which covers the history of our own human lineage.

Key Terms

social intelligence
  hypothesis (p. 194)
extracted foods (p. 194)

neocortex (p. 194)
neocortex ratio (p. 194)

third-party relationships
  (p. 197)

redirected aggression
  (p. 198)
theory of mind (p. 200)

Study Questions

1. There is a positive correlation between brain size and longevity in animal species. One interpretation of this correlation is that selection for longer life spans was the primary force driving the evolution of large brains. An alternative interpretation is that selection for larger brains was the primary force driving the evolution of longer life spans. Explain which of these interpretations is more likely to be correct and why this is the case.

2. We have argued that natural selection is a powerful engine for generating adaptations. If that is the case, then why do organisms grow old and die? Why can't natural selection design an organism that lives forever?

3. Life history traits tend to be bundled in particular ways. Explain how these traits are combined and why we see these kinds of combinations in nature.

4. Primates evolved from small-bodied insectivores that were arrayed somewhere along the fast/short end of the life history continuum. What ecological factors are thought to have favored the shifts toward slower/longer life histories in early primates, monkeys, and apes?

5. Primates take a relatively long time to grow up compared with other animals. Consider the costs and benefits of this life history pattern from the point of view of the growing primate and its mother.

6. What do comparative studies of the size and organization of primate brains tell us about the selective factors that shaped the evolution of primate brains? What are the shortcomings of these kinds of analyses?

7. Monkeys are quite skilled in navigating complicated social situations that they encounter in their everyday lives. They seem to know what others will do in particular situations and can respond appropriately. However, monkeys consistently fail theory-of-mind tests in the laboratory. How can we reconcile these two observations?

8. Monkeys seem to have some concept of kinship. What evidence supports this idea? What kind of variation might you expect to find in monkeys' concepts of kinship within and between species?

9. Suppose that you were studying a group of monkeys and you discovered convincing evidence of empathy or deception. How and why would these data surprise your colleagues?

10. Detailed studies of coalitionary behavior have provided an important source of information about primate cognitive abilities. Explain why coalitions are useful sources of information about social knowledge. What does the pattern of coalitionary support tell us about what monkeys know about other group members?

Further Reading

Byrne, R. W., and A. Whiten, eds. 1988. *Machiavellian Intelligence: Social Expertise and the Evolution of Intellect in Monkeys, Apes, and Humans.* New York: Oxford University Press.

Cheney, D. L., and R. M. Seyfarth. 2007. *Baboon Metaphysics: The Evolution of a Social Mind.* Chicago: University of Chicago Press.

Mitani, J., J. Call, P. Kappeler, R. Palombit, and J. B. Silk, eds. 2012. T*he Evolution of Primate Societies.* Chicago: University of Chicago Press.

Reader, S. M., and K. N. Laland. 2002. "Social Intelligence, Innovation, and Enhanced Brain Size in Primates." *Proceedings of the National Academy of Sciences U.S.A.* 99: 4436–4441.

Whiten, A. W., and R. W. Byrne, eds. 1997. *Machiavellian Intelligence II: Extensions and Evaluations.* New York: Cambridge University Press.

Visit **DIGITAL.WWNORTON.COM/HOWHUMANS8** to
- review this chapter with personalized, interactive questions via InQuizitive
- view videos and animations on this chapter's key topics

15

- **Why Evolution Is Relevant to Human Behavior p. 387**
- **Understanding How We Think p. 390**
- **Social Consequences of Mate Preferences p. 401**
- **How Much Does Evolution Explain about Human Behavior? p. 403**

EVOLUTION AND HUMAN BEHAVIOR

CHAPTER OBJECTIVES

By the end of this chapter you should be able to

A. Evaluate the argument that the application of evolutionary reasoning to understanding contemporary human behavior does not entail genetic determinism.

B. Explain why evolutionary thinking helps us understand how people learn.

C. Discuss reasons why people usually do not mate with close relatives.

D. Explain how natural selection helps us understand why men and women both value good character in a marriage partner, and why men usually care more about youth and women more about control of resources.

Why Evolution Is Relevant to Human Behavior

The application of evolutionary principles to understanding human behavior is controversial. The theory of evolution is at the core of our understanding of the natural world. By studying how natural selection, recombination, mutation, genetic drift, and other evolutionary processes interact to produce evolutionary change, we come to understand why organisms are the way they are. Of course, our understanding of evolution is far from perfect, and other disciplines, most notably chemistry and physics, contribute greatly to our understanding of life. As the great geneticist Theodosius Dobzhansky once said, however, "Nothing in biology makes sense except in the light of evolution."

So far, the way we have applied evolutionary theory in this book is not controversial. We are interested principally in the evolutionary history of our own species, *Homo sapiens*, but we began by using evolutionary theory to understand the behavior of our closest relatives, the nonhuman primates. Forty years ago, when evolutionary theory was new to primatology, this approach generated some controversy, but now most primatologists are committed to evolutionary explanations of behavior. In Part Three, we used evolutionary theory to develop models of the patterns of behavior that might have characterized early hominins. Although some researchers might debate the fine points of this analysis, there is little disagreement about the value of adaptive reasoning in this context. Perhaps this is because the early hominins were simply "bipedal apes," with brains not much larger than the brains of modern chimpanzees. Not many people object to evolutionary analyses of physiological traits, such as lactose tolerance, but they may disagree about particular explanations for those traits. Similarly, most people accept evolutionary explanations about why we live so long and mature so slowly. These traits are clearly part of human biology, and there is a broad consensus that evolutionary theory provides an essential key for understanding them.

The consensus evaporates when we enter the domain of contemporary human behavior. Most social scientists acknowledge that evolution has shaped our bodies, our minds, and our behavior to a limited extent. But many have been very critical of attempts to apply evolutionary theory to contemporary human behavior because they think evolutionary analyses imply that behavior is genetically determined. Genetic determinism of behavior in humans seems inconsistent with the fact that so much of our behavior is acquired through learning and that so much of our behavior and so many of our beliefs are strongly influenced by our culture and environment. The notion that evolutionary explanations imply genetic determinism is based on a fundamental misunderstanding about how the natural world works.

All phenotypic traits, including behavioral traits, reflect the interactions between genes and the environment.

Many people have the mistaken view that genetic transmission and learning are mutually exclusive. That is, they believe that behaviors are either genetic and thus unchangeable or learned and thus controlled entirely by environmental contingencies. This assumption lies at the heart of the "nature–nurture question," a debate that has plagued the social sciences for many years.

The nature–nurture debate is based on a false dichotomy. It assumes that there is a clear distinction between the effects of genes (nature) and the effects of the environment (nurture). People often think that genes are like engineering drawings for a finished machine and that individuals vary simply because their genes carry different specifications. For example, they imagine that Yao Ming is tall because his genes specified an adult height of 2.3 m (7 ft. 6 in.), and Earl Boykins is short because his genes specified an adult height of 1.65 m (5 ft. 5 in.).

However, genes are not like blueprints that specify phenotype. Every trait results from the *interaction* of a genetic program with the environment. Thus genes are more like recipes in the hands of a creative cook, sets of instructions to construct an organism by using materials available in the environment. At each step, this very complex process depends on the nature of local conditions. The expression of any genotype always depends on the environment. People's adult height is shaped by the genes they inherited from their parents, how well nourished they were in childhood, and the nature of the diseases they were exposed to when they were growing up.

The expression of behavioral traits is usually more sensitive to environmental conditions than is the expression of morphological and physiological traits. As we saw in

Chapter 3, traits that develop uniformly in a wide range of environments, such as finger number, are said to be canalized. Traits that vary in response to environmental cues, such as subsistence strategies, are said to be plastic. Every trait, however, whether plastic or canalized, results from the unfolding of a developmental program in a particular environment. Even highly canalized characters can be modified by environmental factors, such as fetal exposure to mutagenic agents or accidents.

Natural selection can shape developmental processes so that organisms develop different adaptive behaviors in different environments.

Some people understand that all traits are influenced by a combination of genes and environment, but they reject evolutionary explanations of human behavior because they have fallen prey to a second, more subtle misunderstanding. Namely, they believe that natural selection cannot create adaptations unless behavioral differences between individuals are caused by genetic differences. If this were true, it would follow that adaptive explanations of human behavior must be invalid because there is no doubt that most of the variation in behavioral traits, such as foraging strategies, marriage practices, and values, is not due to genetic differences but is instead the product of learning and culture.

This belief is false, however, because natural selection shapes learning mechanisms so that organisms adjust their behavior to local conditions in an adaptive way. Recall from Chapter 3 that this is exactly what happens with soapberry bugs. Male soapberry bugs in Oklahoma guard their mates when females are scarce but not when females are abundant. Individual males vary their behavior adaptively in response to the local sex ratio. For this kind of flexibility in male behavior to evolve, there had to be small genetic differences in the male propensity to guard a mated female and small genetic differences in how mate guarding is influenced by the local sex ratio. If such variation exists, then natural selection can mold the responses of males so that they are locally adaptive. In any given population, however, most of the observed behavioral variation occurs because individual males respond adaptively to environmental cues.

Behavior in the soapberry bug is relatively simple. Human learning and decision making are immensely more complex and flexible. We know much less about the mechanisms that produce behavioral flexibility in humans than we do about the mechanisms that produce flexibility in mate guarding among soapberry bugs. Nonetheless, such mechanisms must exist, and it is reasonable to assume that they have been shaped by natural selection. (Note that we are not arguing that all behavioral variation in human societies is adaptive. We know that evolution does not produce adaptation in every case, as we discussed in Chapter 3.) The crucial point here is that evolutionary approaches do not imply that differences in behavior among humans are the product of genetic differences between individuals.

In this chapter and the next, we consider how evolutionary theory can be used to understand the minds and behavior of modern humans. As you will see, researchers from different academic disciplines have followed different approaches in their efforts to understand how evolution has shaped human behavior. Some have focused on how natural selection has shaped the design of the human brain and how the reasoning and learning mechanisms created by selection can be used to understand our behavior. Others have tried to understand how the human capacity for culture and the ability to acquire ideas, beliefs, and values from other group members have influenced the evolution of human behavior. In the rest of this chapter we focus on how the first of these approaches can be used to gain insights about the behavior of contemporary humans. In the next chapter we will see how the two approaches can be combined to understand why humans are so different from all other animals.

Understanding How We Think

Evolutionary analyses provide important insights about how our brains are designed.

The adaptation that most clearly distinguishes humans from other primates is our large and very complex brain. Natural selection hasn't just made our brains big; it has shaped our cognitive abilities in very specific ways and molded the way we think.

Even the most flexible strategies are based on special-purpose psychological mechanisms.

FIGURE 15.1

Rats initially sample small amounts of unfamiliar foods, and if they become ill soon after eating something, they will not eat it again.

One way in which natural selection has shaped the way we think is in selecting for cognitive abilities that help solve the most pressing problems we face in our environment. Psychologists once thought that people and other animals had a few general-purpose learning mechanisms that allowed them to modify any aspect of their phenotypes adaptively. However, a considerable body of empirical evidence indicates that animals are predisposed to learn some things and not others. For example, rats quickly learn to avoid new foods that make them ill. Moreover, rats' food aversions are based solely on the taste of a food that has made them sick, not the food's size, shape, or color. This learning rule makes sense because rats live in a very wide range of environments where they frequently encounter new foods and usually forage at night when it is dark. To determine whether a new food is edible, they taste a small amount and then wait for several hours. If it is poisonous, they become ill, and they do not eat it again. Rats may pay attention to the taste of foods instead of to other attributes because it is often too dark to see what they are eating (**Figure 15.1**). However, there are limits to the flexibility of this learning mechanism. There are certain items that rats will never sample, and in this way their diet is rigidly controlled by genes. Moreover, the learning process is not affected equally by all environmental contingencies. For example, rats are affected more by the association of new tastes with gastric distress than they are with other possible associations.

Natural selection determines the kinds of problems that the brains of particular species are good at solving. To understand the psychology of any species, we must know what kinds of problems its members need to solve in nature.

Our brains may be designed to solve the kinds of problems that our ancestors faced when they lived in small foraging bands.

FIGURE 15.2

Evolutionary psychologists believe that the human mind has evolved to solve the adaptive challenges that confront food foragers because this is the subsistence strategy that humans have practiced for most of our evolutionary history.

We know that people lived in small-scale foraging societies for nearly all of human history (**Figure 15.2**); stratified societies with agriculture and high population density have existed for only a few thousand years (**Figure 15.3**). John Tooby and Leda Cosmides of the University of California, Santa Barbara, argue that complex adaptations such as the brain evolve slowly, so our brains are designed for life in foraging societies. They use the term **environment of evolutionary adaptedness (EEA)** to refer to the social, technological, and ecological conditions under which human mental abilities evolved. Tooby and Cosmides and their colleagues envision the EEA as being much like the world of contemporary hunter-gatherers.

People living in foraging groups face certain kinds of problems that affect their fitness. For example, food sharing is an essential part of life in modern foraging groups. Although vegetable foods are typically distributed only to family members, meat is nearly always shared more widely. Food sharing might be a form of reciprocal altruism. The big problem with reciprocal altruism is that it is costly to interact with individuals who do not reciprocate. Thus Cosmides and Tooby hypothesized that human cognition should be finely tuned to detect cheaters, and they have accumulated a convincing body of experimental data suggesting that people are very attentive to imbalances in social exchange and violations of social contracts.

As we have seen, there is quite a bit of uncertainty about how early humans lived, and this uncertainty adds ambiguity to predictions about human psychology that are based on evolutionary reasoning. Some authorities believe that early members of the genus *Homo* were much like contemporary human foragers. That is, they lived in small bands and subsisted by hunting and gathering. They controlled fire, established home bases, and shared food. They could talk, and they shared cultural beliefs, ideas, and traditions. Other authorities think that the lives of the earliest species of *Homo* were completely unlike those of modern hunter-gatherers. They think that these hominins didn't hunt large game, share food, or have home bases. If early hominins lived like contemporary foragers, then it is reasonable to think that the human brain has evolved to solve the kinds of problems that confront modern foragers, such as detecting freeloaders. On the other hand, if lifeways that characterize contemporary foragers did not emerge until 40 ka, then there might not have been enough time for selection to assemble specialized psychological mechanisms to manage the challenges that foragers face, such as detecting violations of reciprocal obligations.

FIGURE 15.3

Indigenous peoples of the Mississippi Delta constructed these mound structures 2,500 to 1,300 years ago. Monumental architecture like this is based on the ability of one group of people to control the labor of others, a signal of social stratification.

Evolved psychological mechanisms cause human societies to share many universal characteristics.

Much of anthropology (and other social sciences) is based on the assumption that human behavior is not effectively constrained by biology. People have to obtain food, shelter, and other resources necessary for their survival and reproduction. But beyond that, human behavior is unconstrained.

This assumption is not very plausible from an evolutionary perspective. Evolved mechanisms in the human brain probably channel the evolution of human societies and human culture, making some outcomes much more likely than others. So the right question is, What kinds of mental mechanisms do humans have? We are likely to share some mental mechanisms with other animals, but we may also have certain mental mechanisms that differentiate us from other creatures. In the discussion that follows, we examine two examples of cognitive mechanisms that are found in all human societies: inbreeding avoidance and mate preferences.

Inbreeding Avoidance

The offspring of genetically related parents have lower fitness than do the offspring of unrelated parents.

Geneticists refer to matings between relatives as **inbred matings** and contrast them with **outbred matings** between unrelated individuals. The offspring of inbred matings are much more likely to be homozygous for deleterious recessive alleles than are the offspring of outbred matings. As a consequence, inbred offspring are less robust and have higher mortality than the offspring of outbred matings. In Chapter 14, we discussed several genetic diseases, such as phenylketonuria, Tay–Sachs disease, and cystic fibrosis that are caused by a recessive gene. People who are heterozygous for such deleterious recessive alleles are completely unaffected, but people who are homozygous suffer severe, often fatal consequences. Recall that such alleles occur at low frequencies in most human populations. However, there are many loci in the human genome.

FIGURE 15.4

Female chimpanzees avoid mating with closely related males. Although mothers have close and affectionate relationships with their adult sons, matings between mothers and sons are quite uncommon.

Thus, even though the frequency of deleterious recessives at each locus is very small, geneticists have estimated that each person carries the equivalent of two to five lethal recessives. Mating with close relatives is deleterious because it greatly increases the chance that both partners will carry a deleterious recessive allele at the same locus. If inbreeding is deleterious, then we might expect natural selection to favor behavioral adaptations that reduce the chance of inbreeding.

Mating between close relatives is very rare among nonhuman primates.

Remember from Chapter 6 that in all species of nonhuman primates, members of one or both sexes leave their natal groups near the time of puberty. Adult males do not often remain in groups long enough to be able to mate with their own daughters. Dispersal is probably an adaptation to prevent inbreeding. In principle, primates could remain in natal groups and simply avoid mating with close kin. However, this would limit the number of potential mates and might be unreliable if there were much uncertainty about paternity.

Natural selection has provided at least some primates with another form of protection against inbreeding: a strong inhibition against mating with close kin. In matrilineal macaque groups, some males acquire high rank and mate with adult females before they emigrate. However, matings among maternal kin are extremely uncommon.

Experimental studies conducted by Wendy Saltzman of the University of California, Riverside, and her colleagues suggest that reproductive inhibition in callitrichids is due partly to inbreeding aversion. Young females housed with their mothers and fathers do not reproduce; but when fathers are replaced with unrelated males, both mothers and daughters breed. Adult female chimpanzees often have opportunities to mate with their fathers (**Figure 15.4**). More than 40 years of research at Gombe Stream National Park indicate that, in fact, they rarely do. Female chimpanzees seem to have a general aversion to mating with males much older than they are, and males seem to be generally uninterested in females much younger than themselves. These mechanisms may protect females from mating with their fathers, and vice versa.

Humans rarely mate with close relatives.

During the first half of the twentieth century, cultural anthropologists fanned out across the world to study the lives of exotic peoples. Their hard and sometimes dangerous work has given us an enormous trove of information about the spectacular variety of human lifeways. They found that domestic arrangements vary greatly across cultures: Some groups are polygynous, some monogamous, and a few polyandrous. Some people reckon descent through the female line and are subject to the authority of their mother's brother. In some societies, married couples live with the husband's kin, in others they live with the wife's kin, and in some they set up their own households. Some people must marry their mother's brothers' children; others are not allowed to do so.

In all this variety of domestic arrangements, there is not a single ethnographically documented case of a society in which brothers and sisters regularly marry or one in which parents regularly mate with their own children. The only known case of regular brother–sister mating comes from census data collected by Roman governors of Egypt from 20 to 258 C.E. From the 172 census returns that have survived, it is possible to reconstruct the composition of 113 marriages: 12 were between full siblings and 8 between half siblings. These marriages seem to have been both legal and socially approved, as both prenuptial agreements and wedding invitations survive.

The pattern for more distant kin is much more variable. Some societies permit both sex and marriage with nieces and nephews or between first cousins; other societies prohibit sex and marriage among even distant relatives. Moreover, the pattern of mating prohibitions in many societies does not conform to genetic categories. For example, even distant kin on the father's side may be taboo in a given society, whereas maternal cousins may be the most desirable marriage partners in that same society. Sometimes the rules about who can have sex are different from the rules governing who can marry.

Adults are not sexually attracted to the people with whom they grew up.

The fact that inbreeding avoidance is very common among primates suggests that our human ancestors probably also had psychological mechanisms preventing them from mating with close kin. These psychological mechanisms would disappear during human evolution only if they were selected against. However, mating with close relatives is highly deleterious in humans, as it is in other primates. Thus both theory and data predict that modern humans will have psychological mechanisms that reduce the chance of close inbreeding, at least in the small-scale societies in which human psychology was shaped.

There is evidence that such psychological mechanisms exist. In the late nineteenth century, the Finnish sociologist Edward Westermarck speculated that childhood propinquity stifles desire. By this he meant that people who live in intimate association as small children do not find each other sexually attractive as adults. Several lines of evidence provide support for Westermarck's hypothesis:

- *Taiwanese minor marriage.* Until recently, an unusual form of marriage was widespread in China. In **minor marriages**, children were betrothed and the prospective bride was adopted into the family of her future husband during infancy. There, the betrothed couple grew up together like brother and sister. According to Taiwanese informants interviewed by Arthur Wolf, an anthropologist at Stanford University, the partners in minor marriages found each other sexually unexciting. Sexual uninterest was so great that fathers-in-law sometimes had to beat the newlyweds to persuade them to consummate their marriage. Wolf's data indicate that minor marriages produced about 30% fewer children than other arranged marriages did (**Figure 15.5a**) and were much more likely to end in separation or divorce (**Figure 15.5b**). Infidelity was also more common in minor marriages. When modernization reduced parental authority, many young men and women who were betrothed in minor marriages broke their engagements and married others.

- *Kibbutz age-mates.* Before World War II, many Jewish immigrants to Israel organized themselves into utopian communities called *kibbutzim* (plural of **kibbutz**). In

FIGURE 15.5

In minor marriages, the age of the wife when she arrives in her future husband's household (age at adoption) affects both fertility and the likelihood of divorce. (a) The fertility of women adopted at young ages is depressed. (b) The younger a woman is when she arrives in her husband's household, the less likely it is that the marriage will survive.

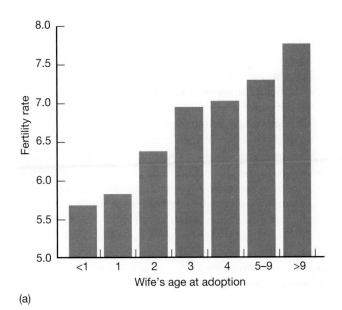

(a)

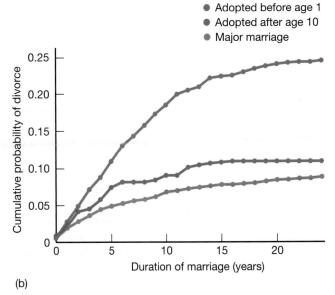

(b)

these communities, children were raised in communal nurseries, and they lived intimately with a small group of unrelated age-mates from infancy to adulthood. The ideology of the kibbutzim did not discourage sexual experimentation or marriage by children in such peer groups, but neither occurred. The Israeli sociologist Joseph Sepher, himself a kibbutznik, collected data on 2,769 marriages in 211 kibbutzim. Only 14 of them were between members of the same peer group, and in all these cases one partner joined the peer group after the age of six. From data collected in his own kibbutz, Sepher found no instances of premarital sex among members of the same peer group.

• *Third-party attitudes toward incest.* As you may have realized already, aversions to inbreeding extend beyond our attitudes toward our own mating behavior to include strong beliefs about appropriate mating behavior by other individuals. We are disgusted not only by the idea of having sex with our parents or our own children but also by the idea of other people having sex with their children. Daniel Fessler of the University of California, Los Angeles, and Carlos Navarrete of Michigan State University think that these kinds of third-party aversions are a form of "egocentric empathy." Westermarck hypothesized that co-residence during childhood generates sexual aversions to particular partners. If that is the case, then the extent of exposure to siblings of the opposite sex during childhood might also be linked to the strength of feelings about one's own behavior and the strength of feelings about the behavior of others. These predictions have been tested in experimental studies conducted by Fessler and Navarette and by another team led by Debra Lieberman at the University of Miami. Both sets of researchers asked subjects (university undergraduates) to contemplate hypothetical cases of consensual sibling incest involving adults. The results from both studies largely confirmed Westermarck's hypothesis. Those who had grown up with opposite-sex siblings had stronger negative responses to the hypothetical scenario than those who had not. Moreover, women generally had stronger aversive responses to the hypothetical scenario than men did.

Evolutionary interpretations of inbreeding avoidance differ sharply from influential theories about incest and inbreeding avoidance in psychology and cultural anthropology.

Incest and inbreeding avoidance play a central role in many influential theories of human society. Thinkers as diverse as Sigmund Freud (the founder of psychoanalysis) and Claude Lévi-Strauss (the father of structuralist anthropology) have asserted that people harbor a deep desire to have sex with members of their immediate family. According to this view, the existence of culturally imposed rules against incest is all that saves society from these destructive passions. This view is not very plausible from an evolutionary perspective. There are compelling theoretical reasons to expect that natural selection will erect psychological barriers to incest and good evidence that it has done so in humans and other primates. Both theory and observation suggest that the family is not the focus of desire; it's a tiny island of sexual indifference.

However, the evolutionary analysis we have outlined here is not quite complete. For example, we might expect the Westermarck effect and egocentric empathy to produce an aversion to minor marriage in China. Yet this practice has persisted for a long time. It is possible that psychological mechanisms are supplemented or perhaps superseded by conscious reasoning. People in many societies believe that incest leads to sickness and deformity, and their beliefs may guide their behavior and shape their cultural practices. Finally, it seems clear that attitudes about incest are not based solely on the deleterious effects of inbreeding. If they were, then all societies would have the same kinds of rules about who can have sexual relationships. Instead, we find considerable variation. For example, some societies encourage first cousins to marry, whereas others prohibit them from doing so.

Human Mate Preferences

Marry	*Not Marry*
Children—(if it Please God)—Constant companion, (& friend in old age) who will feel interested in one,—object *to be* beloved and played with. better than a dog anyhow.—Home, & someone to take care of house—Charms of music & female chit-chat.—These things good for one's health.—*but terrible loss of time.*—	Freedom to go where one liked—choice of Society & *little of it.*—Conversation of clever men at clubs—Not forced to visit relatives, & to bend in every trifle.—to have the expense & anxiety of children—perhaps quarrelling—**Loss of time.**—cannot read in the Evenings—fatness & idleness—Anxiety & responsibility—less money for books & c—if many children forced to gain one's bread.—(But then it is very bad for one's health to work too much)
My God, it is intolerable to think of spending one's whole life, like a neuter bee, working, working, & nothing after all.—No, no won't do.—Imagine living all one's day solitary in smoky dirty London house.—Only picture to yourself nice soft wife on a sofa with good fire, & books, & music perhaps—Compare this vision with the dingy reality of Grt. Marlbro St.	Perhaps my wife won't like London; then the sentence is banishment & degradation into indolent, idle fool (Burkhardt and Smith, 1986, p. 444).
Marry—Mary—Marry Q.E.D.	

These are the thoughts of 29-year-old Charles Darwin, recently returned from his five-year voyage on the HMS *Beagle*. Soon after writing these words, Darwin married his cousin Emma, the daughter of Josiah Wedgwood, the progressive and immensely wealthy manufacturer of Wedgwood china (**Figure 15.6**). By all accounts, Charles and Emma were a devoted couple. Emma bore 10 children and nursed Charles through countless bouts of illness. Charles toiled over his work and astutely managed his investments, parlaying his modest inheritance and his wife's more substantial one into a considerable fortune.

Darwin's frank reflections on advantages and disadvantages of marriage were very much those of a conventional, upper-class Victorian gentleman. But people of every culture, class, and sex have faced the problem of choosing mates. Sometimes people choose their own mates, and other times parents arrange their children's marriages. But everywhere, people care about the kind of person they will marry.

Evolutionary theory generates some testable predictions about the psychology of human mate preferences.

For much of their evolutionary history, humans have lived in foraging societies. The adaptive challenges that men and women face in these kinds of societies are likely to have shaped their mating strategies. For women, this might have meant choosing men who would provide them with access to resources. Recall from Chapter 11 that there is considerable interdependence between men and women in foraging societies. Women mainly gather plant foods, and men are mainly responsible for hunting. Women's consumption exceeds their production for much of their reproductive life. Children do not begin to provide substantial amounts of their own food until they reach adolescence. Thus, for women, it might be important to choose a mate who will be a good provider.

Men's reproductive success depends largely on the fertility of their mating partners, so it is plausible that selection favored men who focused on this attribute. Women's fertility is highest when they are in their 20s and declines to zero when women reach menopause, at about 50 years of age (**Figure 15.7**). Thus selection should have favored men who chose young and healthy mates. Because picture IDs were scarce in the Pleistocene, selection may have shaped men's psychology so that they are attracted to cues

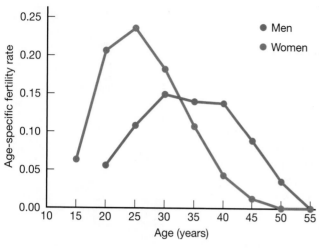

FIGURE 15.7

Age-specific fertility rates give the probability of producing a child at particular ages. !Kung women have their first child between the ages of 15 and 19 and have the highest fertility rate in their 20s. Women's fertility falls to zero by age 50. !Kung men do not begin to reproduce until their early 20s, and their fertility rates are fairly stable in their 30s and 40s, dropping to low levels in their 50s.

that reliably predict youth and health, such as smooth skin, good muscle tone, symmetrical features, and shiny hair.

For both men and women, it is important to find mates whom they can get along with. Human children depend on their parents for a remarkably long time. During this period, both parents provide food and shelter for their children. Because parental investment lasts for many years, adaptive thinking predicts that both men and women will value traits in their partners that help them sustain their relationships. Both are likely to value personal qualities such as compatibility, agreeableness, reliability, and tolerance.

If evolution has shaped the psychology of human mating strategies, then we would expect to find common patterns across societies.

David Buss, a psychologist at the University of Texas at Austin, was among the first to test the evolutionary logic underlying human mating preferences and tactics. Buss enlisted colleagues in 33 countries to administer standardized questionnaires about the qualities of desirable mates to more than 10,000 men and women. Most of the data were collected in Western industrialized nations, and most samples represent university students in urban populations within those countries (**Figure 15.8**). In the questionnaires, people were asked to rate several traits of potential mates—good looks, good financial prospects, compatibility, and so on—according to their desirability. Respondents were also asked about their preferred age at marriage and the preferred age difference between themselves and their spouse.

People generally care most about the personal qualities of their mates.

Men and women around the world rate mutual attraction or love above all other traits (**Table 15.1**). The next most highly desired traits for both men and women are personal attributes, such as dependability, emotional stability and maturity, and a pleasing disposition. Good health is the fifth most highly rated trait for men and the seventh for women. Good financial prospect is the thirteenth most highly rated trait

FIGURE 15.8

People in 33 countries (*red*) were surveyed about the qualities of an ideal mate.

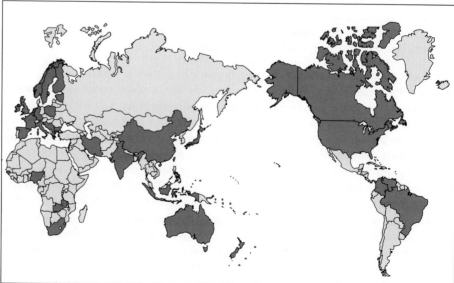

CHAPTER 15: Evolution and Human Behavior

TABLE 15.1

Trait	Ranking of Trait by:	
	Males	**Females**
Mutual attraction/love	1	1
Dependable character	2	2
Emotional stability and maturity	3	3
Pleasing disposition	4	4
Good health	5	7
Education and intelligence	6	5
Sociability	7	6
Desire for home and children	8	8
Refinement, neatness	9	10
Good looks	10	13
Ambition and industriousness	11	9
Good cook and housekeeper	12	15
Good financial prospect	13	12
Similar education	14	11
Favorable social status or rating	15	14
Chastity*	16	18
Similar religious background	17	16
Similar political background	18	17

Men and women from 33 countries around the world (shown in Figure 15.8) were asked to rate the desirability of a variety of traits in prospective mates. The rankings of the values assigned to each trait, on average, are given here. Subjects were asked to rate each trait from 0 (irrelevant or unimportant) to 3 (indispensable). Thus, high ranks (low numbers) represent traits that were generally thought to be important.

*Chastity was defined in this study as having no sexual experience before marriage.

by men and the twelfth by women. Good looks are rated tenth by men and thirteenth by women. It is interesting, and somewhat surprising, that neither sex seems to value chastity highly. Perhaps this is because people were asked to evaluate the desirability of sexual experience before marriage (that is, virginity), not fidelity during their marriage.

Men and women show the differences in mate preferences predicted by parental investment theory.

Even though the ranking of the scores assigned to these traits is similar for men and women, there are consistent differences between men and women in how desirable they think these traits are. Buss found that people's sex had the greatest effect on their ratings of the following traits: "good financial prospect," "good looks," "good cook and housekeeper," and "ambition and industriousness." As the evolutionary model predicts,

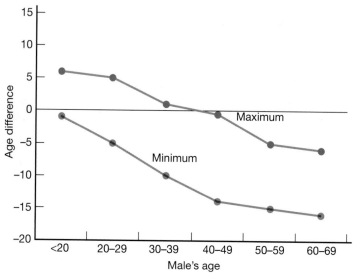

(a) Men's preferences

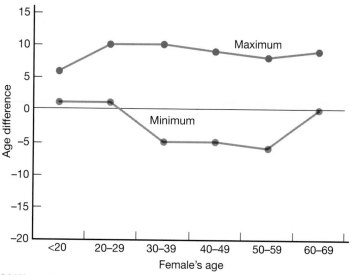

(b) Women's preferences

FIGURE 15.9

Mate preferences by sex. (a) In personal advertisements, all but the youngest men state preferences for women who are younger than themselves. As men get older, the age difference between themselves and preferred mates increases. (b) Women typically prefer men who are somewhat older than themselves, and these preferences remain the same as women get older.

women value good financial prospects and ambition more than men do, and men value good looks more than women do. A person's sex has a smaller and somewhat less uniform effect on ratings of chastity. In 23 populations, men value chastity significantly more than women do; in the remaining populations, men and women value chastity equally. There are no populations in which women value chastity significantly more than men do.

Men and women differ about the preferred ages of their partners.

Evolutionary reasoning suggests that men's mate preferences will be strongly influenced by the reproductive potential of prospective mates. Therefore, we would predict men to choose mates with high fertility or high reproductive value. By the same token, we would expect women to be less concerned about their partner's age than about their ability to provide resources for them and their offspring.

A considerable amount of evidence suggests that men consistently seek and marry partners who are younger than they are and that women seek and marry partners somewhat older than themselves. Douglas Kenrick of Arizona State University and Richard Keefe surveyed marriage records in two cities in the United States and in a small Philippine village, as well as personal advertisements in the United States, northern Europe, and India. In all these cases, they found a similar pattern. As men get older, the age difference between them and their wives increases. Thus young men marry women slightly younger than themselves, and older men marry partners considerably younger than themselves. As women get older, there is little change in the age difference between them and their husbands. Newspaper advertisements in which advertisers specify the range of ages for prospective mates demonstrate a very similar pattern (**Figure 15.9**). Henry Harpending of the University of Utah has found very similar patterns among the Herero, a pastoralist group in the northern Kalahari Desert of Botswana, in which marriages are unstable, divorce is common, and women have a considerable amount of financial independence.

Although men advertise for and marry progressively younger women, the actual age of their partners does not seem to fit the prediction that males will choose fertile mates. Older men seek and marry women who are considerably younger than themselves but not women who are young enough to produce children. Men's choices about whom to date and whom to marry may be driven by multiple factors, not just women's fertility. Older men may desire younger women, but they may also want to find someone who shares their taste in music, has similar goals in life, and so on. Furthermore, men's preferences and their marriages may reflect their own attractiveness in the mating market. Older men may want young women but know they will have to settle for partners closer to their own age. Together, the data taken from personal advertisements and from marriage records reflect individual desires tempered by pragmatism.

Men and women vary about the preferred number of partners.

In addition to having different criteria for the ideal mate, men and women may also have different mating tactics. Because women devote nine months to each pregnancy and nurse their children for even longer, selection is likely to have favored a psychology that makes them cautious about involvement in sexual relationships that would expose them to the risks of pregnancy. (Of course, today birth control reduces the risk of pregnancy for women, but effective methods of contraception are a recent innovation. Human mating tactics evolved in a world without such technology.) Women are likely to prefer stable, committed relationships with men who are willing and able to help care for them and their offspring. Because the costs of conception are borne mainly by women, men can afford to be more flexible in their mating tactics and to have a psychology that makes them more open to mating opportunities that do not involve long-term commitments. However, we would expect men to form committed long-term relationships because children who receive care from both parents are more likely to thrive.

David Schmitt of Bradley University has coordinated a comprehensive cross-cultural study of human sexuality, sampling people, mainly university students, in 62 countries around the world. In this survey, people were asked about the traits that they valued in potential mates and were also asked about various aspects of their mating tactics. For example, they were asked the number of sexual partners they would like to have over various intervals ranging from 6 months to 30 years. For all intervals, men reported preferring more sexual partners than women did (**Figure 15.10**). This difference seems to be common cross-culturally (**Figure 15.11**), although the magnitude of the sex difference and the number of partners desired vary considerably.

Differences in mating tactics may contribute to misunderstandings between men and women.

When you meet someone you're attracted to, you probably feel excitement and some degree of uncertainty. Some of this uncertainty arises because you are not sure whether the other person is as attracted to you as you are to him or her. And some of this uncertainty arises because you don't know what the other person's intentions are. Martie Haselton of the University of California, Los Angeles, and David Buss have pointed out that this uncertainty generates different kinds of problems for men and women. To understand the logic of their argument, let's think about what kinds of mistakes you could make in deciding whether someone was attracted to you. A false positive arises if you think the other person is attracted to you, when in fact that's not the case. A false negative occurs if you think the other person doesn't like you, when he or she really does. Both kinds of errors are costly: A false positive could lead you to make an overture that would be rejected ("Sorry, I need to wash my hair"); a false negative could prevent you from

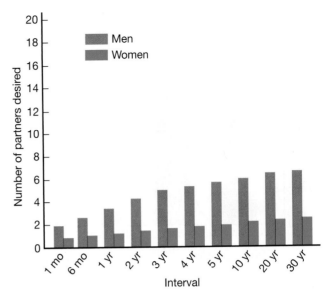

FIGURE 15.10

Men typically prefer more sexual partners across all intervals than women do. Note, however, that there is also more variability in men's preferences than in women's preferences indicating that some men prefer many partners, whereas others prefer fewer partners.

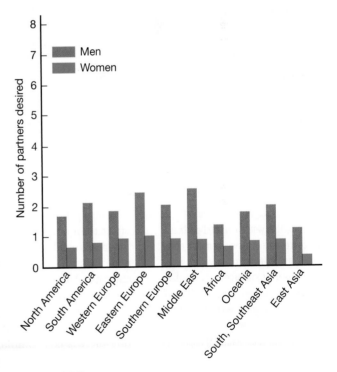

FIGURE 15.11

In every world region, men prefer significantly more sexual partners than women do over a one-month interval.

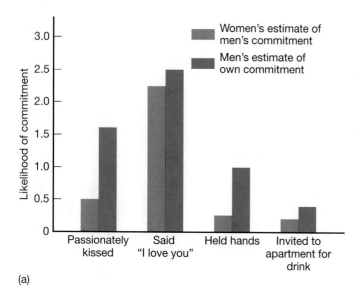

(a)

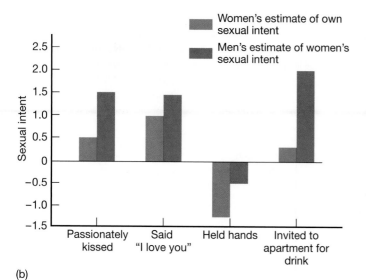

(b)

FIGURE 15.12

Men and women were asked to estimate how they would interpret particular courtship signals by members of the opposite sex and how they would rate the same signals by members of their own sex, using a scale from +3 (very likely) to −3 (very unlikely). (a) Men and women estimated the extent of commitment implied by several courtship signals. Women tended to underestimate men's interest in commitment in comparison with men's own estimates of their interest in commitment. (b) Men and women estimated the likelihood of sexual intent implied by the same signals. Men tended to overestimate women's sexual intent in comparison with women's perceptions of their own intent.

making any overture at all (and you will have nothing better to do than wash your hair).

Now think about the kinds of errors that can arise when there is uncertainty about the other person's intentions about the relationship. Haselton and Buss hypothesize that natural selection will predispose men and women to bias their judgments about new partners' sexual intentions and commitment in different ways. Women, who could become pregnant, are expected to be cautious about their partner's intentions, and as a result they will make more false negative errors than false positive errors. Put another way, evolutionary reasoning predicts that women are more likely to underestimate men's commitment than to overestimate it. Men, who are interested in pursuing both short-term and long-term relationships, are expected to minimize the chance of missing sexual opportunities, and as a result they will make more false positive errors than false negative errors. That is, they are likely to overestimate women's sexual interest more often than they underestimate it.

Haselton and Buss have conducted several studies on college students in the United States to test this hypothesis. They have asked men and women to evaluate sexual intent and commitment in members of their own sex and the opposite sex, to imagine how they would interpret various kinds of signals directed to themselves (for example, holding hands, declaring love), and to recall instances when their own intentions were misunderstood by members of the opposite sex. The results conform to Haselton and Buss's predictions: Men tend to overestimate women's sexual intent, and women tend to underestimate men's interest in commitment (**Figure 15.12**).

Culture predicts people's mate preferences better than their sex does.

Both of the large cross-cultural data sets reveal considerable variation from country to country. Buss and his colleagues found that the country of residence has a greater effect than a person's sex on variation in all of the 18 traits in Table 15.1, except for "good financial prospect." This means that knowing where a person lives tells you more about what he or she values in a mate than knowing the person's sex. Of the 18 traits, chastity (defined in Buss's study as no sexual experience before marriage) shows the greatest variability among populations. In Sweden, men rate chastity at 0.25, and women rate it at 0.28 on a scale of 0 (irrelevant) to 3 (indispensable). In contrast, Chinese men rate chastity 2.54, and Chinese women rate it 2.61 (**Figure 15.13**), indicating that there is more similarity between men and women from the same population than there is among members of each sex from different populations.

This result illustrates an important point: Evolutionary explanations that invoke an evolved psychology and cultural explanations that are based on the social and cultural milieu are not mutually exclusive. The cross-cultural data suggest that some uniformities in people's mate preferences are the result of evolved psychological mechanisms. People everywhere want to marry kind, caring, trustworthy people. Men want to marry young women, and women want to marry prosperous men. But this is not the whole story. The cross-cultural data also suggest that mate preferences are strongly influenced by the cultural and economic environment in which we live. Ultimately, culture also arises out of our evolved psychology, and the cultural variation in mate

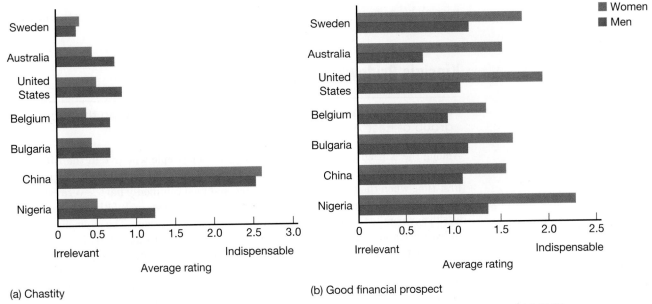

(a) Chastity

(b) Good financial prospect

FIGURE 15.13

Culture accounts for substantial variation in mate preferences. The average ratings given by men and women in several countries surveyed are shown for the trait with (a) the highest interpopulation variability ("chastity") and (b) the lowest interpopulation variability ("good financial prospect").

preferences that the cross-cultural data reveal must, therefore, also be explicable in evolutionary terms. However, the way our evolved psychology shapes the cultures in which we live is complicated and poorly understood, and many interesting questions remain unresolved. Evolutionary theory does not yet explain, for example, why chastity is considered essential in China but unimportant in Sweden.

Evolutionary analyses of mate choice have generated considerable controversy.

As we explained at the beginning of this chapter, evolutionary analyses of human behavior generate considerable controversy. Work on human mate choice is no exception. Many critics have complained that evolutionary analyses simply reflect and reinforce Western cultural values, which celebrate women's youth and beauty and men's wealth and power. They argue that researchers are not studying evolved preferences but rather are learning about cultural values and beliefs. In response, advocates of evolutionary analyses argue that the cross-cultural uniformity of mate preferences and mating tactics reflects evolved psychological predispositions that are modified, but not created, by culture.

Other critics have accepted the general logic of evolutionary reasoning but have questioned the methods used to assess mate preferences and mating tactics. Most of the early work was based on pencil-and-paper tests in which people, often undergraduates, were asked about their preferences and their personal experiences. These kinds of data may be biased in several ways. For example, cultural norms may lead men to exaggerate their sexual experience and women to understate their desire for sexual variety, even on anonymous surveys.

Social Consequences of Mate Preferences

You might wonder how people's mate preferences influence their actual decisions and choices about marriage partners. In this section, we describe the findings from one ethnographic study suggesting that these kinds of preferences actually influence people's behavior in social situations and, consequently, shape the societies in which they live.

Kipsigis Bridewealth

Evolutionary theory explains marriage patterns among the Kipsigis, a group of East African pastoralists.

Among the Kipsigis, a group of Kalenjin-speaking people who live in the Rift Valley province of Kenya, women usually marry in their late teens, men usually marry for the first time when they are in their early 20s, and men commonly have several wives—a practice called polygyny. As in many other societies, the groom's father makes a **bridewealth** payment to the father of the bride at the time of marriage. The payment, tendered in livestock and cash, compensates the bride's family for the loss of her labor and gives the groom rights to her labor and the children she bears during her marriage. The amount of the payment is settled through protracted negotiations between the father of the groom and the father of the bride. The average bridewealth in the 1980s consisted of six cows, six goats or sheep, and 800 Kenyan shillings. This is about one-third of the average man's cattle holdings, one-half of his goat and sheep herd, and two months' wages for men who hold salaried positions. Because men marry polygynously, there is competition over eligible women. Often the bride's father entertains several competing marriage offers before he chooses a groom for his daughter. The prospective bride and groom have little voice in the decisions their fathers make.

Monique Borgerhoff Mulder, an anthropologist at the University of California, Davis, reasoned that Kipsigis bridewealth payments would provide a concrete index of the qualities that each party values in prospective spouses. The groom's father is likely to prefer a bride who will bear his son many healthy children. His bridewealth offer is expected to reflect the potential reproductive value of the prospective bride. The groom's father is also expected to prefer that his son marry a woman who will devote her labor to his household. Kipsigis women who remain near their own family's households are likely to be called on to help their mothers with the harvest and to assist their mothers in childbirth. Thus the groom's father may prefer a woman whose natal family is distant from his son's household. The bride's father is likely to have a different perspective on the negotiations. Because wealthy men can provide their wives with larger plots of land to farm and more resources, we would expect the bride's father to prefer that his daughter marry a relatively wealthy man. At the same time, because the bride's family will be deprived of her labor and assistance if she moves far away from their land, the bride's father is likely to prefer a groom who lives nearby. The fathers of the bride and groom are expected to weigh the costs and benefits of prospective unions in their negotiations over bridewealth payments. For example, although the bride's father may prefer a high bridewealth payment, he may settle for a lower payment if the groom is particularly desirable. To determine whether these preferences affected bridewealth payments, Borgerhoff Mulder recorded the number of cows, sheep, and goats as well as the amount of money that each groom's family paid to the bride's family.

Plump women whose menarche occurred at an early age fetched the highest bridewealth payments.

Borgerhoff Mulder found that bridewealth increased as the bride's age at the time of **menarche** (her first menstruation) decreased (**Figure 15.14**). That is, the highest bridewealths were paid for the women who were youngest when they first menstruated. Among the Kipsigis, age at menarche is a reliable index of women's reproductive potential. Kipsigis women who reach menarche early have longer reproductive life spans, higher annual fertility, and higher survivorship among their offspring than women who mature at later ages.

CHAPTER 15: Evolution and Human Behavior

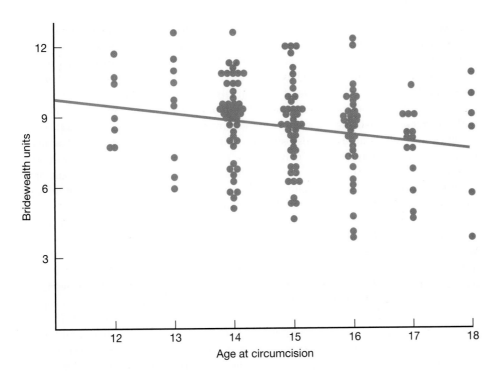

FIGURE 15.14

Kipsigis girls who mature early fetch larger bridewealth payments than older girls do. Among the Kipsigis, girls undergo circumcision (removal of the clitoris) within a year of menarche. The largest bridewealths were paid for the girls who underwent menarche and circumcision at the youngest ages. Bridewealth is transformed into standardized units to account for the fact that the value of livestock fluctuates.

Borgerhoff Mulder wondered how a man assessed his prospective bride's reproductive potential because men often do not know their bride's exact age, nor her age at reaching menarche. One way to be sure of a woman's ability to produce children would be to select one who had already demonstrated her fertility by becoming pregnant or producing a child. However, bridewealth payments for such women were typically lower than bridewealth payments for women who had never conceived. Instead, bridewealth payments were associated with the physical attributes of women. Brides whom the Kipsigis considered plump commanded significantly higher bridewealth payments than brides considered skinny. The plumpness of prospective brides may be a reliable correlate of the age at menarche because menarcheal age is determined partly by body weight. Plumpness may also be valued because a woman's ability to conceive is related to her nutritional status.

Bridewealth payments are also related to the distance between the bride's home and the groom's home; the farther she moves, the less likely she is to provide help to her mother, and the higher the bridewealth payment will be. However, there is no relationship between the wealth of the father of the groom and the bridewealth payment. The bride's father does not lower the bridewealth payment to secure a wealthy husband for his daughter. Although this finding was unexpected, Borgerhoff Mulder suggested that it may be related to the fact that differences in wealth among the Kipsigis are unstable over time. A wealthy man who has large livestock herds may become relatively poor if his herds are raided, reduced by disease, or diverted to pay for another wife. Although land is not subject to these vicissitudes, the Kipsigis traditionally have not held legal title to their lands.

How Much Does Evolution Explain about Human Behavior?

The examples and evidence presented in this chapter demonstrate that evolution can help us understand our minds and behavior. In a way, this should not be very surprising. After all, there is no reason to think that the biological cost of mating with close relatives would be different for us from how it is for other primates, so it makes sense that humans would avoid inbreeding just as other primates do. It is somewhat more surprising to find that we seem to share some of the proximate mechanisms that reduce inbreeding, such as a deep-seated aversion to mating with individuals with whom we have had close contact early in life. It seems likely that we inherited these mechanisms from the common ancestor of humans and chimpanzees, and they were preserved in both lineages because they served an important adaptive function. Although some societies have elaborated on these shared mechanisms, such as adding rules about which relatives can and cannot marry, none allow matings between very close kin. It is interesting to contemplate how a better understanding of evolution might have altered the thinking of both Sigmund Freud and Claude Lévi-Strauss and influenced the intellectual history of the twentieth century.

Evolutionary theory yields insights about many aspects of our behavior, but it is easy to come up with examples of common behavior that seem to contradict evolutionary logic. What possesses someone to parachute out of a plane or devote their lives to helping others? Critics of evolutionary analyses of human behavior are quick to point to such examples and use them to bolster the argument that evolution has little relevance to contemporary human behavior. In response to such critics, evolutionary psychologists argue that our minds and behavior are adapted for life in the environment of evolutionary adaptedness, not the present world. Our appetites for salt, sugar, and fat, for example, were shaped in an environment in which these nutrients were scarce, not one in which it is cheap and easy to "super-size me." Similarly, our capacity for friendship and altruism toward unrelated individuals may have been shaped in an environment in which people routinely lived in small groups composed of close kin, and cooperation was favored by kin selection or reciprocity.

But even people living in foraging societies, whose lives most closely resemble the lives of our ancestors in the EEA, are strikingly different from those of any other creature on Earth. Foraging peoples have occupied virtually every terrestrial habitat on the planet. To survive in such a wide range of habitats they have needed well-developed cognitive abilities, the ability to devise new solutions to adaptive challenges, and the capacity to acquire knowledge from others. Foragers are also much more cooperative than any other mammal, even those that live in small, close-knit societies. In the final chapter of the book, we consider how evolutionary processes that shaped human cognition and culture have played a role in making humans such distinctive creatures.

Key Terms

environment of evolutionary
  adaptedness (EEA)
  (p. 390)

inbred matings (p. 391)
outbred matings (p. 391)

minor marriages (p. 393)
kibbutz (p. 393)

bridewealth (p. 402)
menarche (p. 402)

Study Questions

1. Much of the behavior of all primates is learned. Nonetheless, we have suggested many times that primate behavior has been shaped by natural selection. How can natural selection shape behaviors that are learned?

2. What is the nurture–nature debate? Explain why this debate is based on a flawed understanding of how evolution shapes behavior.

3. Many of the things that we do are consistent with general predictions derived from evolutionary

theory. We love our children, help our relatives, and avoid sex with close kin. But there are also many aspects of the behavior of members of our own society that seem unlikely to increase individual fitness. What are some of these behaviors?

4. In some species of primates, there seems to be an aversion to mating with close kin. The aversion seems to be stronger for females than for males. Why do you think this might be the case? Under what conditions would you expect that difference between the sexes to disappear?

5. Experiments conducted by evolutionary psychologists suggest that people are much better at solving problems that involve detecting violations of social rules or social conventions ("If a person drinks alcohol, then he must be 21") than logically equivalent problems that involve violations of nonsocial norms ("If a person goes to Boston, then he takes the train"). Explain why this might be the case.

6. In Chapter 6, we said that the reproductive success of most male primates depends on the number of females with which they mate. Here we discussed

Buss's argument that a man's reproductive success will depend mainly on the health and fertility of his mate. Why are humans different from most primates? Among what other primate species should we expect males to attend to the physical characteristics of females when choosing mates?

7. According to evolutionary theory, why should men value fidelity in prospective mates more than women should?

8. In Buss's cross-cultural survey, what was the most important attribute in a mate for both men and women? Does this result falsify his evolutionary reasoning?

9. Are Borgerhoff Mulder's observations about the Kipsigis consistent with Buss's cross-cultural results? Explain why or why not.

10. Some people who read about evolutionary analyses of human mating patterns might come to the conclusion that it is justifiable for men to prefer younger partners over older ones or for women to prefer wealthier partners over poorer ones. Consider this conclusion in light of the naturalistic fallacy that we discussed in Chapter 6.

Further Reading

Barkow, J. H., L. Cosmides, and J. Tooby, eds. 1995. *The Adapted Mind: Evolutionary Psychology and the Generation of Culture.* New York: Oxford University Press.

Barrett, L., R. Dunbar, and J. Lycett. 2002. *Human Evolutionary Psychology.* Princeton, N.J.: Princeton University Press.

Buss, D. 2011. *Evolutionary Psychology: The New Science of the Mind.* 4th ed. London: Pearson.

Visit DIGITAL.WWNORTON.COM/HOWHUMANS8 to
• review this chapter with personalized, interactive questions via InQuizitive
• view videos and animations on this chapter's key topics

16

- **Evolution and Human Culture p. 408**
- **Cooperation p. 417**
- **Is Human Evolution Over? p. 425**

CULTURE, COOPERATION, AND HUMAN UNIQUENESS

CHAPTER OBJECTIVES

By the end of this chapter you should be able to

A. Describe how cumulative cultural adaptation allows humans to evolve more rapidly to a wider range of habitats than other mammal species can.

B. Assess how different learning mechanisms can sustain cultural traditions.

C. Assess possible reasons why, despite cultural traditions being common in other species, cumulative cultural adaptation is very rare.

D. Discuss why adaptive modes of cultural learning can lead to maladaptive behavior.

E. Compare the pattern and scope of cooperation in humans to that of other mammal species.

F. Explain why the pattern and scale of human cooperation are puzzling from an evolutionary perspective.

As we conclude this book, we turn to a final question: What has made humans a unique species? Some readers will think that this is a trivial question; others, a controversial one. It may seem trivial because every species is unique, just as every snowflake is different from every other snowflake. But others may think the question is controversial because humans are products of the same evolutionary processes that have shaped all other forms of life on the planet. As we have emphasized throughout this book, each one of us is descended from a tiny shrewlike insectivore that lived among the dinosaurs more than a hundred million years ago. That small creature was gradually transformed by natural selection into a monkey-like animal clambering through the Oligocene forests of Africa; then to one of the many Miocene apes; then to a bipedal australopith in the woodlands of East Africa 2 Ma; and then to the genus *Homo*, which was the first of our ancestors to venture out of Africa; and finally to *Homo sapiens*, the brainy tool-addicted creature that now lives in practically every part of the world. We share approximately 96% of our genome with chimpanzees and bonobos, our physiology and morphology are only slightly modified versions of the standard primate model, and much of our behavior and psychology can be understood in the same terms as the behavior and psychology of other animals. Many would argue that the claim that humans are unique denies our knowledge of our evolutionary origins and obscures our place in nature.

But humans are an outlier in the natural world. Contemporary human biomass (the sum of all our weights) is eight times the biomass of all other wild terrestrial vertebrates combined and equals the biomass of all of the more than 14,000 species of ants. This is not just a consequence of agricultural and modern industrial technology. Human hunter-gatherers were outliers in the natural world even before the origin of agriculture. As we learned in Chapter 13, modern humans left Africa about 60,000 years ago and by 12,000 years ago they occupied every terrestrial habitat on Earth except Antarctica and a few remote islands. Their geographical and ecological range was larger than that of any other creature. As we have seen, most primates are limited to a narrow range of habitats on a single continent. We find chimpanzees in central African forests, baboons in African woodlands and savannas, and capuchins in the forests of Central and South America. The animals with the largest ranges are big predators such as wolves and lions, but their ranges are still much smaller than the range of human foragers 12,000 years ago. Foragers were able to accomplish this because they were better at rapidly adapting to a wide range of environments than any other creature.

Our goal in this chapter is to explain how and why this happened.

One reason humans have become so successful is that we are smarter than other animals. Over the last 2 million years human brains have become about three times the size of chimpanzee brains, and as we saw in Chapter 8, larger brains seem to lead to more complex cognition. We are better at causal reasoning, theory of mind, and other reasoning tasks that help us learn how to solve new problems. And this would have helped humans make a living in new environments. However, we want to convince you that although we are smart, we are not nearly smart enough to solve the problems humans need to solve to survive and thrive in such a wide range of habitats. Two more ingredients are essential parts of the human recipe. The first is culture. Unlike other creatures, people can learn from one another in a way that leads to the accumulation of locally adaptive knowledge, tools, and social institutions, and this allows humans to solve adaptive problems collectively that are too hard for individuals to solve on their own. The second ingredient is cooperation. People cooperate far more than any other mammal. This allows for specialization, exchange, and division of labor, which in turn vastly amplify the ability of people to extract resources from their environments. The three Cs—cognition, culture, and cooperation—have made humans a runaway ecological success.

Evolution and Human Culture

Foraging populations solve problems that are beyond the inventive capacity of individuals.

You learned in Chapter 13 that by 45 ka modern people were living above the Arctic Circle near the Yenesei River. The people who left Africa 60 ka were tropical foragers living in a hot, dry coastal environment. To adapt to the high Arctic they had to create an entirely new way of life. We don't know very much about the Yana River people, but we do know a lot about the Central Inuit, foragers who lived at about the same latitude in the Canadian Arctic.

The Central Inuit lived in small groups and made a living mainly by hunting and fishing. They depended on a tool kit crammed with complex, highly refined, and well-designed implements. Winter temperatures average about −25°C (−13°F), so survival required warm clothes. The Central Inuit made cleverly designed clothes, mainly from caribou skins, that were both light and warm. To make these kinds of clothes, you need a host of complex skills; you must know how to cure and soften hides, spin thread, carve needles from bone, and cut and stitch well-fitting garments. But even the best clothing is not enough during winter storms; shelter is mandatory. The Central Inuit made snow houses that were so well designed that interior temperatures were about 10°C (50°F).

There is no wood in these environments, so people carved soapstone lamps and filled them with rendered seal fat to light their homes, cook their food, and melt ice for drinking water. During the winter, the Central Inuit hunted seals with multipiece toggle harpoons, mainly by ambushing them at their breathing holes, and moved their camps by using dogsleds. During the summer, they used the leister—a three-pronged spear with a sharp central spike and two hinged, backward-facing points—to harvest Arctic char caught in stone weirs (**Figure 16.1**). They also hunted seals and walrus in open water from kayaks. Later in summer and into the fall, the Central Inuit shifted to caribou, which they hunted with sophisticated composite bows made from driftwood and sinew. And these items and technologies are only part of the Central Inuit tool kits.

Having an extensive tool kit, however, is still not enough to survive in the Arctic environment; you also need a vast amount of knowledge. You need to know the habits of the animals that you hunt, how to move on ice, how to judge the weather, and where food can be found as the seasons change. You also need social rules and customs that allow groups of people to work together in such difficult conditions.

Do you think that you could acquire all the local knowledge necessary to live in the Arctic on your own? You are smart and probably did well on the SAT. You can probably drive a car, operate a computer, and understand something about physics. So if individual cognition *alone* is the key to the human ability to adapt to a wide range of environments, you should be able to figure out how to survive in the Arctic. This is exactly the way that other animals learn about their environments—they rely mainly on information encoded in their genes and personal experience to figure out how to find food, make shelter, and in some cases make tools.

We're pretty sure you'd fail because this experiment has been repeated many times, and the outcome is almost always the same. We think of it as "the lost European explorer experiment." Over the last couple of centuries, various European explorers have become stranded in unfamiliar habitats. Despite desperate efforts and ample learning time, these hardy men and women suffered or died because they could not figure out how to adapt to the habitat they found themselves in. The Franklin Expedition of 1846 illustrates this point. Sir John Franklin, a Fellow of the Royal Society and an experienced Arctic traveler, set out to find the Northwest Passage and spent two ice-bound winters in the Arctic. Everyone on his team eventually perished from starvation and scurvy (**Figure 16.2**). Their fate was tragic but also instructive. Members of the expedition spent their second winter on King William Island. The Central Inuit have lived around King William Island for at least 700 years, and this area is rich in animal resources. But the British explorers starved because they did not have the necessary local knowledge to make a living. Even though they had the same basic cognitive abilities as the Inuit and they had two years to use those abilities to figure out how to survive, they failed to acquire the skills necessary to subsist in the northern habitat.

Results from this version of the lost European explorer experiment and many others

FIGURE 16.1

The Inuit use many specialized tools to make a living in the Arctic. Here a man holds a leister, a specialized fishing spear.

FIGURE 16.2

Sir John Franklin, member of the Royal Society and leader of an expedition lost in the northern reaches of North America.

suggest that the technologies of foragers and other relatively "simple" societies are way beyond the inventive capacity of individuals. It's not hard to see why. Kayaks, bows, and dogsleds are complicated artifacts with multiple interacting parts made of many materials. Working out the best design, or even a workable design, for something like this from scratch is very hard to do. The Inuit could make the tools that they needed and master all the tasks that they needed to stay alive in the Arctic because they could draw on a vast pool of information that was known by other people in their population. They could gain access to this information by watching them, asking questions, or being taught. That is, unlike other organisms, humans rely on culturally acquired information, and it is the ability to make use of culturally acquired information that has made our species such a spectacular evolutionary success.

Humans rely on the accumulation of culturally acquired information to survive.

For many anthropologists, culture is what makes us human. Each of us is immersed in a cultural milieu that influences the way we see the world, shapes our beliefs about right and wrong, and endows us with the knowledge and technical skills to get along in our environment. Despite the central importance of culture in anthropology, there is little consensus about how or why culture arose in the evolution of the human lineage. In the discussion that follows, we present a view of the evolution of human culture that one of us (R. B.) developed with Peter Richerson at the University of California, Davis. Although we believe strongly in this approach to understanding the evolution of culture, there is not a broad consensus among anthropologists that this or any other particular view of the origins of culture is correct.

There are many definitions of **culture**. When thinking about the role of culture in human evolution, we think it is useful to define culture as *information acquired by individuals through some form of social learning.* For example, a child may learn that it is important to defer to her elders from watching her parents interact with her grand-

FIGURE 16.3

Chimpanzees display a variety of behaviors that seem to vary from group to group. Here, chimpanzees raise their arms while grooming.

parents. She may also be corrected if she fails to behave appropriately. When individuals acquire different behaviors as a result of some form of social learning, then we observe cultural variation. The properties of culture are sometimes quite different from the properties of other forms of environmental variation. If people acquire behavior from others through teaching or imitation, then different populations living in similar ecological environments may behave very differently because they acquire different behaviors from members of the previous generation.

Culture is common among other animals, but cumulative cultural evolution is rare.

Over the last few decades, primatologists have documented a great deal of behavioral variation across groups in various species, most notably chimpanzees, orangutans, and capuchins. For example, chimpanzees living on the western shores of Lake Tanganyika raise their arms and clasp hands while they groom (**Figure 16.3**), but chimpanzees living on the eastern shore of the lake don't do this. Orangutans in some areas use sticks to pry seeds out of fruits, but orangutans at other sites have not mastered this technique and cannot extract the seeds. Capuchins show considerable variation in foraging techniques and social conventions. For example, capuchins at some sites participate in long bouts of mutual hand sniffing, but capuchins at other sites never display this behavior. In some cases, scientists have documented the appearance, diffusion, and eventual extinction of behavioral variants. There are also examples of cultural traditions in a variety of species outside the primates, such as fish, birds, cetaceans, meerkats, and rodents. These traditions encompass a diverse

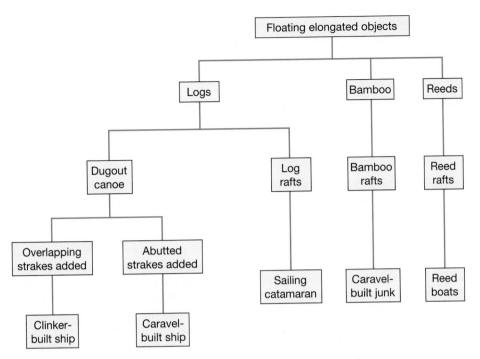

FIGURE 16.4

We can trace how certain technological innovations have developed. In China, the first boats were elongated structures that floated on the water. Some were made of logs, others of bamboo or reeds. Floating logs were transformed into canoes with the addition of a keel. Other types of ships, including Chinese junks, have a square hull and no keel.

array of ecologically significant behaviors, including food preferences, foraging techniques, and alarm calls.

In human populations, culturally transmitted adaptations can gradually accumulate over many generations (**Figures 16.4** and **16.5**), resulting in complex behaviors that no individual could invent on his or her own. In other animals, there are very few examples of this kind of cumulative cultural evolution. The best-documented case of cumulative cultural evolution comes from studies of song dialects in songbirds, such as cowbirds. Cowbirds lay their eggs in the nests of other bird species (a good trick in itself), so chicks don't hear the songs of their own parents when they are growing up. Once they leave the nests of their foster parents, young birds begin to imitate the

FIGURE 16.5

(a) Bamboo rafts may have been the precursors of (b) the great Chinese junks.

(a)

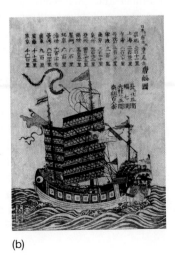

(b)

songs of cowbirds in the neighboring area. The form of the song in each local population gradually changes, and dialect variation among populations can be used to create song trees just as genetic variation can be used to construct gene trees. The songs of whales and other cetaceans seem to evolve in the same way as birdsong. This is impressive, but in these cases, cumulative cultural evolution is limited to a single domain, song dialect, and other behaviors are not culturally transmitted. Humans are an outlier in the extent of cumulative cultural evolution.

Why culture in other species does not accumulate is not clear.

Social learning creates traditions because experienced individuals do something (perform a behavior, make a tool, vocalize), and this makes it more likely that naive individuals will do something similar. A variety of social learning mechanisms lead to traditions, and it is useful to think of these mechanisms as ranging along a continuum. At one end of the continuum are mechanisms that do not preserve innovations and, therefore, cannot lead to cumulative cultural evolution. For example, **social facilitation** occurs when the activity of one animal increases the chance that other animals will learn the behavior on their own. Social facilitation could account for the persistence of tool use in the following scenario: Young chimpanzees accompany their mothers while they are foraging. In populations in which females use stones to break open nuts, infants and juveniles spend a lot of time around nuts and hammer stones. Young chimpanzees fool around with stone hammers and anvils until they master the skill of opening the nuts. They do not learn the skill by watching their mothers. This means that if a talented (or lucky) individual finds a way to improve nut cracking, the innovation will not spread to other members of the group.

At the other end of the continuum are mechanisms that preserve innovations. For example, **observational learning** (sometimes called imitation) occurs when naive animals learn how to perform an action by watching the behavior of experienced, skilled animals. If a chimpanzee female invents a new nut-cracking technique, then the innovation will be preserved if her offspring imitate it. Imitation allows innovations to persist because unskilled individuals can acquire new or improved techniques by observing the actions of others. Cumulative cultural evolution may occur if a series of innovations arises, gets copied, and spreads throughout the group.

In between social facilitation and observational learning are other mechanisms, such as **emulation**. Emulation occurs when naive individuals learn the end state of the behavior (a cracked nut) but not the behavior that generated that end state (pounding with a hammer stone). This can lead to the spread of innovations when individuals can learn on their own how to produce the end state, but not if the end state is difficult to achieve. For example, suppose one chimpanzee absconds with a can of tuna from the storage tent at the research camp and manages to open the can by using the same hammer-and-anvil technique that she uses to crack open nuts. The innovation (opening tuna cans) could spread once chimpanzees learn the goal (tuna) because the chimpanzees already know how to pound open nuts. However, if a new technique is needed to open the can, say, prying open the lid with a sharp stone, then emulation would not preserve the innovation.

Several recent studies suggest that monkeys and apes are capable of a form of observational learning. For example, chimpanzees at Gombe strip the leaves from slender twigs and use the twigs as probes to fish for termites. Elizabeth Lonsdorf, of Franklin and Marshall College, and her colleagues videotaped young chimpanzees while their mothers were fishing for termites. She found that young females watched their mothers carefully as they fished for termites, but young males were considerably less attentive (**Figure 16.6**). Lonsdorf also discovered that not all females used the same fishing techniques; some females consistently used longer twigs than others. Young females tended to use the same kinds of tools that their mothers used, but young males did not adopt the techniques that their mothers used.

White-faced capuchins also seem to learn some foraging techniques by observation. The monkeys feed on seeds of *Luhea* fruits, which they obtain by pounding the fruits against a hard surface or scrubbing the fruit along a rough surface. The two techniques seem to be equally effective, but adults tend to use one technique or the other, not both. Susan Perry of the University of California, Los Angeles, monitored the development of *Luhea* processing techniques among immature monkeys. She found that the juveniles try out both techniques when they are young but eventually settle on only one. Those that associate most often with pounders tend to adopt the pounding technique and those that associate most with scrubbers tend to adopt the scrubbing technique. Thus capuchins seem to learn *Luhea* foraging techniques through observation.

More evidence of observational learning comes from a set of experiments on captive chimpanzees conducted by Andrew Whiten of the University of St. Andrews and his colleagues. In these experiments, the animals are presented with a task, such as extracting a reward from a box that can be opened in two ways. Naive chimpanzees in one group observe the behavior of a group member that has been trained to open the box one way; naive chimpanzees in a second group learn a different technique (**Figure 16.7**). Chimpanzees tend to use the technique that they have seen demonstrated, suggesting that they must have learned the technique through imitation. Similar types of experiments provide evidence of social learning in vervet monkeys, capuchin monkeys, and lemurs.

So why don't chimpanzees make stone tools, bows, and arrows or build canopies over their nests to shelter them from the rain? We are not sure, but there are several possibilities. First, although the naturalistic data and experiments show that chimpanzees and capuchins can learn by observing others, the process is not very accurate. Most copy the behavior of demonstrators, but some don't. Repeated over generations, inaccurate social learning would rapidly degrade the innovations. Second, once chimpanzees have learned one way of getting inside the box, they are not inclined to learn another way, even if it is more efficient. Similarly, capuchins seem to settle on one technique for extracting seeds from *Luhea* fruits. This limits their ability to acquire progressively better skills and technology.

The third factor that may limit the development of complex culture repertoires in chimpanzees (and by extension other primates) is that chimpanzees do not blindly copy all the details of behaviors that they observe. Oddly enough, blind copying may be an important requirement for cumulative cultural evolution. In one set of experiments, chimpanzees observed human experimenters open the boxes in a way that included irrelevant, nonfunctional behaviors along with those required to get inside the box. Chimpanzees tend to acquire only behaviors necessary to actually open the box. In a parallel experiment conducted with people, the subjects faithfully copied all the irrelevant behaviors as well as the relevant ones. Faithful copying may be important for cumulative cultural evolution because many of the things that we learn are complicated and difficult to understand. (For example, why do you need to beat the eggs before adding them to the flour when you make a cake?) If people, like chimpanzees, copied only what they could understand, complicated tools and behavioral routines could not evolve. Doing something because you have seen others do it, even if you don't understand why they did it, may be important. But clearly, this could lead to unfortunate consequences.

FIGURE 16.6

Young female chimpanzees carefully watch their mothers fish for termites, and they tend to acquire the same kinds of techniques that their mothers use. Males are much less attentive to their mothers and do not match their mothers' techniques.

FIGURE 16.7

A young chimpanzee is trying to open a box in one of Whiten's experiments.

Suppose that you are trying to learn how to fletch an arrow. Your mentor stops to scratch an itch or swat away a fly. The learner has to separate these irrelevant actions from the relevant ones. Psychologists George Gergely and Gergely Csibra of the Central European University think that learners can solve this problem only if demonstrators provide cues about which components of the behavior are important and which are not. Doing so need not involve overt verbal instruction; instead demonstrators can use subtle cues such as the direction of their gaze or pointing.

Culture Is an Adaptation

Cumulative cultural adaptation is not a by-product of intelligence and social life.

Chimpanzees and capuchins are among the world's cleverest creatures. In nature, they use tools and perform many complex behaviors; in captivity, they can be taught very complicated tasks. Chimpanzees and capuchins live in social groups and have ample opportunity to observe the behavior of other individuals, and yet the best evidence suggests that neither chimpanzees nor capuchins make much use of observational learning in their daily lives. Thus the learning mechanisms that allow cumulative cultural adaptation, whatever they are, may not simply be a by-product of intelligence and opportunities for observing others.

This conclusion suggests, in turn, that the psychological mechanisms that enable humans to learn in a way that gives rise to cumulative cultural evolution are adaptations that have been shaped by natural selection because culture is beneficial (**Figure 16.8**). Of course, this need not be the case. These mechanisms may be by-products of some other adaptation that is unique to humans, such as language. But given the great importance of culture in human societies, it is important to think about the possible adaptive advantages of culture.

Culture allows humans to exploit a variety of environments by using a universal set of mental mechanisms.

Humans can live in a wider variety of environments than other primates because culture allows us to accumulate better strategies for exploiting local environments much more rapidly than genetic inheritance can produce adaptive modifications. Animals such as baboons adapt to different environments by using various learning mechanisms. For example, they learn how to acquire and process the food they eat. Baboons in the lush wetlands of the Okavango Delta of Botswana learn how to harvest roots of water plants and how to hunt young antelope. Baboons living in the harsh desert of nearby Namibia must learn how to find water and process desert foods. All such learning mechanisms require prior knowledge about the environment: where to search for food, what strategies can be used to process the food, which flavors are reinforcing, and so on. More detailed and more accurate knowledge allows more accurate adaptation because it allows animals to avoid errors and acquire a more specialized set of behaviors.

In most animals, this knowledge is stored in the genes. Imagine that you captured a group of baboons from the Okavango Delta and moved them to the Namibian desert. It's a very good bet that the first few months would be tough for the baboons, but after a relatively short time, the transplanted group of baboons would probably be hard to tell from their neighbors. They would eat the same foods, have the same activity patterns, and have the same kinds of grooming relationships. The transplanted baboons would become similar to the local baboons because they acquire a great deal of information about how to be a baboon genetically; it is hardwired. Of

FIGURE 16.8

Infants are prone to spontaneous imitation of the behaviors they observe. Here, a 13-month-old infant flosses her two teeth.

course, the transplanted baboons would have to learn where to find water, where to sleep, which foods are edible, and which foods are toxic, but they would be able to do this without contact with local baboons because they have a built-in ability to learn such things on their own.

Human culture allows accurate adaptation to a wider variety of environments because *cumulative* cultural adaptation provides more accurate and more detailed information about the local environment than genetic inheritance systems can provide. The Inuit could make kayaks and do all the other things they needed to do to stay alive in the harsh environment of the Arctic because they could make use of a vast pool of useful information stored in the minds of other people in their population. The information contained in this pool is accurate and adaptive because the combination of individual learning and human social learning leads to rapid, cumulative adaptation. Even if most individuals blindly imitate the behavior of others, some individuals may occasionally come up with a better idea, and this will nudge traditions in an adaptive direction. Observational learning preserves the many small nudges and exposes the modified traditions to another round of nudging. This process generates adaptation more quickly than genetic inheritance does. The complexity of cultural traditions can explode to the limits of our capacity to learn them.

Culture can lead to evolutionary outcomes not predicted by ordinary evolutionary theory.

The importance of culture in human affairs has led many anthropologists to conclude that evolutionary thinking has little to contribute to understanding human behavior. They argue that evolution shapes genetically determined behaviors but not behaviors that are learned, and so culture is independent of biology. This argument is a manifestation of the nature–nurture controversy, and we explained at the beginning of the last chapter why this reasoning is flawed. Although many anthropologists have rejected evolutionary thinking about culture, many evolutionists have made the opposite mistake. They reject the idea that culture makes any *fundamental* difference in the way that evolution has shaped human behavior and psychology. If natural selection shaped the genes underlying the psychological machinery that gives rise to human behavior, the machinery must have led to fitness-enhancing behavior, at least in ancestral environments. If the adaptation doesn't enhance fitness in modern environments, that's because our evolved psychology is designed for life in a different kind of world.

We think both sides in this argument are wrong. Humans cannot be understood without the complex interplay between biology and culture. This is because cumulative cultural evolution is rooted in a new evolutionary trade-off between benefits and costs. Human social learning mechanisms are beneficial because they allow humans to accumulate vast reservoirs of adaptive information over many generations, leading to the cumulative cultural evolution of highly adaptive behaviors and technology. Because this process is much faster than genetic evolution, it allows human populations to develop cultural adaptations to local environments: kayaks in the Arctic and blowguns in the Amazon. The ability to adjust rapidly to local conditions was highly adaptive for early humans because the Pleistocene was a time of extremely rapid fluctuations in world climates. However, the psychological mechanisms that create this benefit come with a built-in cost. Remember that the advantage of learning from others is that it avoids the need for everyone to figure out everything for themselves. We can simply do what others do. But to get the benefits of social learning, people have to be credulous, generally accepting that other people are doing things in a sensible and proper way.

This credulity helps us learn complicated things, but it also makes us vulnerable to the spread of maladaptive beliefs and behaviors. If everyone in our community believes that it's beneficial to bleed sick people or that it's a good idea to treat corn with lime, we

FIGURE 16.9

Cultural evolution may permit the spread of ideas and behaviors that do not contribute to reproductive success. Dangerous sports, such as rock climbing, may be examples of such behaviors.

believe that, too. This is how we get wondrous adaptations such as kayaks and blowguns. But we have little protection against the perpetuation of maladaptations that somehow arise. Even though the capacities that give rise to culture and shape its content must be (or at least must have been) adaptive on average, the behavior observed in any particular society at any particular time may reflect evolved maladaptations. Examples of these sorts of maladaptations are not hard to find.

Maladaptive beliefs can spread because culture is not acquired just from parents.

The logic of natural selection applies to culturally transmitted information in much the same way that it does to genes. Beliefs compete for our memory and our attention, and not all beliefs are equally likely to be learned or remembered. Beliefs are heritable, often passing from one individual to another without major change. As a result, some beliefs spread, and others are lost. However, the rules of cultural transmission are different from the rules of genetic transmission, so the outcome of selection among beliefs can be different from the outcome of selection on genes. The basic rules of genetic transmission are simple. With some exceptions, every gene that an individual carries in his body is equally likely to be incorporated into his gametes, and the only way that those genes can be transmitted is through his offspring. Thus only genes that increase reproductive success will spread. Cultural transmission is much more complicated. Beliefs are acquired and transmitted throughout an individual's life, and they can be acquired from grandparents, siblings, friends, co-workers, teachers, and even completely impersonal sources such as books, television, and now the Internet.

Most important, ideas and beliefs can spread even if they do not enhance reproductive fitness. If ideas about dangerous activities such as rock climbing and heroin use spread from friend to friend, these ideas can persist even though they reduce survival and individual reproductive success (**Figure 16.9**). Beliefs about heaven and hell can spread from priest to parishioner, even if the priest is celibate and has no offspring of his own to influence. Moreover, cultural variants may accumulate and be transmitted within groups of people who form clans, fraternities, business firms, religious sects, or political parties. This process can generate groups that are defined by cultural values and traditions, not by genetic relatedness.

Culture is part of human biology, but culture makes human evolution qualitatively different from that of other organisms.

The fact that culture can lead to outcomes not predicted by conventional evolutionary theory does not mean that human behavior has somehow transcended biology. The idea that culture is separate from biology is a popular misconception that cannot withstand scrutiny. Culture is generated from organic structures in the brain that were produced by the processes of evolution. However, cultural transmission leads to new evolutionary processes. Thus to understand the whole of human behavior, evolutionary theory must be modified to account for the complexities introduced by these poorly understood processes.

The fact that culture can lead to outcomes that would not be predicted by conventional evolutionary theory does not mean that ordinary evolutionary reasoning is useless. The fact that there are processes that lead to the spread of risky behaviors such as rock climbing does not mean that these are the only processes that influence cultural behavior. In the last chapter we saw that many aspects of human psychology probably have been shaped by natural selection so that people learn to behave adaptively. We love our children and feel strong aversions to mating with close relatives. There is every reason to suspect that these predispositions play an important role in shaping human cultures. As long as this is the case, ordinary evolutionary reasoning will be useful for understanding human behavior.

Cooperation

Humans are more cooperative than other mammals.

Most mammals live solitary lives, meeting only to mate and raise their young. Among social species, cooperation is limited to relatives and, perhaps, small groups of reciprocators. After weaning, individuals acquire virtually all the food that they eat themselves. There is little division of labor, no trade, and no large-scale conflict. The sick, hungry, and disabled must fend for themselves. The strong take from the weak without fear of sanctions by third parties. Seventeenth-century philosopher Thomas Hobbes (**Figure 16.10**) famously described life in the state of nature as "the warre of all against all." Amend Hobbes to account for nepotism, and his picture of the state of nature is not so far off for most mammals.

FIGURE 16.10

The English political philosopher Thomas Hobbes.

In stark contrast, cooperation is an essential component of the economies of all foraging societies. Arizona State University anthropologist Kim Hill illustrates the difference with the following anecdote. Human hunter-gatherers and nonhuman primates both forage for fruit in trees. When a party of chimpanzees comes upon a fruiting tree, they all climb the tree and gather as much fruit as they can. Human hunter-gatherers send a couple of young guys up into the tree to shake the branches so that the fruit falls to the ground where everybody can easily harvest it. The young men are willing to go up into the tree because they know there will be fruit waiting for them when they get down, and this cooperative arrangement allows people to harvest the fruit more efficiently.

This kind of cooperative activity pervades human hunter-gatherer societies. Hill has studied the Aché, a hunter-gatherer group living in the forests of Paraguay, for more than 20 years (**Figure 16.11**). Here is a list of the cooperative foraging behaviors he recorded:

> Cuts a trail for others to follow; makes a bridge for others to cross a river; carries another's child; climbs a tree to flush a monkey for another hunter; allows another to shoot at prey when ego has first (best) shot; allows another to dig out an armadillo or extract honey or larva when ego encountered it; yells whereabouts of escaping prey; calls the location of a resource for another individual to exploit while ego continues searching; calls another to come to a pursuit of a peccary, paca, monkey, or coati; waits for others to join a pursuit, thus lowering own return rate; tracks peccaries when ego has no arrows (for other men to kill); carries game shot by another hunter; climbs fruit trees to knock down fruit for others to collect; cuts down palms (for others to take heart or fiber); opens a "window" in a tree to test for palm starch (for others to come take); carries the palm fiber others have collected; cuts down fruit trees for others to collect the fruit; brings a bow, arrow, ax, or other tool to another in a pursuit; spends time instructing another on how to acquire a resource; lends bow or ax to another when it could be used by ego; helps to look for another's arrows; prepares or repairs another man's bow and arrows in the middle of a pursuit; goes back on the trail to warn others of wasp nest; walks toward other hunters to warn of fresh jaguar tracks or poisonous snakes; removes dangerous obstacles from the trail before others arrive (Hill, 2002, pp. 113–114).

In each case, one individual helps another individual and incurs some cost in doing so. Such helping behavior is not structured by kinship among the Aché. Only a very small percentage of helping behavior is directed toward kin. Men help unrelated men, and women tend to help their husbands. Food produced by cooperative foraging is shared throughout the band.

FIGURE 16.11

The Aché are a group in Paraguay who lived solely by hunting and gathering until the 1970s and still acquire much of their food by foraging. Here, two Aché women cooperate to extract starch from a palm tree.

Human cooperation increases our ability to adapt.

Although the members of other mammal species don't engage in the division of labor, trade, mutual aid, and the construction of large-scale capital facilities, there are animals that do all these things, and they have been spectacular ecological successes and have radiated into a vast range of habitats. Multicellular organisms arose when groups of single-celled creatures evolved specialization and exchange, and multicellular organisms have been able to occupy a dramatically large number of niches. Their success indicates that the benefits of cooperation among cells were present in niches as different as those occupied by plants and animals; ecologies as different as aquatic, terrestrial, and subterranean habitats; and climates as varied as tropical and tundra. Similarly, eusocial insects have a very wide range of lifeways—some ant species herd aphid "cows," protect their herds from predators, and subsist on sweet "honeydew" produced by their carefully tended domesticates. Others are like farmers, carefully tending and fertilizing fungus gardens. Army ants, which have several castes of workers specialized for different tasks, can work together to build bridges, defend the colony, and manage traffic. Like humans, the eusocial insects have been a spectacular ecological success. Ants, for example, make up 2% of insect species but more than a third of insect biomass; in tropical forests, ants outweigh all vertebrates combined.

We believe that cooperation has played a similar role in the human expansion across the globe. Specialization is beneficial because it is efficient to subdivide labor among individuals who specialize in one or a few specific tasks. Exchange allows the output of efficient production to be shared. If one individual specializes in building houses, a second in farming, and a third in making music, and they trade their products, all three will typically enjoy better housing, food, and music than if they tried to produce everything themselves. The same goes for mutual aid. When an individual is sick and cannot forage, others can greatly improve her fitness by providing food at relatively small cost to themselves. Cooperative child care can greatly increase the ability of parents to produce food and other resources.

Humans cooperate in large groups of unrelated individuals.

One of the most striking differences between people and other social mammals is the scale on which humans cooperate. In most other mammals, cooperation is limited to small groups of kin and reciprocators. The most striking exception is a spectacularly homely subterranean African rodent called the naked mole rat, which lives in underground colonies numbering about 80 individuals (**Figure 16.12**). Colonies of naked mole rats work much like the colonies of ants or termites. There is a single reproducing female, and colony members forage cooperatively, maintain the burrow, and defend the colony. The members of a colony are closely related to one another. Other mammals that cooperate in sizable groups, such as African wild dogs, also are closely related. Human societies differ from other cooperative species because they can mobilize many *unrelated* individuals for collective enterprises. This is obviously true of modern societies in which government institutions such as courts and police regulate behavior. But, as it turns out, societies without such institutions also can mobilize many cooperators.

The joint production of capital facilities, such as roads and bridges, relies on large-scale cooperative behavior. Each worker invests time and labor, but all members of the community will travel on the road or use the bridge to cross the river. In modern societies, contracts enforced by governments mean that workers are guaranteed to be compensated directly. But in small-scale societies, in which workers don't receive wages for their labor or sign legally binding contracts, communities can also organize large-scale construction projects. For example, before the twentieth century, there were massive runs of salmon up the Trinity, Klamath, and other western coastal rivers. The Native American groups living along these rivers constructed large weirs, which act like fences, across the rivers to harvest the salmon as they swam upstream to spawn (**Figure 16.13**). The Yurok constructed a weir across the Klamath River at Kepel. Cutting the wood for this weir required the labor of

FIGURE 16.12

The naked mole rat is a subterranean rodent that lives in large cooperative colonies with a single reproducing female. Individuals within a colony are closely related.

CHAPTER 16: Culture, Cooperation, and Human Uniqueness

FIGURE 16.13

A salmon weir built across the Trinity River in northern California by members of the Hupa tribe in the early twentieth century. The weir remained in place for a short period during the early summer run of king salmon. By blocking the path of the migrating salmon, it allowed the Native Americans to harvest many salmon by using nets. Many people cooperated in constructing the weir and harvesting the salmon.

hundreds of men from several villages, and the construction involved 70 workers over an extended period. During the 10 days of the salmon run, huge numbers of salmon were collected, dried, and shared among members of the tribe.

Warfare is a particularly interesting case of large-scale cooperation for two reasons. First, warfare has played an undeniably important role in human history. Second, our ability to wage war is remarkable because war creates an especially high-stakes collective action problem. Individual warriors risk injury or death, whereas victorious military actions benefit all group members. People engage in armed conflict with neighboring groups in almost all human societies. In foraging societies, the size of warring groups is typically small, but even societies that have no formal institutions can mobilize sizable war parties under the right circumstances. A recent study of warfare among the Turkana, an African pastoralist society, conducted by Sarah Mathew of Arizona State University, provides a good example.

The Turkana herd cows and sheep in the arid savanna of northwestern Kenya (**Figure 16.14**). They live in mobile settlements numbering a few hundred people. The Turkana are divided into approximately 20 territorial sections— geographic regions within which herdsmen from each territory are free to graze. Men also belong to age groups, which are composed of similar-aged men who tend to herd and fight together. There is no recognized political or military authority; no elected officials, official police, or fighting forces. The Turkana often engage in armed combat with members of other ethnic groups that live just outside the border of Turkana territory. Victors may acquire livestock to supplement their herds and new grazing land, and they may also deter attacks by other groups. However, going to war has sizable costs for individuals; Mathew's data indicate that warriors have a 1% chance of dying each time they go on a raid. The Turkana cooperate in large numbers; on average 300 warriors are mobilized for each raid (**Figure 16.15**), and the warriors come from several settlements, territorial sections, and age groups (**Figure 16.16**). This means that most of the men in

FIGURE 16.14

The Turkana are a group of nomadic herders who live in northern Kenya.

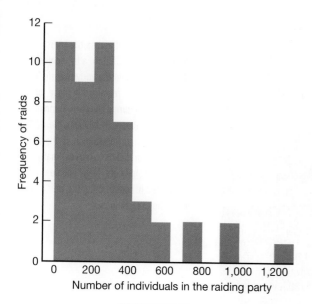

FIGURE 16.15

The distribution of the size of raiding parties among the Turkana. The horizontal axis gives the number of warriors participating in a raid, and the height of the vertical bars gives the fraction of the sample of raids that had that number of warriors. The average size was about 300 fighters and the largest parties consisted of more than 1,000 individuals. This distribution means that a single individual has only a small effect on the success of the raid.

these large raiding parties are unrelated to one another and many members of the war party barely know one another.

Notice that cooperation does not always produce nice or socially desirable outcomes. When the Yurok construct a weir, they catch more salmon, and everyone in the group gets more food. When other group members give food to a woman too sick to forage, she and her children are better off. When the Turkana go off on a raid, some are wounded, suffer, and may die; the threat of attacks and counterattacks forces everyone to put effort into guarding herds, wasting resources that could be used for more productive purposes.

Human cooperation is regulated through prosocial sentiments and culturally transmitted norms enforced by rewards and punishments.

People are much more cooperative than other mammals, but they are not angels. Like other organisms, people are motivated by their own well-being and the welfare of their kin. The effect of each individual's contribution to large-scale collective enterprises is small. Selfish motives will tempt people to free ride, that is, to hide behind a tree when the shooting starts or feign illness when it is time to cut timber for the weir. If people succumb to these motives, there will be no cooperation. So what prevents free riding and sustains cooperation?

For most animals the answer is some combination of kinship and reciprocity. When individuals cooperate with kin, free riding can reduce their inclusive fitness. A naked mole rat who shirks its duties reduces the fitness of kin, and because relatedness is high, this effect can be enough to prevent free riding. In some primates, reciprocity plays an important role. Here, free riders are punished by retaliation by injured parties. A baboon who fails to reciprocate grooming may not get groomed by its partner next time.

While similar motives undoubtedly play a role in human cooperation, especially on smaller scales, they are not the whole story. Prosocial sentiments and the enforcement of culturally evolved moral norms by third parties play a crucial role in sustaining human cooperation.

Humans are not just exceptionally clever and cooperative creatures; we are also unusually nice ones. We donate to charity, give blood, return lost wallets, and give directions to bewildered tourists. As we noted earlier, individuals go to war, risking their lives to gain rewards that will mainly benefit others. Empathy motivates us to feel compassion for others, even people we don't know and will never meet. We have

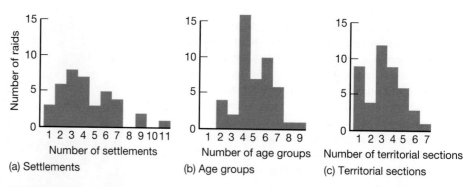

(a) Settlements (b) Age groups (c) Territorial sections

FIGURE 16.16

Membership in Turkana raiding parties is drawn from several (a) settlements, (b) age groups, and (c) territorial sections. This distribution means that warriors fight with many individuals they do not know well, suggesting that cooperation is not maintained by reciprocity.

prosocial sentiments, such as generosity and a sense of fairness, and feel concern for the welfare of others. Such sentiments may motivate us to perform altruistic acts. As Abraham Lincoln once said, "When I do good, I feel good. When I do bad, I feel bad. That's my religion."

However, some researchers believe that people perform these kinds of acts for largely selfish reasons. They point out that heroes get to ride in parades, crusaders for justice become famous, and generous donors get their names on brass plaques. And, in some cases, we may expect recipients to reciprocate in the future. In an effort to get at the nature of people's social preferences, behavioral economists have designed a set of simple games in which individuals are faced with decisions that will affect their own welfare and the welfare of others. For example, in the dictator game, one player (the proposer) is given a sum of money. The proposer can keep all the money or can allocate some amount to another player. In the standard form of the game, the offer is relayed anonymously; the two players never meet and never interact again. This is meant to eliminate the possibility that proposers will take advantage of opportunities to gain reputational benefits or expectations based on reciprocity. Although proposers are free to keep all the money for themselves, not everyone does this. In fact, proposers typically allocate 20% to 30% of their endowments to the other player.

The ultimatum game adds a second step to the dictator game. As before, the proposer is given a monetary endowment and makes an anonymous allocation. But in this game the recipient decides whether to accept or reject the proposer's offer. If the recipient accepts the offer, each player gets the designated amount; if the recipient rejects the offer, neither one gets any money. A recipient who rejects an offer above zero will actually lose money. Nonetheless, recipients typically reject offers of less than 20%. This is striking because recipients incur a cost when they reject a low offer, and they seem willing to punish proposers who make low offers, even though they are strangers and will not interact again.

You might think that these results reflect some peculiarity of industrialized societies or college students, who are usually the subjects of such experiments. But the ultimatum game has now been played by thousands of people in dozens of countries all over the world. Joseph Henrich, now at Harvard University, coordinated a project in which the ultimatum game was played in a dozen small-scale societies around the world (**Figure 16.17**). Henrich and his colleagues found considerable variation across societies in the size of offers and the likelihood that low offers would be rejected (**Figure 16.18**). However,

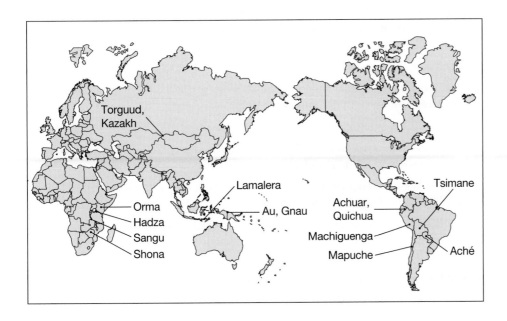

FIGURE 16.17

Populations in which the ultimatum game experiments were performed.

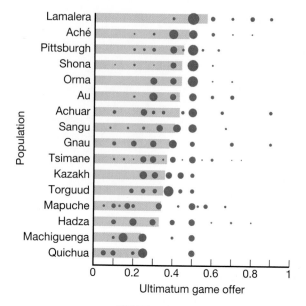

FIGURE 16.18

Results from cross-cultural ultimatum game experiments. The horizontal axis gives the fraction of the total monetary endowment offered by the proposer. The yellow bar gives the mean offer in each society, and the diameter of the blue circles gives the fraction of proposers who offered that fraction of the endowment. So, for example, most Lamalera participants offered half of the endowment, and the mean offer was slightly greater than a half. Among the Quichua, the most common offer was about 25% of the endowment, and the mean offer was about the same.

in all societies, the more unequal an offer was, the more likely it was that it would be rejected.

Third-party enforcement of culturally evolved moral norms sustains human cooperation.

In the ultimatum game, recipients are often willing to punish proposers who make low offers even when they don't know their identity and won't interact again. They seem to be motivated by a sense of what constitutes an acceptable offer and what is simply unfair. Their behavior represents one example of what behavioral economists refer to as third-party enforcement of culturally evolved moral norms. That system plays an important role in sustaining cooperation. To see how this works, let's revisit Turkana warfare. Warriors have many opportunities to free ride. They can desert before the battle begins. During the battle they can lag behind, hide, or otherwise reduce their own risk of getting killed. After the battle they can make off with more than their share of the cows. Moreover, some free riding occurs in about 50% of raids. Why doesn't free riding spread? The answer is that cowards and other free riders are punished. Mathew's research indicates that punishment takes two forms. First, there is direct punishment, usually by members of the free rider's age group. The first violation usually results in verbal sanctions; the free rider is ridiculed and told not to do it again. Further violations elicit corporal punishment and fines—the violator's age-mates tie him to a tree, beat him, and then slaughter one of his cows for a feast. Second, free riders lose various kinds of social support. They are less attractive as mates and less likely to get help from others when they need it. For example, a Turkana man traveling away from his settlement can count on getting shelter and food from other Turkana because they are obliged to provide such hospitality. However, there is no obligation to provide hospitality to a man who has a reputation for cowardice.

Norms enforced by third-party sanctions regulate a variety of behaviors in even the simplest foraging societies. Anthropologist Kim Hill surveyed the ethnographic literature and compiled a long list of norms that regulate behavior:

- *Marriage.* Whom you can marry based on age, kin relationship, or ritual group membership and whether it is permissible to have more than one wife or husband.

- *Food production.* What land is yours to exploit, what kinds of plants and animals you may harvest, and what economic activities are permissible.

- *Food sharing.* Whom you must share with, how much they receive, and who receives which cuts of meat.

- *Food consumption.* What kinds of food you may eat based on your age, sex, reproductive status, and ritual group membership.

- *Display rights.* What kinds of rituals you may participate in.

- *Residence.* Where you may live and with which people, again based on your sex, age, reproductive status, and ritual group membership.

- *Politics.* Who has political power and who can be a leader based on kinship, ritual membership, sex, age, and other factors.

- *Conflict.* Who is a legitimate opponent in ritual dueling and divining, what kinds of conflict are just and what kinds are not, and whether you are obligated to participate in conflicts with other groups.

- *Life history.* When you can have sex and who must invest in children.

- *Pollution.* Where and when you can relieve yourself, dispose of waste, and other potentially polluting activities.

Notice that some norms regulate victimless crimes. For example, it is very common for norms to prohibit sex among siblings or parents and offspring. These behaviors don't injure third parties, yet third parties sometimes go to great efforts to suppress such behaviors.

It seems likely that third-party enforcement of norms makes it easier to maintain cooperation than simple reciprocity for several reasons. First, it can increase the magnitude of penalties imposed on free riders. With reciprocation, a man who cheats his partner will lose the benefits of that relationship. With community-enforced norms, the violator may face more severe punishment and the loss of social support from nearly everyone in the community. Second, third-party norm enforcement can increase the chance that violators are detected. Without community monitoring and enforcement, a child who tells her mother that she is too sick to gather firewood or mind the goats can go out and play with her friends when her mother is out of camp. With community monitoring and enforcement, the cost of malingering will be much greater—she can't play when anyone is around the camp.

The extent of human cooperation is an evolutionary puzzle.

All the available evidence suggests that the societies of our Pliocene ancestors were like those of other social primates. Sometime over the last several million years, important changes occurred in human psychology that supported larger, more cooperative societies. Given the magnitude and complexity of the changes in human societies, the most plausible hypothesis is that they were the product of natural selection. However, the standard theory of the evolution of social behavior is consistent with Hobbes's vision of "the warre of all against all" tempered by a bit of nepotism, not observed human behavior. Apes fill the bill, but not humans.

Scientists have advanced two kinds of explanations for the high level of human cooperation. The **mismatch hypothesis** holds that the psychological machinery that supports human cooperation evolved in small hunter-gatherer societies with high genetic relatedness (**Figure 16.19**). Although high relatedness does not lead to very much cooperation in other primates, some special ecological situation may have favored it in early hominin populations. For example, a shift to hunting and the production of highly dependent infants may have favored male parental investment, food sharing, and cooperative hunting. In this kind of social environment, natural selection may have favored a psychology

FIGURE 16.19

Hunter-gatherers often live in small, nomadic groups.

that made people more cooperative. Prosocial emotions, such as shame and guilt, may have been favored by selection because it motivated people to follow cooperative social norms. Because groups were small and made up of relatives, selection may have favored cooperation and psychological mechanisms that promote cooperation. Our evolved psychology misfires in contemporary societies in which most people live in groups with much lower degrees of relatedness.

The mismatch hypothesis has several weaknesses. First, surveys by Kim Hill and his colleagues indicate that the members of contemporary hunter-gatherer bands are not very closely related. People often move from one band to another so that the social world of modern hunter-gatherers typically encompasses about 500 people who all speak the same language. So the mismatch hypothesis is plausible only if ancestral hunter-gatherers lived in small, closed groups like other primates, not in the kinds of groups that characterize modern foragers. Second, the mismatch hypothesis cannot easily explain the scale of cooperation observed in contemporary societies. People, even people in small-scale societies, cooperate in large groups with people they do not know. The simplest version of the mismatch hypothesis suggests that people should be acutely sensitive to cues of kinship and reciprocity. They should be motivated to cooperate with relatives and people they know and be suspicious of strangers.

The **cultural group selection** hypothesis holds that extensive human cooperation is a side effect of rapid cultural adaptation. Systems of rewards and punishments can stabilize a variety of moral norms, including noncooperative ones, on different scales. As long as the cost of being punished exceeds the cost of following the norm, obeying the norm will be advantageous for individuals. It doesn't matter what the norm requires. Mutually enforced sanctions could maintain cooperative or noncooperative norms: "You may steal your neighbor's cows to feed your family," or "You may not steal your neighbor's cows to feed your family." Similarly, punishment can maintain norms at different scales. "Do not steal a clan member's cattle, but the cattle of other clans are for brave men to steal," or "Do not steal the cattle of someone from your tribe, but the cattle of other tribes are for brave men to steal." These are both group-beneficial norms, but one benefits clans, whereas the other benefits tribes. The list of possible variations is nearly endless. As a result, different groups may tend to evolve toward different equilibria—one set of norms is enforced in one group, a different set in another group, a third set in a third group, and so on. This tendency will be opposed by migration and other kinds of social contact. Cultural adaptation is more rapid than genetic adaptation. Indeed, if we are correct, this is the reason we have culture—to allow different groups to accumulate different adaptations to diverse environments. As a result we expect that as culture became more important in the human lineage, behavioral differences between groups increased.

In Chapter 1 we saw that three conditions are necessary for adaptation by natural selection: First, there must be a struggle for existence so that not all individuals survive and reproduce. Second, there must be variation so that some types are more likely to survive and reproduce than others. And finally, variation must be heritable so that the offspring of survivors resemble their parents. We argued that selection typically occurs at the levels of individuals because these three conditions don't hold for groups. Groups may compete with one another and groups may vary in their ability to survive and grow, but the factors that lead to group-level variation in competitive ability are not transmitted from one generation to another, so there is no cumulative adaptation at the level of groups. The cultural group selection hypothesis emphasizes that once rapid cultural adaptation in human societies gave rise to stable (heritable), between-group differences, the stage was set for a variety of selective processes to generate adaptations at the group level.

Different human groups have different norms and values, and the cultural transmission of these traits can cause differences that can persist for long periods. The norms and values that predominate in a group may well affect the probability that the group survives, whether it is economically successful, whether it expands, and whether it is imitated by its neighbors (**Figure 16.20**). For example, suppose that groups with norms

FIGURE 16.20

The Nuer and Dinka are two groups who live in South Sudan. Each of these groups includes several tribes that compete for grazing land. During the nineteenth century, the Nuer expanded at the expense of the Dinka because all the Nuer tribes shared norms about tribal membership and obligations that allowed them to organize much larger war parties than those organized by the Dinka.

that promote military success are more likely to survive than groups lacking this sentiment. This creates a selective process that leads to the spread of such norms.

These two hypotheses are not mutually exclusive. Some of the psychological machinery necessary to create and enforce norms could easily have evolved in small groups of related individuals, and then these mechanisms made possible the norms that enforced more extensive and larger-scale cooperation. However, we argue that the mismatch hypothesis alone is not enough to understand the profound differences that have evolved between humans and other primates or to understand how humans have achieved such high levels of cooperation.

Is Human Evolution Over?

Students in our courses often wonder whether human evolution is over, and it seems a sensible question to consider as we come to the end of the story of human evolution. As we have seen, modern humans are the product of millions of years of evolutionary change. But so are cockroaches, peacocks, and orchids. All the organisms that we see around us, including people, are the products of evolution, but they are not finished products. They are simply works in progress, and this applies to us as well.

In one sense, however, human evolution is over. Because cultural change is much faster than genetic change, most of the changes in human societies since the origin of agriculture, almost 10 ka, and perhaps even before this point, have been the result of cultural, not genetic, evolution. Most of the evolution of human behavior and human societies is not driven by natural selection and the other processes of organic evolution; rather, it is driven by learning and other psychological mechanisms that shape cultural evolution. However, this fact does not mean that evolutionary theory or human evolutionary history is irrelevant to understanding contemporary human behavior. Natural selection has shaped the physiological mechanisms and psychological machinery governing learning and other mechanisms of cultural change, and understanding human evolution can yield important insights into human nature and the behavior of modern peoples.

Key Terms

culture (p. 410)
social facilitation (p. 412)

observational learning
  (p. 412)
emulation (p. 412)

mismatch hypothesis
  (p. 423)

cultural group selection
  (p. 424)

Study Questions

1. The verb *ape* means "to copy or imitate." Is its meaning consistent with what we now know about the learning processes of other primates?

2. Why is cumulative cultural change likely to require emulation or observational learning?

3. Primatologists have documented many examples of behaviors that vary across populations, and some of those researchers have concluded that this variation is a form of culture. Explain why this is or is not a reasonable conclusion.

4. Some things that we do seem to be maladaptive (think about skydiving, drug abuse, and collecting classic cars). Some people would argue that these behaviors provide evidence that natural selection has no important impact on modern humans. Is this a reasonable argument? Why or why not?

5. Famous people, such as successful athletes and movie stars, are hired to sell all kinds of products— from underwear to cars—that have nothing to do with their professional accomplishments. How does the theory of cultural evolution help to explain why this might be a successful advertising strategy?

6. How do the dictator and ultimatum games provide evidence of prosocial sentiments? How crucial are anonymity and cross-cultural results for the conclusion that people are prosocial?

7. How does the pattern of cooperation in human groups differ from the pattern of cooperation we described in Chapter 7?

8. Thinking about warfare as a form of cooperation seems odd. Explain why evolutionary anthropologists think of war as a form of cooperation and why the existence of large-scale warfare poses a puzzle for evolutionary anthropologists.

9. What is the evidence that people cooperate in large, weakly related groups? Why is this phenomenon a puzzle from an evolutionary perspective?

10. In Chapter 7, we said that genetic group selection is usually not an important force in nature because migration reduces the amount of genetic variation between groups. Explain why movement between groups does not create the same problems for cultural group selection.

Further Reading

Boyd, R., and P. J. Richerson. 2009. "Culture and the Evolution of Human Cooperation." *Philosophical Transactions of the Royal Society (B)* 364: 3281–3288.

Cronk, L., and B. Leech. 2013. *Meeting at Grand Central: Understanding the Social and Evolutionary Roots of Cooperation.* Princeton, N.J.: Princeton University Press.

Hill, K., M. Barton, and M. Hurtado. 2009. "The Emergence of Human Uniqueness: Behavioral Characters

Underlying Behavioral Modernity." *Evolutionary Anthropology* 18: 187–200.

Mesoudi, A. 2010. *Cultural Evolution.* Chicago: University of Chicago Press.

Richerson, P. J., and R. Boyd. 2005. *Not by Genes Alone: How Culture Transformed Human Evolution.* Chicago: University of Chicago Press.

Visit DIGITAL.WWNORTON.COM/HOWHUMANS8 to

- review this chapter with personalized, interactive questions via InQuizitive
- view videos and animations on this chapter's key topics

EPILOGUE

There Is Grandeur in This View of Life...

Here we end our account of how humans evolved. As we promised in the Prologue, the story has not been a simple one. We began, in Part One, by explaining how evolution works: how evolutionary processes create the exquisite complexity of organic design and how these processes give rise to the stunning diversity of life. Next we used these ideas in Part Two to understand the ecology and behavior of nonhuman primates: why they live in groups, why the behavior of males and females differs, why animals compete and cooperate, and why primates are so smart compared with other kinds of animals. Then, in Part Three, we combined our understanding of how evolution works and our knowledge of the behavior of other primates with information gleaned from the fossil record to reconstruct the history of the human lineage. We traced each step in the transformation from a shrewlike insectivore living at the time of dinosaurs; to a monkeylike creature inhabiting the Oligocene swamps of northern Africa; to an apelike creature living in the canopy of the Miocene forests; to the small-brained, bipedal hominins who ranged over Pliocene woodlands and savannas; to the large-brained and technically more skilled early members of the genus *Homo*, who migrated to most of the Old World; and, finally, to creatures much like ourselves who created spectacular art, constructed simple structures, and hunted large and dangerous game just 100 ka. Finally, in Part Four, we turned to look at ourselves—to assess the magnitude and significance of genetic variation in the human species, and to try to explain how and why humans have become such a successful and unusual species.

FIGURE E.1

Charles Darwin died in 1882 and was buried in Westminster Abbey beneath the monument to Isaac Newton.

Evolutionary analyses of human behavior are not always well received. In Darwin's day, many people were deeply troubled by the implications of this theory. One Victorian matron, informed that Darwin believed humans to be descended from apes, is reported to have said, "Let us hope that it is not true, and if it is true, that it does not become widely known." Darwin's theory profoundly changed the way we see ourselves. Before Darwin, most people believed that humans were fundamentally different from other animals. Human uniqueness and human superiority were unquestioned. But we now know that all aspects of the human phenotype are products of organic evolution—the same processes that create the diversity of life around us. Nonetheless, many people still feel that we diminish ourselves by explaining human behavior in the same terms that we use to explain the behavior of chimpanzees or soapberry bugs or finches.

In contrast, we think the story of human evolution is breathtaking in its grandeur. With a few simple processes, we can explain how we arose, why we are the way we are, and how we relate to the rest of the universe. It is an amazing story. But perhaps Darwin himself (**Figure E.1**) put it best in the final pass of *On the Origin of Species*:

It is interesting to contemplate an entangled bank, clothed with many plants of many kinds, with birds singing on the bushes, with various insects flitting about, and with worms crawling through the damp earth, and to reflect that these elaborately constructed forms, so different from each other, and dependent on each other in so complex a manner, have all been produced by laws acting around us. These laws, taken in the largest sense, being Growth with Reproduction; Inheritance which is almost implied by reproduction; Variability from the indirect and direct action of the external conditions of life, and from use and disuse; a Ratio of Increase so high as to lead to a Struggle for Life, and as a consequence, Natural Selection, entailing Divergence of Character and the Extinction of less-improved forms. Thus, from the war of nature, from famine and death, the most exalted object which we are capable of conceiving, namely, the production of the higher animals, directly follows. There is grandeur in this view of life, with it several powers having been originally breathed into a few forms or only one; and that, whilst this planet has gone cycling on according to the fixed law of gravity, from so simple a beginning endless forms most beautiful and most wonderful have been, and are being evolved. [From C. Darwin, 1859, 1964, *On the Origin of Species*, facs. of 1st ed. (Cambridge, Mass.: Harvard University Press), p. 490.]

APPENDIX

The Skeletal Anatomy of Primates

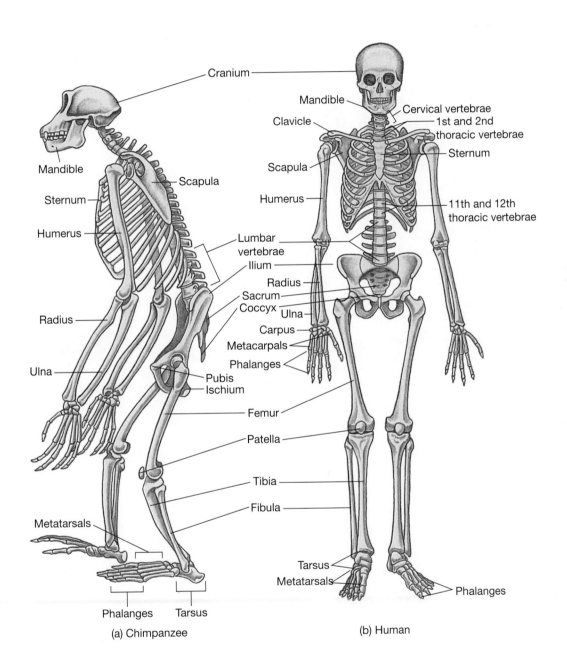

(a) Chimpanzee

(b) Human

GLOSSARY

abductor A muscle whose contraction moves a limb away from the midline of the body. The abductors that connect the pelvis to the femur act to keep the body upright during bipedal walking. (Ch. 10)

Acheulean A Mode 2 tool industry found at sites dated at 1.6 Ma to 0.3 Ma and associated with *Homo ergaster* and some archaic *Homo sapiens*. Named after the French village of Saint-Acheul, where it was first discovered, the Acheulean industry is dominated by teardrop-shaped hand axes and blunt cleavers. (Ch. 11)

activator A protein that increases transcription of a regulated gene. Compare *repressor*. (Ch. 2)

adaptation A feature of an organism created by the process of natural selection. (Ch. 1)

adaptive radiation The process in which a single lineage diversifies into several species, each characterized by distinctive adaptations. The diversification of the mammals at the beginning of the Cenozoic era is an example of an adaptive radiation. (Ch. 4)

adenine One of the four bases of the DNA molecule. The complementary base of adenine is thymine. (Ch. 2)

affiliative Friendly. (Ch. 7)

alkaloids Secondary compounds produced and kept in plant tissues to make the plant distasteful or even poisonous to herbivores. (Ch. 5)

allele One of two or more alternative forms of a gene. For example, the A and S alleles are two forms of the gene controlling the amino acid sequence of one of the subunits of hemoglobin. (Ch. 2)

alliance An interaction in which two or more animals jointly initiate aggression against, or respond to aggression from, one or more other animals. Also called *coalition*. (Ch. 7)

allopatric speciation Speciation that occurs when two or more populations of a single species are geographically isolated from each other and then diverge to form two or more new species. Compare *parapatric speciation* and *sympatric speciation*. (Ch. 4)

altruism (altruistic, adj.) Behavior that reduces the fitness of the individual performing the behavior (the actor) but increases the fitness of the individual affected by the behavior (the recipient). (Ch. 7)

amino acids Molecules that are linked in a chain to form proteins. There are 20 amino acids, all of which share the same molecular backbone but have a different side chain. (Ch. 2)

analogy (analogous, adj.) Similarity between traits that is due to convergent evolution, not common descent. For example, the fact that humans and kangaroos are both bipedal is an analogy. Compare *homology*. (Ch. 4)

ancestral trait A trait that appears earlier in the evolution of a lineage or clade. Ancestral traits are contrasted with *derived traits*, which appear later in the evolution of a lineage or clade. For example, the presence of a tail is ancestral in the primate lineage, and the absence of a tail is derived. Systematists must avoid using ancestral similarities when constructing phylogenies. (Ch. 4)

angiosperms The flowering plants. The radiation of the angiosperms during the Cretaceous period may have played an important role in the evolution of the primates. (Ch. 9)

anticodon The sequence of bases on a transfer RNA molecule that binds complementarily to a particular *codon*. For example, for the codon ATC the corresponding anticodon is TAG because A binds to T, and G binds to C. (Ch. 2)

apatite crystal A crystalline material found in tooth enamel. (Ch. 9)

arboreal Active predominantly in trees. Compare *terrestrial*. (Ch. 4)

argon–argon dating A sophisticated variant of the potassium–argon dating method that allows very small samples to be dated accurately. (Ch. 9)

Aurignacian An early Upper Paleolithic stone tool industry found in Europe at sites that date to after 45 ka. (Ch. 13)

bachelor male A male that has not been able to establish residence in a bisexual group. Bachelor males may live alone or reside in all-male groups. (Ch. 6)

balanced polymorphism A steady state in which two or more alleles co-exist in a population. This state occurs when heterozygotes have a higher fitness than any homozygote. (Ch. 14)

basal metabolic rate The rate of energy use required to maintain life when an animal is at rest. (Ch. 5)

base One of four molecules—adenine, guanine, cytosine, and thymine—that are bound to the DNA backbone. Different sequences of bases encode the information necessary for protein synthesis. (Ch. 2)

biface A flat stone tool made by working both sides of a core until there is an edge along the entire circumference. See also *hand ax*. (Ch. 11)

bilaterally symmetrical Describing an animal whose morphology on one side of the midline is a mirror image of the morphology on the other side. (Ch. 5)

binocular vision Vision in which both eyes can focus together on a distant object to produce three-dimensional images. See also *stereoscopic vision*. (Ch. 5)

biochemical pathway Any of the chains of chemical reactions by which organisms regulate their structure and chemistry. (Ch. 2)

biological species concept The concept that species is defined as a group of organisms that cannot interbreed in nature. Adherents of the biological species concept believe that the resulting lack of gene flow is necessary to maintain differences between closely related species. Compare *ecological species concept*. (Ch. 4)

bipedal Describing locomotion in which the animal walks upright on two (hind) legs. Compare *quadrupedal*. (Ch. 9)

blade A stone tool made from a flake that is at least twice as long as it is wide. Blades dominate the tool traditions of the Upper Paleolithic. (Ch. 13)

blending inheritance A model of inheritance, widely accepted during the nineteenth century, in which the hereditary material of the mother and father was thought to combine irreversibly in the offspring. (Ch. 1)

bridewealth The collection of valuable items that is transferred from the groom's family to the bride's family at the time of marriage. (Ch. 15)

camera-type eye An eye in which light passes through a transparent opening and is then focused by a lens on photosensitive tissue. Camera-type eyes are found in vertebrates, mollusks, and some arthropods. (Ch. 3)

canalized Describing traits that are very insensitive to environmental conditions during development, resulting in similar phenotypes in a variety of environments. Compare *plastic*. (Ch. 3)

canine The sharp, pointed tooth that lies between the incisors and the premolars in primates. (Ch. 5)

carbohydrates Certain organic molecules with the formula $C_nH_{2n}O_n$, including common sugars and starches. (Ch. 5)

carbon-14 dating A dating method based on an unstable isotope of carbon with an atomic weight of 14. Carbon-14 is produced in the atmosphere by cosmic radiation and is taken up by living organisms. After organisms die, the carbon-14 present in their bodies decays to a stable isotope (nitrogen-14) at a constant rate. By measuring the ratio of carbon-14 to the stable isotope of carbon (carbon-12) in organic remains, scientists can estimate the length of time that has passed since the organism died. The carbon-14 method is useful for dating specimens that are younger than about 40,000 years. Also called *radiocarbon dating*. (Ch. 9)

character A trait or attribute of the phenotype of an organism. (Ch. 1)

character displacement The result of competition between two species that causes the members of different species to become morphologically or behaviorally more different from each other. (Ch. 4)

Châtelperronian An Upper Paleolithic tool industry found in France and Spain that dates from 36 ka to 32 ka and is associated with Neanderthal fossil remains. (Ch. 13)

chimera A combination of more than one genetic lineage within a single individual. (Ch. 7)

chorion The outer membrane that surrounds the fetus in utero and gives rise to the placenta. (Ch. 7)

chromosome A linear body in the cell nucleus that carries genes and appears during cell division. Staining cells with dyes reveals that different chromosomes are marked by different banding patterns. (Ch. 2)

cladistic taxonomy A system for classifying organisms in which patterns of descent are the only criteria used. Compare *evolutionary taxonomy*. (Ch. 4)

cleaver A biface stone tool with a broad, flat edge. Cleavers are common at Acheulean sites. (Ch. 11)

coalition See *alliance*. (Ch. 7)

codon A sequence of three DNA bases on a DNA molecule that constitutes one "word" in the message used to create a specific protein. There are 64 codons. Compare *anticodon*. (Ch. 2)

coefficient of relatedness (r) An index measuring the degree of genetic closeness between two individuals. The index ranges from 0 (for no relation) to 1 (which occurs only between an individual and itself or between identical twins). For example, the coefficient of relatedness between an individual and its parents or its siblings is 0.5. (Ch. 7)

collected food A type of food resource, such as a leaf or fruit, that can be gathered and eaten directly. (Ch. 11)

combinatorial control The control of gene expression in which more than one regulatory protein is used and expression is allowed only in a specific combination of conditions. (Ch. 2)

comparative method A method for establishing the function of a phenotypic trait by comparing species. (Ch. 4)

compound eye An eye in which the image is formed by many discrete photoreceptors. Compound eyes are found in insects and other arthropods. (Ch. 3)

conspecifics Members of the same species. (Ch. 5)

continental drift The movement over the surface of the globe of the immense plates of relatively light material that make up the continents. (Ch. 9)

continuous variation Phenotypic variation in which there is a continuum of types. Height in humans is an example of continuous variation. Compare *discontinuous variation*. (Ch. 1)

convergence The evolution of similar adaptations in unrelated species. The evolution of camera-type eyes in both vertebrates and mollusks is an example of convergence. See also *analogy*. (Ch. 1)

core A piece of stone from which smaller flakes are removed. Cores and/or flakes may themselves be useful tools. (Ch. 11)

correlated response An evolutionary change in one character caused by selection on a second, correlated character. For example, selection favoring only long legs will also increase arm length if arm length and leg length are positively correlated. (Ch. 3)

cortex The original, unmodified surface of a stone used to make stone tools. (Ch. 11)

cross In genetics, a mating between chosen parents. (Ch. 2)

crossing over The exchange of genetic material between homologous chromosomes during meiosis. Crossing over causes recombination of genes carried on the same chromosome. (Ch. 2)

crural index The ratio of the length of the shin bone (tibia) to the length of the thigh bone (femur). (Ch. 12)

cultural group selection A process in which competition between culturally different groups leads to the spread of cultural practices prevalent in the successful groups. (Ch. 16)

culture Information stored in human brains that is acquired by imitation, teaching, or some other form of social learning and that can affect behavior or some other aspect of the individual's phenotype. (Ch. 16)

cytosine One of the four bases of the DNA molecule. The complementary base of cytosine is guanine. (Ch. 2)

dental formula The number of incisors, canines, premolars, and molars in the upper and lower jaws. (Ch. 5)

deoxyribonucleic acid See *DNA*. (Ch. 2)

derived trait A trait that appears later in the evolution of a lineage or clade. Derived traits are contrasted with *ancestral traits*, which appear earlier in the evolution of a lineage or clade. For example, the absence of a tail is derived in the hominin lineage, and the presence of a tail is ancestral. Systematists seek to use derived similarities when constructing phylogenies. (Ch. 4)

development All the processes by which the single-celled zygote is transformed into a multicellular adult. (Ch. 3)

diastema (diastemata, pl.) A gap between adjacent teeth. (Ch. 10)

diploid Referring to cells containing pairs of homologous chromosomes, in which one chromosome of each pair is inherited from each parent. Also referring to organisms whose somatic (body) cells are diploid; all primates are diploid. Compare *haploid*. (Ch. 2)

discontinuous variation Phenotypic variation in which there is a discrete number of phenotypes with no intermediate types. Pea color in Mendel's experiments is an example of discontinuous variation. Compare *continuous variation*. (Ch. 1)

diurnal Active only during the day. Compare *nocturnal*. (Ch. 5)

dizygotic twins Twins that result from the fertilization of two separate eggs by two separate sperm. Dizygotic twins are no more closely related than other full siblings. Compare *monozygotic twins*. (Ch. 14)

DNA Deoxyribonucleic acid, the molecule that carries hereditary information in almost all living organisms. DNA consists of two very long sugar–phosphate backbones (called "strands") to which the bases adenine, cytosine, guanine, and thymine are bound. Hydrogen bonds between the bases bind the two strands. (Ch. 2)

dominance The ability of one individual to intimidate or defeat another individual in a pairwise (dyadic) encounter. In some cases, dominance is assessed from the outcome of aggressive encounters; in other cases, dominance is assessed from the outcome of competitive encounters. (Ch. 6)

dominance matrix A square table constructed to keep track of dominance interactions among a group of individuals. Usually winners are listed down the left side and losers are listed across the top, and the number of times each individual defeats another is entered in the cells of the matrix. Individuals are ordered in the matrix so as to minimize the number of entries below the diagonal. This ordering is then used to construct the dominance hierarchy. (Ch. 6)

dominant Describing an allele that results in the same phenotype whether in the homozygous or the heterozygous state. Compare *recessive*. (Ch. 2)

ecological species concept The concept that natural selection plays an important role in maintaining the differences between species and that the absence of interbreeding between two populations is not a necessary condition for defining them as separate species. Compare *biological species concept*. (Ch. 4)

EEA See *environment of evolutionary adaptedness*.

electron-spin-resonance dating A technique used to date fossil teeth by measuring the density of electrons trapped in apatite crystals in teeth. (Ch. 9)

emulation A form of social learning in which naïve individuals acquire information about the end state of behavior but do not acquire information about the process required to generate the end state. (Ch. 16)

endocranial volume The volume inside the braincase. (Ch. 10)

environment of evolutionary adaptedness (EEA) The past environment(s) in which currently observed adaptations were shaped. For example, the psychological mechanisms that cause contemporary humans to overeat were probably shaped in an environment of evolutionary adaptedness in which overeating was rarely a problem. (Ch. 15)

environmental covariation The effect on phenotypes that occurs when the environments of parents and offspring are similar. Because environmental covariation causes the phenotypes of parents and offspring to be similar, it can falsely increase estimates of heritability. (Ch. 14)

environmental variation Phenotypic differences between individuals that exist because those individuals developed in different environments. Compare *genetic variation*. (Ch. 3)

enzyme A protein that serves as a catalyst, increasing the rate at which particular chemical reactions occur at a given temperature. Enzymes can control the chemical composition of cells by causing some chemical reactions to occur much faster than others. (Ch. 2)

equilibrium A steady state in which the composition of the population does not change. (Ch. 1)

estrus A period during the reproductive cycle of most mammals (and most primates) when the female is receptive to mating and can conceive. (Ch. 6)

eukaryotes Organisms whose cells have cellular organelles, cell nuclei, and chromosomes. All plants and animals are eukaryotes. Compare *prokaryotes*. (Ch. 2)

evolutionary taxonomy A system for classifying organisms that uses both patterns of descent and patterns of overall similarity. Compare *cladistic taxonomy*. (Ch. 4)

exon A segment of the DNA in eukaryotes that is translated into protein. Compare *intron*. (Ch. 2)

extracted food Food that is embedded in a matrix, encased in a hard shell, or otherwise difficult to extract. Extracted foods require complicated, carefully coordinated techniques to process. (Chs. 8, 11)

F_0, F_1, and F_2 generations A system for keeping track of generations in breeding experiments. The initial generation is called the F_0 generation, the offspring of the F_0 generation constitute the F_1 generation, and the offspring of the F_1 generation constitute the F_2 generation. (Ch. 2)

falciparum malaria A severe form of malaria. The sickle-cell allele for hemoglobin is common in West Africa because it confers resistance to falciparum malaria in the heterozygous state. (Ch. 14)

family A taxonomic level above genus but below order. A family may contain several genera, and an order may contain several families. Humans belong to the family Hominidae, and the other great apes belong to the family Pongidae. (Ch. 4)

fecundity The biological capacity to reproduce. In humans, fecundity may be greater than fertility (the actual number of children produced) when people limit family size. (Ch. 1)

femur The thigh bone. (Ch. 10)

fixation A state that occurs when all the individuals in a population are homozygous for the same allele at a particular locus. (Ch. 3)

flake A small chip of stone knocked from a larger stone core. (Ch. 11)

folivore (folivorous, adj.) An animal whose diet consists mostly of leaves. (Ch. 5)

foramen magnum The large hole in the bottom of the cranium through which the spinal cord passes. (Ch. 10)

fossil A trace of life more than 10,000 years old preserved in rock. Fossils can be mineralized bones, plant parts, impressions of soft body parts, or tracks. (Ch. 9)

founder effect A form of genetic drift that occurs when a small population colonizes a new habitat and then greatly increases in number. Random genetic changes due to the small size of the initial population are amplified by later population growth. (Ch. 14)

frugivore (frugivorous, adj.) An animal whose diet consists mostly of fruit. (Ch. 5)

gametes In animals, eggs and sperm. (Ch. 2)

gene A segment of the chromosome that produces a recognizable effect on phenotype and segregates as a unit during gamete formation. (Ch. 2)

gene flow The movement of genes from one population to another, or from one part of a population to another, as the result of interbreeding. (Ch. 4)

gene frequency The fraction of the genes at a genetic locus that are a particular allele (also called allele frequency). For example, a population that contains 250 AA individuals, 200 AS individuals, and 50 SS individuals has 700 copies of the A allele and 300 copies of the S allele; therefore, the frequency of the S allele is 0.3. (Ch. 3)

gene tree A phylogenetic tree tracing the pattern of descent for a particular gene. (Ch. 13)

genetic distance A measure of the overall genetic similarity of individuals or species. The best estimates of genetic distance use many genes. (Ch. 4)

genetic drift Random change in gene frequencies due to sampling variation that occurs in any finite population. Genetic drift is more rapid in small populations than in large populations. (Ch. 3)

genetic variation Phenotypic differences between individuals that result from the fact that those individuals have inherited different genes from their parents. Compare *environmental variation*. (Ch. 14)

genome All the genetic information carried by an organism. (Ch. 2)

genomewide association studies Studies that look for statistical associations between phenotypic traits (for example, stature) and a great many genetic markers located throughout the genome. An association between a particular marker and a phenotypic trait indicates that a gene near that marker affects the trait. (Ch. 14)

genotype The combination of alleles that characterizes an individual at some set of genetic loci. For example, in populations with only the A and S alleles at the hemoglobin locus, that locus has only three possible genotypes: AA, AS, and SS. (SA is the same as AS.) Compare *phenotype*. (Ch. 2)

genotypic frequency The fraction of individuals in a population that have a particular genotype. (Ch. 3)

genus (genera, pl.) A taxonomic category below family and above species. There may be several species in a genus and several genera in a family. (Ch. 4)

Gondwanaland The more southerly of the two supercontinents that existed from about 120 Ma to 100 Ma. Gondwanaland included the continental plates that now make up Africa, South America, Antarctica, Australia, New Guinea, Madagascar, and the Indian subcontinent. (Ch. 9)

grooming The process of picking through hair to remove dirt, dead skin, ectoparasites, and other material. Grooming is a common form of affiliative behavior among primates. (Ch. 7)

guanine One of the four bases of the DNA molecule. The complementary base of guanine is cytosine. (Ch. 2)

gum A sticky carbohydrate that some trees produce in response to physical damage. Gum is an important food for many primates. (Ch. 5)

gummivore (gummivorous, adj.) An animal whose diet consists mostly of gum. (Ch. 5)

gymnosperms A group of plants that reproduce without flowering. Modern gymnosperms include pines, redwoods, and firs. (Ch. 9)

haft To attach a spear point, ax head, or similar implement to a handle. Hafting greatly increases the force that can be applied to the tool. (Ch. 12)

Hamilton's rule A rule predicting that altruistic behavior among relatives will be favored by natural selection if $rb > c$, where r is the *coefficient of relatedness* between actor and recipient, b is the sum of the benefits of performing the behavior on the fitness of the recipient(s), and c is the cost, in decreased fitness of the donor, of performing the behavior. See also *kin selection*. (Ch. 7)

hand ax The most common type of biface stone tool found in Acheulean sites. It is flat and teardrop shaped with a sharp point at the narrow end. (Ch. 11)

haplogroup The mtDNA genotypes that descend from a node in the phylogenetic tree. (Ch. 13)

haploid A cell with only one copy of each chromosome. Gametes are haploid, as are the cells of some asexual organisms. Compare *diploid*. (Ch. 2)

haplorrhine Any member of the group containing tarsiers and anthropoid primates. The system that classifies primates into haplorrhines and strepsirrhines is a cladistic alternative to the evolutionary systematic taxonomy, in which primates are divided into prosimians and anthropoids, and tarsiers are grouped with prosimians. Compare *strepsirrhine*. (Ch. 5)

haplotype A particular set of alleles at some number of genetic loci that are transmitted together on the same chromosome. (Ch. 14)

Hardy–Weinberg equilibrium The unchanging frequency of genotypes that results from sexual reproduction and occurs in the absence of other evolutionary forces such as natural selection, mutation, or genetic drift. (Ch. 3)

hemoglobin A protein in blood that carries oxygen, including two α (alpha) and two β (beta) subunits. (Ch. 2)

heritability The fraction of the phenotypic variation in the population that is the result of genetic variation. (Ch. 14)

heterozygous Referring to a diploid organism whose cells carry two alleles for a particular genetic locus. Organisms that are heterozygous are called "heterozygotes." Compare *homozygous*. (Ch. 2)

hind-limb dominated A form of locomotion that depends mainly on the hind legs for power and propulsion. (Ch. 5)

home base A temporary camp that members of a group return to each day. At the home base, food is shared, processed, cooked, and eaten; subsistence tools are manufactured and repaired; and social life is conducted. (Ch. 11)

hominin Any member of the family Hominidae, including all species of *Australopithecus* and *Homo*. (Ch. 10)

hominoid Any member of the superfamily Hominoidea, which includes humans, all the living apes, and many extinct apelike and human-like species from the Miocene, Pliocene, and Pleistocene epochs. (Ch. 4)

Homo heidelbergensis Middle Pleistocene hominins from Africa and western Eurasia. These hominins had large brains and very robust skulls and postcrania. (Ch. 12)

homologous chromosomes Sets of chromosomes have the same genetic loci, but often these loci contain different alleles. Human cells contain 23 pairs of homologous chromosomes. One member of each pair comes from the mother and the other from the father. (Ch. 2)

homology (homologous, adj.) Similarity between traits that is due to common ancestry, not convergence. For example, the reason that gorillas and baboons are both quadrupedal is that they are both descended from a quadrupedal ancestor. Compare *analogy*. (Ch. 4)

homozygous Referring to a diploid organism whose chromosomes carry two copies of the same allele at a single genetic locus. Organisms that are homozygous are called "homozygotes." Compare *heterozygous*. (Ch. 2)

humerus The bone in the upper part of the forelimb (arm). (Ch. 10)

hunted food Live animal prey captured by human foragers or nonhuman primates. (Ch. 11)

hybrid zone A geographic region where two or more populations of the same species or two species overlap and interbreed. Hybrid zones usually occur at the habitat margins of the respective populations. (Ch. 4)

ilium (ilia, pl.) One of the three bones in the pelvis. (Ch. 10)

inbred mating Mating between closely related individuals. Also called *inbreeding*. Compare *outbred mating*. (Ch. 15)

inbreeding See *inbred mating*.

incisors The front teeth in mammals. In anthropoid primates, incisors are used for cutting, and there are two on each side of the upper and lower jaw. (Ch. 5)

independent assortment The principle, discovered by Mendel, that each of the genes at a single locus on a pair of homologous chromosomes is equally likely to be transmitted when gametes (eggs and sperm) are formed. This happens because during meiosis the probability that a particular chromosome will enter a gamete is 0.5 and is independent of whether other nonhomologous chromosomes enter the same gamete. Thus, knowing that an individual received a particular chromosome from its mother (and thus a particular allele) tells nothing about the probability that it received other, nonhomologous chromosomes from its mother. (Ch. 2)

infraorder The taxonomic level between order and superfamily. An order may contain several infraorders, and an infraorder may contain several superfamilies. (Ch. 5)

Initial Upper Paleolithic The earliest Upper Paleolithic industry in Europe found at sites that date to between 50 ka and 45 ka. (Ch. 13)

insectivore (insectivorous, adj.) An animal whose diet consists mostly of insects. (Ch. 5)

insulin A protein that is created by the pancreas and is involved in the regulation of blood sugar. (Ch. 14)

intersexual selection A form of sexual selection in which females choose with whom they mate. The result is that traits making males more attractive to females are selected for. Compare *intrasexual selection*. (Ch. 6)

intrasexual selection A form of sexual selection in which males compete with other males for access to females. The result is that traits making males more successful in such competition are selected for, such as large body size or large canines. Compare *intersexual selection*. (Ch. 6)

intron A segment of the DNA in eukaryotes that is not translated into protein. Compare *exon*. (Ch. 2)

isotope A chemical element with the same atomic number as another element but having a different atomic weight. Unstable isotopes spontaneously change into more stable isotopes. (Ch. 9)

kibbutz (kibbutzim, pl.) An agricultural settlement in Israel, usually organized according to collectivist principles. (Ch. 15)

kin selection A theory stating that altruistic acts will be favored by selection if the product of the benefit to the recipient and the degree of relatedness (r) between the actor and recipient exceed the cost to the actor. See also *Hamilton's rule*. (Ch. 7)

knapping The process of manufacturing stone tools. (Ch. 11)

knuckle walking A form of quadrupedal locomotion in which, in the forelimbs, weight is supported by the knuckles rather than by the palm or outstretched fingers. Chimpanzees and gorillas are knuckle walkers. (Ch. 4)

lactase persistence Retention of the capacity to synthesize the enzyme lactase, which is necessary to digest the main carbohydrates in fresh milk after weaning. (Ch. 14)

lactase-phlorizin hydrolase (LPH) An enzyme produced in the small intestine that breaks down lactose in milk. The term is frequently shortened to lactase. (Ch. 14)

lactation (lactate, v.) Production of milk by the mammary glands in females; also the period during which milk is produced for nursing offspring. Lactation is a characteristic feature of mammals. (Ch. 3)

lactose A sugar present in mammalian milk. Most mammals—including most humans—lose the ability to digest lactose as adults. (Ch. 14)

Laurasia The more northerly of the two supercontinents that existed from roughly 150 Ma to 120 Ma. Laurasia included what are now North America, Greenland, Europe, and parts of Asia. (Ch. 9)

LCT The structural gene that codes for lactase-phlorizin hydrolase (lactase). (Ch. 14)

Levallois technique A three-step toolmaking method used by Neanderthals. The knapper first makes a core having a precisely shaped convex surface, then makes a striking platform at one end of the core, and finally knocks a flake off the striking platform. (Ch. 12)

linked Referring to genes located on the same chromosome. The closer together two loci are, the more likely they are to be linked. Compare *unlinked*. (Ch. 2)

locus (loci, pl.) The position that a particular gene occupies on a chromosome. (Ch. 2)

long noncoding RNA (lncRNA) RNA molecules longer than 200 nucleotides. LncRNA has many functions, including gene regulation. (Ch. 2)

lordosis The S-shaped curvature typical of the human spine. (Ch. 10)

macroevolution Evolution of new species, families, and higher taxa. Compare *microevolution*. (Ch. 4)

maladaptive Detrimental to fitness. (Ch. 3)

mandible The lower jaw. Compare *maxilla*. (Ch. 5)

marsupial A mammal that gives birth to live young that continue their development in a pouch equipped with mammary glands. Marsupials include kangaroos and opossums. (Ch. 1)

mate guarding A behavior in which the male defends his mate after copulation to prevent other males from mating with her. (Ch. 3)

mating system The form of courtship, mating, and parenting behavior that characterizes a particular species or population. An example is polygyny. (Ch. 5)

matrilineage Individuals related through the maternal line. (Ch. 7)

maxilla The upper jaw. Compare *mandible*. (Ch. 5)

meiosis The process of cell division in which haploid gametes (eggs and sperm) are created. Compare *mitosis*. (Ch. 2)

menarche First menstruation. (Ch. 15)

messenger RNA (mRNA) A form of RNA that carries specifications for protein synthesis from DNA to the ribosomes. (Ch. 2)

microevolution Evolution of populations within a species. Compare *macroevolution*. (Ch. 4)

microlith A very small stone flake. Typical of African Later Stone Age industries, microliths were probably hafted onto wood handles to make spears and axes. (Ch. 13)

microRNA (miRNA) Short segments of RNA that are involved in the translation of mRNA into protein and gene expression. Some are involved in regulating development and cell differentiation in complex organisms. (Ch. 2)

microsatellite loci Regions within DNA sequences in which short sequences of DNA are repeated multiple times—GTGTGT or ACTACTACT. They are also known as short tandem repeats. (Ch. 13)

Middle Stone Age (MSA) The stone tool industries of sub-Saharan Africa and southern and eastern Asia that existed 250 ka to 40 ka. The MSA is the counterpart of the Middle Paleolithic (Mousterian) in Europe. The MSA industries varied, but flake tools were manufactured in all of them. (Ch. 13)

mineralization (mineralized, adj.) The process by which organic material in the bones of dead animals is replaced by minerals from the surrounding rock, creating fossils. (Ch. 9)

minor marriage A form of marriage, formerly widespread in China, in which children were betrothed in infancy and then raised together in the household of the prospective groom. (Ch. 15)

mismatch hypothesis The idea that human minds are adapted to life in small-scale foraging societies and that this causes maladaptive behavior in complex, urban societies. (Ch. 16)

mitochondrial DNA (mtDNA) DNA in the mitochondria that is particularly useful for evolutionary analyses for two reasons: (1) Mitochondria are inherited only from the mother and, thus, there is no recombination, and (2) mtDNA accumulates mutations at relatively high rates, thus serving as a more accurate molecular clock for changes in the last few million years. (Ch. 12)

mitosis The process of division of somatic (normal body) cells through which new diploid cells are created. Compare *meiosis*. (Ch. 2)

Mode 1 A category of simple stone tools made by removing flakes from cores without any systematic shaping of the core. Both the flakes and the cores were probably used as tools themselves. Tools in the Oldowan industry are Mode 1 tools. (Ch. 11)

Mode 2 A category of stone tools in which cores are shaped into symmetrical bifaces by the removal of flakes. The Acheulean industry is typified by Mode 2 tools. (Ch. 11)

Mode 3 A category of stone tools made by striking large symmetrical flakes from carefully prepared stone cores by using the Levallois technique. The Mousterian industry in Europe and the Middle Stone Age industries in Africa are typified by Mode 3 tools. (Ch. 12)

Mode 4 A category of stone tools in which blades are common. Mode 4 tools are found in some Middle Stone Age industries in Africa, and they predominate in the Upper Paleolithic industries of Europe. (Ch. 13)

Mode 5 A category of stone tools in which microliths are common. The African Later Stone Age industries are typified by Mode 5 tools. (Ch. 13)

modern synthesis An explanation for the evolution of continuously varying traits that combines the theory and empirical evidence of both Mendelian genetics and Darwinism. (Ch. 3)

molars The broad, square back teeth that are generally adapted for crushing and grinding in primates. Anthropoid primates have three molars on each side of the upper and lower jaws. (Ch. 5)

molecular clock The hypothesis that genetic change occurs at a constant rate and thus can be used to measure the time elapsed since two species shared a common ancestor. The molecular clock is based on observed regularities in the rate of genetic change along different phylogenetic lines. (Ch. 4)

monozygotic twins Twins that result from the fertilization of one egg by a single sperm. Early in development the fertilized egg splits to create two zygotes. Compare *dizygotic twins*. (Ch. 14)

morphology The form and structure of an organism; also a field of study that focuses on the form and structure of organisms. (Ch. 1)

most recent common ancestor (MRCA) The most immediate ancestor of individuals belonging to two different species or lineages. (Ch. 13)

Mousterian industry A stone tool industry characterized by points, side scrapers, and denticulates (tools with small toothlike notches on the working edge) but an absence of hand axes. The Mousterian is generally associated with Neanderthals in Europe. (Ch. 12)

mRNA See *messenger RNA*.

MSA See *Middle Stone Age*.

mtDNA See *mitochondrial DNA*.

multiparous A female who has had more than one pregnancy. (Ch. 6)

mutation A spontaneous change in the chemical structure of DNA. (Ch. 3)

natural selection The process that produces adaptation. Natural selection is based on three postulates: (1) The availability of resources is limited; (2) organisms vary in the ability to survive and reproduce; and (3) traits that influence survival and reproduction are transmitted from parents to offspring. When these three postulates hold, natural selection produces adaptation. (Ch. 1)

Neanderthal A form of archaic *Homo sapiens* found in western Eurasia from about 127 ka to about 30 ka. Neanderthals had large brains and elongated skulls with very large faces. They were also characterized by very robust bodies. (Ch. 12)

negative selection Selection against novel mutants that preserves the existing genotype. (Ch. 14)

negatively correlated Describing a statistical relationship between two variables in which larger values of one variable tend to co-occur with smaller values of the other variable. For example, the size and number of seeds produced by an individual plant are negatively correlated in some plant populations. Compare *positively correlated*. (Ch. 3)

neocortex Part of the cerebral cortex; generally thought to be most closely associated with problem solving and behavioral flexibility. In mammals, the neocortex covers virtually the entire surface of the forebrain. (Ch. 8)

neocortex ratio The size of the neocortex in relation to the rest of the brain. (Ch. 8)

neotony The retention of juvenile traits into later stages of life. (Ch. 14)

niche The way of life, or "trade," of a particular species—what foods it eats and how the food is acquired. (Ch. 4)

NIDD See *non–insulin-dependent diabetes*.

nocturnal Active only during the night. Compare *diurnal*. (Ch. 5)

noncoding RNA Molecules of RNA that do not code for proteins, including transfer RNA, ribosomal RNA, and microRNAs. (Ch. 2)

non–insulin-dependent diabetes (NIDD) A form of diabetes in which cells of the body do not respond properly to levels of insulin in the blood. NIDD has a genetic basis. (Ch. 14)

nonsynonymous substitution Substitution of one nucleotide for another in a DNA sequence that changes the amino acid coded for. (Ch. 14)

nucleus (nuclei, pl.) The distinct part of the cell that contains the chromosomes. Eukaryotes (fungi, protozoans, plants, and animals) all have nucleated cells; prokaryotes (bacteria) do not. (Ch. 2)

observational learning A form of learning in which animals observe the behavior of other individuals and thereby learn to perform a new behavior. Compare *social facilitation*. (Ch. 16)

occipital torus A horizontal ridge at the back of the skull in *Homo ergaster*, *Homo erectus*, and archaic *Homo sapiens*. (Ch. 11)

Oceania A region of the South Pacific that includes Polynesia, Melanesia, and Micronesia. (Ch. 14)

Oldowan A set of simple stone tools made by removing flakes from cores without any systematic shaping of the core. Both the flakes and the cores were probably used as tools. This industry is found in Africa at sites that date from about 2.5 Ma. (Ch. 11)

olfaction (olfactory, adj.) The sense of smell. (Ch. 5)

opposable Most primates, including humans, have an opposable thumb, which means that they touch all of their other fingers on the same hand with the thumb. Most primates, but not humans, also have an opposable big toe and can bend their big toe to touch the other toes on the same foot. (Ch. 5)

organelle A portion of the cell that is enclosed in a membrane and has a specific function; examples are mitochondria and the nucleus. (Ch. 2)

out-group A taxonomic group that is related to a group of interest and can be used to determine which traits are ancestral and which are derived. (Ch. 4)

outbred mating Mating between unrelated individuals. Compare *inbred mating*. (Ch. 15)

pair bonding A mating system in which a male and female form an exclusive mating relationship. Most primates that live in pairs mate mainly with one another but may sometimes mate with outsiders. Thus, most pair-living primates are not strictly monogamous. (Ch. 5)

paleontologist A scientist who studies fossilized remains of plant and animal species. (Ch. 9)

Pangaea The massive single continent that contained all of Earth's dry land until about 120 Ma. (Ch. 9)

parapatric speciation A two-step process of speciation in which (1) selection causes the differentiation of geographically separate, partially isolated populations of a species and (2) later the populations become reproductively isolated as a result of reinforcement. Compare *allopatric speciation* and *sympatric speciation*. (Ch. 4)

parent–offspring conflict Conflict that arises between parents and their offspring over how much the parents will invest in the offspring. These conflicts stem from the opposing genetic interests of parents and offspring. (Ch. 7)

pastoralists People who make a living herding livestock. (Ch. 14)

phenotype The observable characteristics of organisms. Individuals with the same phenotype may have different genotypes. Compare *genotype*. (Ch. 2)

phenotypic matching A mechanism for kin recognition in which animals assess similarities between themselves and others. (Ch. 7)

phylogeny The evolutionary relationships among a group of species, usually diagrammed as a "family tree." (Ch. 4)

pick A triangle-shaped biface stone tool found in Acheulean sites. (Ch. 11)

placental mammal A mammal that gives birth to live young that developed in the uterus and were nourished by blood delivered to a placenta. (Ch. 1)

plastic Describing traits that are very sensitive to environmental conditions during development, resulting in different phenotypes in different environments. Compare *canalized*. (Ch. 3)

pleiotropic effects Phenotypic effects created by genes that influence multiple characters. (Ch. 3)

plesiadapiform Any member of a group of primatelike mammals that lived during the Paleocene (65 Ma to 55 Ma). Although many paleontologists do not consider them to have been primates, the plesiadapiforms probably were similar to the earliest primates that lived around the same time. (Ch. 9)

polyandry A mating system in which a single female forms a stable pair bond with two males at the same time. Polyandry is generally rare among mammals, but it is thought to occur in some species of marmosets and tamarins. Compare *polygyny*. (Ch. 5)

polygyny A mating system in which a single male mates with many females. Polygyny is the most common

mating system among primate species. Compare *polyandry*. (Ch. 5)

population genetics The branch of biology dealing with the processes that change the genetic composition of populations through time. (Ch. 3)

porphyria variegata A genetic disease caused by a dominant gene in which carriers of the gene develop a severe reaction to certain anesthetics. (Ch. 14)

positively correlated Describing a statistical relationship between two variables in which larger values of one variable tend to co-occur with larger values of the other variable. For example, in human populations the height and weight of individuals are positively correlated. Compare *negatively correlated*. (Ch. 3)

positively selected Describing selection that favors new genotypes and thus leads to genetic change. (Ch. 14)

postcranium (postcrania, pl.; postcranial, adj.) The skeleton excluding the skull. (Ch. 9)

potassium–argon dating A radiometric method of dating the age of a rock or mineral by measuring the rate at which potassium-40, an unstable isotope of potassium, is transformed into argon. This method can be used to date volcanic rocks that are at least 500,000 years old. (Ch. 9)

prehensile Describing the ability of hands, feet, or tails to grasp objects, such as food items or branches. (Ch. 5)

premolars The teeth that lie between the canines and molars. (Ch. 5)

pressure flaking A method for finishing stone tools. The toolmaker presses the edge of the tool with a sharp item, such as a piece of bone or antler, to remove small flakes. (Ch. 13)

primary structure The sequence of amino acids that make up a protein. (Ch. 2)

primiparous Refers to a female who has given birth for the first time. (Ch. 6)

proconsulid Any member of a group of early Miocene hominoids that includes the genus *Proconsul*. (Ch. 9)

prokaryotes Organisms that lack a cell nucleus or separate chromosomes. Bacteria are prokaryotes. Compare *eukaryotes*. (Ch. 2)

protein A large molecule that consists of a long chain of amino acids. Many proteins are enzyme catalysts; others perform structural functions. (Ch. 2)

protein-coding genes Genes that encode instructions for making proteins. (Ch. 2)

Punnett square A diagram that uses gene (or allele) frequencies to calculate the genotypic frequencies for the next generation. (Ch. 2)

quadrupedal Describing locomotion in which the animal moves on all four limbs. Compare *bipedal*. (Ch. 4)

radioactive decay Spontaneous change from one isotope of an element to another isotope of the same element or to an entirely different element. Radioactive decay occurs at a constant rate that can be measured precisely in the laboratory. (Ch. 9)

radiocarbon dating See *carbon-14 dating*. (Ch. 9)

radiometric method Any dating method that takes advantage of the fact that isotopes of certain elements change spontaneously from one isotope to another at a constant rate. (Ch. 9)

rain shadow An area of reduced rainfall found on the lee (downwind) side of large mountains and mountain ranges. (Ch. 9)

recessive Describing an allele that is expressed in the phenotype only when it is in the homozygous state. Compare *dominant*. (Ch. 2)

reciprocal altruism A theory that altruism can evolve if pairs of individuals take turns giving and receiving altruism during many encounters. (Ch. 7)

recombination The creation of new genotypes as a result of the random segregation of chromosomes and of crossing over. (Ch. 2)

redirected aggression A behavior in which the recipient of aggression threatens or attacks a previously uninvolved party. For instance, if A attacks B and B then attacks C, B's attacks are an example of redirected aggression. (Ch. 8)

regulatory gene A DNA sequence that regulates the expression of a structural gene, often by binding to an activator or repressor. (Ch. 2)

reinforcement The process in which selection acts against the likelihood of hybrids occurring between members of two phenotypically distinctive populations, leading to the evolution of mechanisms that prevent interbreeding. (Ch. 4)

repressor A protein that decreases transcription of a regulated gene. Compare *activator*. (Ch. 2)

reproductive isolation A relationship in which no gene flow occurs between two populations. (Ch. 4)

ribonucleic acid See *RNA*. (Ch. 2)

ribosome A small organelle composed of protein and nucleic acid that temporarily holds together the messenger RNA and transfer RNAs during protein synthesis. (Ch. 2)

RNA Ribonucleic acid, a long molecule that plays several important roles in protein synthesis. RNA differs from DNA in that it has a slightly different chemical backbone and it contains the base uracil instead of thymine. (Ch. 2)

rock shelter A site sheltered by an overhang of rock. (Ch. 12)

sagittal crest A sharp fin of bone that runs along the midline of the skull that increases the area available for the attachment of chewing muscles. (Ch. 10)

sampling variation The variation in the composition of small samples drawn from a large population. (Ch. 3)

scapula (scapulae, pl.) Shoulder blade. (Ch. 12)

secondary compounds Toxic (poisonous) chemical compounds produced by plants and concentrated in plant tissues to prevent animals from eating the plant. (Ch. 5)

selection–mutation balance An equilibrium that occurs when the rate at which selection removes a deleterious gene is balanced by the rate at which mutation introduces that gene. The frequency of genes at selection–mutation balance is typically quite low. (Ch. 14)

selective sweep A process in which one allele increases in a population as a result of positive selection. (Ch. 14)

sex ratio The number of individuals of one sex in relation to the number of the opposite sex. By convention, sex ratios are generally expressed as the number of males to the number of females. (Ch. 3)

sexual dimorphism Differences in body size or morphology between sexually mature males and females. (Ch. 5)

sexual selection A form of natural selection that results from differential mating success in one sex. In mammals, sexual selection usually occurs in males and may be due to male–male competition. (Ch. 6)

sexual selection infanticide hypothesis A hypothesis postulating that infanticide has been favored by sexual selection because males who kill unweaned infants can enhance their own reproductive prospects if they (1) kill infants whose deaths hasten their mothers' resumption of cycling, (2) do not kill their own infants, and (3) can mate with the mothers of the infants that they kill. (Ch. 6)

sickle-cell anemia A severe form of anemia that afflicts people who are homozygous for the sickle-cell gene. (Ch. 2)

single-nucleotide polymorphism (SNP, pronounced "snip") Occurs when members of a population differ at a particular nucleotide position in the genome. (Ch. 14)

SLI See *specific language impairment*.

SNP See *single-nucleotide polymorphism*.

social facilitation The situation that occurs when the performance of a behavior by older individuals increases the probability that younger individuals will acquire that behavior on their own. Social facilitation does not mean that young individuals copy the behavior of older individuals. For example, the feeding behavior of older individuals may bring younger individuals in contact with the foods that adults are eating and, therefore, increase the chance that younger individuals acquire a preference for those foods. Compare *observational learning*. (Ch. 16)

social intelligence hypothesis The hypothesis that the relatively sophisticated cognitive abilities of higher primates are the outcome of selective pressures that favored intelligence as a means to gain advantages in social groups. (Ch. 8)

social organization The size, age–sex composition, and degree of cohesiveness of primate social groups. (Ch. 5)

solitary A term used for animals that do not live in social groups and do not form regular associations with conspecifics. (Ch. 5)

species (sing. and pl.) A group of organisms classified together at the lowest level of the taxonomic hierarchy. Biologists disagree about how to define a species. See *biological species concept* and *ecological species concept*. (Ch. 1)

specific language impairment (SLI) A family of language disorders in which the affected person experiences difficulty using language but is of otherwise normal intelligence. Evidence suggests that at least some cases of SLI are hereditary. (Ch. 14)

spliceosomes Organelles that splice the mRNA in eukaryotes after the introns have been snipped out. (Ch. 2)

stabilizing selection Selection pressures that favor average phenotypes. Stabilizing selection reduces the amount of variation in the population but does not alter the mean value of the trait. (Ch. 1)

stasis A state or period of stability during which little or no evolutionary change in a lineage occurs. (Ch. 1)

stereoscopic vision Vision in which three-dimensional images are produced because each eye sends a signal of the visual image to both hemispheres in the brain. Stereoscopic vision requires binocular vision. (Ch. 5)

strategy A complex of behaviors deployed in a specific functional context, such as mating, parenting, or foraging. (Ch. 6)

stratum (strata, pl.) A geological layer. (Ch. 9)

strepsirrhine Any member of the group containing lemurs and lorises. The system classifying primates into haplorrhines and strepsirrhines is a cladistic alternative to the evolutionary systematic taxonomy, in which primates are divided into prosimians and anthropoids, and tarsiers are grouped with prosimians. Compare *haplorrhine*. (Ch. 5)

subnasal prognathism The condition in which the part of the face below the nose is pushed out. (Ch. 10)

superfamily The taxonomic level that lies between infraorder and family. An infraorder may contain several superfamilies, and a superfamily may contain several families. For example, humans are a member of the superfamily Hominoidea, which contains the families Hominidae and Pongidae. (Ch. 4)

sutures Wavy joints between bones that mesh together and are separated by fibrous tissue. (Ch. 12)

sympatric speciation A hypothesis that speciation can result from selective pressures favoring different phenotypes within a population without positing

geographic isolation as a factor. Compare *allopatric speciation* and *parapatric speciation*. (Ch. 4)

synonymous substitution Substitution of one nucleotide for another in a DNA sequence that does not change the amino acid coded for. (Ch. 14)

systematics A branch of biology that is concerned with the procedures for constructing phylogenies. Compare *taxonomy*. (Ch. 4)

tapetum (tapeta, pl.) A layer behind the retina in some organisms that reflects light. (Ch. 9)

taphonomy The study of the processes that affect the state of the remains of an organism from the time the organism dies until it is fossilized. (Ch. 11)

taurodont root A single broad tooth root in molars, resulting from the fusion of three roots. Taurodont roots were characteristic of Neanderthals. (Ch. 12)

taxonomy A branch of biology that is concerned with the use of phylogenies for naming and classifying organisms. Compare *systematics*. (Ch. 4)

temporalis muscle A large muscle involved in chewing. The temporalis muscles attach to the side of the cranium and to the mandible. (Ch. 10)

terrestrial Active predominantly on the ground. Compare *arboreal*. (Ch. 4)

territory A fixed area occupied by animals that defend the boundaries against intrusion by other individuals or groups of the same species. (Ch. 5)

tertiary structure The three-dimensional folded shape of a protein. (Ch. 2)

testes (testis, sing.) The male organs responsible for producing sperm. (Ch. 4)

theory of mind The capacity to be aware of the thoughts, knowledge, or perceptions of other individuals. A theory of mind may be a prerequisite for deception, imitation, teaching, and empathy. Researchers generally think that humans, and possibly chimpanzees, are the only primates to possess a theory of mind. (Ch. 8)

thermoluminescence dating A technique used to date crystalline materials by measuring the density of trapped electrons in the crystal lattice. (Ch. 9)

third-party relationships Relationships among other individuals. For example, monkeys and apes are believed to understand something about the nature of kinship relationships among other group members. (Ch. 8)

thymine One of the four bases of the DNA molecule. The complementary base of thymine is adenine. (Ch. 2)

torque A twisting force that generates rotary motion. (Ch. 10)

toxin A chemical compound that is poisonous or toxic. (Ch. 3)

trait A characteristic of an organism. (Ch. 1)

transfer RNA (tRNA) A form of RNA that facilitates protein synthesis by first binding to amino acids in the cytoplasm and then binding to the appropriate site on the mRNA molecule. There is at least one distinct form of tRNA for each amino acid. (Ch. 2)

transitive Describing a property of triadic (three-way) relationships in which the relationships between the first and second elements and the second and third elements automatically determine the relationship between the first and third elements. For example, if A is greater than B and B is greater than C, then A is greater than C. In many primate species, dominance relationships are transitive. (Ch. 6)

transposable elements Segments of DNA that move from one location to another within the genome of a single individual. (Ch. 14)

tRNA See *transfer RNA.*

Uluzzian A stone tool industry found in Italy and the Balkans at sites that date to after 45 ka. The Uluzzian industry has characteristics of both Middle and Upper Paleolithic industries. (Ch. 13)

unlinked Referring to genes on different chromosomes. Compare *linked.* (Ch. 2)

Upper Paleolithic The period from about 45 ka to about 10 ka in Europe, North Africa, and parts of Asia. The tool kits from this period are dominated by blades. (Ch. 13)

uracil One of the four bases of the RNA molecule. Uracil corresponds to the base thymine in DNA; as with thymine, its complementary base is adenine. (Ch. 2)

uranium–lead dating A method of dating zirconium crystals in igneous rocks that is based on the ratio of uranium to lead. This method can be used to date stalactites, stalagmites, and flow stone formed by precipitation in limestone caves and has been particularly useful for dating hominin remains found in caves in South Africa. (Ch. 9)

variant The particular form of a trait. For example, blue eyes, brown eyes, and gray eyes are variants of the trait eye color. (Ch. 2)

variation among groups Differences in the average phenotype or genotype between groups. (Ch. 14)

variation within groups Differences in phenotype or genotype between individuals in a group. (Ch. 14)

viviparity Giving birth to live young. (Ch. 5)

zygomatic arch A cheekbone. (Ch. 9)

zygote The cell formed by the union of an egg and a sperm. (Ch. 2)

CREDITS

Whittaker/Alamy Stock Photo; **Figure 5.26**: Satellite image by DigitalGlobe; **Figure 5.27a**: Robert Boyd; **Figure 5.27b**: Robert Boyd; **Figure 5.27c**: David Tipling Photo Library/Alamy Stock Photo; **Figures 5.27d, e**: Robert Boyd; **Figures 5.28a–c**: Robert Boyd; **Figure 5.33**: Tim Davenport/Wildlife Conservation Society.

CHAPTER 6

Photos: **Figure 6.CO**: Roine Magnusson/age fotostock; **Figure 6.1**: Joan Silk; **Figure 6.2**: Arco Images GmbH/Alamy; **Figure 6.3**: Kathy West; **Figure 6.4**: Mark Conlin/Getty Images; **Figure 6.6**: Kathy West; **Figure 6.7**: Yasuo Tomishige/The Asahi Shimbun via Getty Images; **Figure 6.12b**: Bazuki Muhammed/Reuters/Newscom; **Figure 6.13**: K. G. Preston-Mafham/Premaphotos Wildlife; **Figure 6.16**: Carola Borries; **Figure 6.18**: Joan Silk; **Figure 6.20a**; bluelake/Shutterstock; **Figure 6.20b**: Matt Gibson/Shutterstock; **Figure 6.21a**: Robert Boyd/Joan Silk; **Figure 6.21b**: Robert Boyd; **Figure 6.22**: Joan Silk; **Figure 6.25b**: Martin Harvey/Photolibrary/Getty Images; **Figure 6.26**: Toni Angermayer/Science Source; **Figure 6.28**: nikpal/iStock/Getty Images Plus; **Figures 6.30 and 6.36**: Joan Silk.

Drawn art: **Figure 6.5**: Figure 10.3 from *The Evolution of Primate Societies* by John C. Mitani, et al. © 2012 by The University of Chicago. Reprinted by permission of the University of Chicago Press; **Figure 6.10**: Figure 3 from S. C. Alberts, et al. (2013). "Reproductive aging patterns in primates reveal that humans are distinct." *Proceedings of the National Academy of Sciences* 110(33), 13440–1344. Reprinted with permission; **Figure 6.19**: Figure from L. Barrett & S. P. Henzi (2000). "Are baboon infants Sir Philip Sydney's offspring?" *Ethology* 106(7), 645–658. Reprinted by permission of John Wiley & Sons; **Figure 6.34a**: Figure from M. Heistermann, et al. (2001). "Loss of oestrus concealed ovulation and paternity confusion in free-ranging Hanuman langurs." *Proceedings of the Royal Society of London. Series B: Biological Sciences* 268:1484, 2445–2451. Reprinted by permission of the Royal Society; **Figure 6.34b**: Figure from M. Heistermann, et al. (2001). "Loss of oestrus concealed ovulation and paternity confusion in free-ranging Hanuman langurs." *Proceedings of the Royal Society of London. Series B: Biological Sciences* 268:1484, 2445–2451. Reprinted by permission of the Royal Society; **Figure 6.35**: Figure 2 from E. K. Roberts, et al. (2012). "A Bruce effect in wild geladas." *Science* 335(6073), 1222–1225. Reprinted with permission from AAAS.

CHAPTER 7

Photos: **Figure 7.CO**: Anup Shah/Nature Picture Library; **Figure 7.1**: K. G. Preston-Mafham/Premaphotos Wildlife; **Figure 7.2**: AP Photo/Rajesh Nirgude; **Figure 7.3**: Joan Silk; **Figure 7.8a**: Kathy West; **Figure 7.8b**: Joan Silk; **Figures 7.9a, b**: Joan Silk; **Figure 7.11a**: A. J. Kazem & A. Widdig (2013). "Visual phenotype matching: cues to paternity are present in rhesus macaque faces." *PLOS One* 8(2), e55846. Reprinted by permission of the Public Library of Science; **Figure 7.12a**: Adrian Hepworth/Alamy Stock Photo; **Figure 7.12b**: Marina Cords; **Figure 7.12c**: Joan Silk; **Figure 7.12d**: Robert Ross/Getty Images; **Figure 7.14**: Joan Silk; **Figure 7.17b**: Joan Silk; **Figure 7.18**: Terry Whitaker/Frank Lake Picture Agency/Corbis via Getty Images; **Figure 7.19**: Joan Silk.

Drawn art: **Figure 7.11b**: Figure from A. J. Kazem & A. Widdig (2013). "Visual phenotype matching: cues to paternity are present in rhesus macaque faces." *PLOS One* 8(2), e55846. Reprinted by permission of the Public Library of Science.

CHAPTER 8

Photos: **Figure 8.CO**: Frans Lanting/National Geographic Creative; **Figure 8.1**: Bettmann/Corbis via Getty Images; **Figure 8.2**: W. Perry Conway/Corbis via Getty Images; **Figure 8.3**: Joan Silk; **Figure 8.4**: Gallo Images/Corbis via Getty Images; **Figure 8.6a**: Fiona Rogers/Visuals Unlimited/Getty Images; **Figure 8.7**: Michael Nichols/National Geographic/Getty Images; **Figure 8.8**: Wolfgang Kohler, The Mentality of Apes. Routledge & Kegan Paul, Ltd., London, 1927; **Figure 8.9a**: Frans Lanting/Mint Images/age fotostock; **Figure 8.9b**: woddle1000/iStock/Getty Images Plus; **Figure 8.11a**: Mary Beth Angelo/Science Source; **Figure 8.11b**: Michael Nichols/National Geographic Creative; **Figure 8.12**: Robert Boyd & Joan Silk; **Figure 8.13**: Joan Silk; **Figure 8.15a**: Joan Silk; **Figure 8.15b**: Ross/Tom Stack Associates/Alamy Stock Photo; **Figure 8.16**: E. Menzel; **Figure 8.19**: E. Hermann, J. Call, M. V. Hernandez-Lloreda, B. Hare, and M. Tomasello (2007). "Humans Have Evolved Specialized Skills of Social Cognition: The Cultural Intelligence Hypothesis." *Science* 317:1360–1366.

Drawn art: **Figure 8.5a, b**: Figure 10.11 from *The Evolution of Primate Societies* by John C. Mitani, et al. © 2012 by The University of Chicago. Reprinted by permission of the University of Chicago Press; **Figure 8.18a, b**: Reprinted from *Current Biology*, Vol. 15, Issue 5, Jonathan I. Flombaum and Laurie R. Santos, "Rhesus Monkeys Attribute Perceptions to Others," pp. 447–452, Copyright © 2005 Elsevier Ltd., with permission from Elsevier.

CHAPTER 9

Photos: **Figure 9.CO**: Magdalena Rehova/Alamy; **Figure 9.3a**: kjekol/iStock/Getty Images Plus; **Figure 9.7**: Doug M. Boyer/Duke University Department of Evolutionary Anthropology; **Figure 9.12**: Shaun Curry/AFP/Getty Images; **Figure 9.21**: Christophe Ratier/NHPA.UK; **Figure 9.22**: Photograph courtesy Laura MacLatchy. MacLatchy, L. (2004). "The Oldest Ape." *Evolutionary Anthropology* 13: 90–103. **Figure 9.26**: Photo courtesy Salvador Moyà-Solà. Salvador Moyà-Solà, Meike Köhler, David M. Alba, Isaac Casanovas-Vilar, Jordi Galindo. "Pierolapithecus catalaunicus, a New Middle Miocene Great Ape from Spain." *Science* 19 Nov. 2004: Vol. 306, Issue 5700, pp. 1339–1344 DOI: 10.1126/science.1103094.

Drawn art: **Figure 9.1a, b**: Figure from *Mammal Evolution: An Illustrated Guide* by R. J. G. Savage, pp. 38–39, 1986. Copyright © 1986 by Facts On File, Inc., an imprint of Infobase Publishing. Reprinted with permission of the publisher; **Figure 9.2**: Figure 5.3 from Robert D. Martin. *Primate Origins and Evolution: A Phylogenetic Reconstruction.* © 1990 R. D. Martin. Reprinted by permission of Princeton University Press; **Figure 9.7**: Artwork of Carpolestes simpsoni by Doug M. Boyer, from "Paleontology: Primate Origins Nailed" by Eric J. Sargis, *Science* 298, Nov. 22, 2002, p. 1564. Reprinted with permission; **Figure 9.8**: Figure from *The Cambridge Encyclopedia of Human Evolution*, edited by Steve Jones, Robert Martin, and

David Pilbeam, p. 200. Copyright © Cambridge University Press 1992. Reprinted with the permission of Cambridge University Press; **Figure 9.10a, b**: Figure 3 from Kenneth D. Rose, "The Earliest Primates," *Evolutionary Anthropology*, Vol. 3, Issue 5 (1994): 159–173. Copyright © 1994 Wiley-Liss, Inc., A Wiley Company. Reprinted with permission of Wiley-Liss, Inc., a subsidiary of John Wiley & Sons, Inc.; **Figure 9.11a, b**: This figure was published in *Primate Adaptation and Evolution*, J. G. Fleagle, (Academic Press, 1988). Copyright © 1988 Elsevier Ltd. Reprinted by permission; **Figure 9.23**: This figure was published in *Primate Adaptation and Evolution*, J. G. Fleagle, (Academic Press, 1988). Copyright © 1988 Elsevier Ltd. Reprinted by permission; **Figure 9.24**: Figure 8.21 from *Principles of Human Evolution, 2nd Edition* by Roger Lewin and Robert Foley. © 2004 by Blackwell Science Ltd, a Blackwell Publishing company. Reproduced with permission of Blackwell Publishing Ltd.; **Figure 9.25**: Figure 2.23 from Robert D. Martin. *Primate Origins and Evolution: A Phylogenetic Reconstruction.* © 1990 R. D. Martin. Reprinted by permission of Princeton University Press.

CHAPTER 10

Photos: **Figure 10.CO**: Anup Shah/Animals Animals/age fotostock; **Figure 10.4**: Sabena Jane Blackbird/Alamy Stock Photo; **Figure 10.5**: Brigitte Senuta, Martin Pickford, Dominique Gommery, Pierre Meind, Kiptalam Cheboie, Yves Coppens. "First hominid from the Miocene (Lukeino Formation, Kenya)" Comptes Rendus de l'Académie des Sciences - Series IIA - Earth and Planetary Science 332 (2001) 137–144. 2001 Académie des sciences/Éditions scientifiques et médicales Elsevier SAS. Tous droits réservés S1251-8050(01)01529-4/FL A; **Figure 10.6a**: Image courtesy Robert Eckhardt. Galik K, Senut B, Pickford M, Gommery D, Treil J, Kuperavage AJ, Eckhardt RB. "External and Internal Morphology of the BAR 1002'00 Orrorin tugenensis Femur." 2004, *Science* 305, 1450–1453; **Figure 10.6b, c**: C. Owen Lovejoy "The natural history of human gait and posture: Part 2. Hip and thigh." *Gait & Posture*, Volume 21, Issue 1, January 2005, Pages 113–124; Figure 10.7: Redrawn from Y. Haile-Selassie, G. Suwa, and T. D. White, "Late Miocene Teeth from Middle Awash, Ethiopia, and Early Hominid Dental Evolution." 2004, *Science* 05 Mar. 2004: Vol. 303, Issue 5663, pp. 1503–1505; **Figure 10.8**: Tim D. White/Provided by David Brill; **Figure 10.9**: Tim D. White & Gen Suwa/Provided by David Brill; **Figure 10.11**: C. Owen Lovejoy, Gen Suwa and colleagues/Provided by David Brill; **Figure 10.16**: National Museum of Kenya; **Figure 10.17**: Eric Lafforgue/Art in All of Us/Corbis via Getty Images; **Figure 10.18**: John Reader/Science Source; **Figure 10.19**: courtesy Professor Zeray AlemSeged/DRP; **Figure 10.20**: Yohannes Haile-Selassie, Luis Gibert, Stephanie M. Melillo, Timothy M. Ryan, Mulugeta Alene, Alan Deino, Naomi E. Levin, Gary Scott & Beverly Z. Saylor. "New species from Ethiopia further expands Middle Pliocene hominin diversity." *Nature* 521, 483–488 (28 May 2015) doi:10.1038/nature14448; **Figure 10.22**: Courtesy of Lee R. Berger and The University of The Witwatersrand; **Figure 10.28**: John Reader/Science Source; **Figure 10.29**: Martin Harvey/Getty Images; **Figure 10.30**; National Museum of Kenya; **Figure 10.33**: Album/Prisma/Newscom; **Figure 10.36**: Courtesy of Meave Leakey/National Museums of Kenya/photo by Robert Campbell.

Drawn art: **Figure 10.3**: Figure from ""The evolution of human bipedality: ecology and functional morphology," by K. D. Hunt. Reprinted by permission of the author; **Figure 10.5**: Three individual drawings, showing the angles of articulation for the knee, in lateral view: (1.) modern human; (2.) *A. afarensis*; (3.) ape. From *LUCY: The Beginnings of Humankind* by Donald C. Johanson and Maitland A. Edey. © 1981 Luba Dmytryk Gudz\Brill Atlanta. Reprinted with permission; **Figure 10.22**: Figure 4.2, © 1999 by Kathryn Cruz-Uribe, from *The Human Career: Human Biological and Cultural Origins, Second Edition* by Richard G. Klein. © 1989, 1999 by The University of Chicago. Reprinted by permission of the University of Chicago Press; **Figure 10.23**: Figure 4.24 from *The Human Career: Human Biological and Cultural Origins, Second Edition* by Richard G. Klein. © 1989, 1999 by The University of Chicago. Reprinted by permission of the University of Chicago Press; **Figure 10.34**: Figure 2 from "The Diets of Early Hominins," by Peter S. Ungar and Matt Sponheimer. *Science* 334 (6053). Reprinted with permission from AAAS.

CHAPTER 11

Photos: **Figure 11.CO**: Peter Bostrom; **Figure 11.2**: Fred Spoor, Philipp Gunz, Simon Neubauer, Stefanie Stelzer, Nadia Scott, Amandus Kwekason & M. Christopher Dean. "Reconstructed Homo habilis type OH 7 suggests deep-rooted species diversity in early Homo." *Nature* 519, 83–86 (05 March 2015) doi:10.1038/nature14224; **Figure 11.3**: Javier Trueba/MSF/Science Photo Library/Science Source; **Figure 11.9**: imageBROKER/Alamy Stock Photo; **Figure 11.10**: David Lordkipanidze, Georgian State Museum, Georgian Academy of Sciences/Leo Gabunia, Abesalom Vekua, David Lordkipanidze, Carl C. Swisher, Reid Ferring, Antje Justus, Medea Nioradze, Merab Tvalchrelidze, Susan C. Antón, Gerhard Bosinski, Olaf Jöris, Marie-A.-de Lumley, Givi Majsuradze, Aleksander Mouskhelishvili. "Earliest Pleistocene Hominid Cranial Remains from Dmanisi, Republic of Georgia: Taxonomy, Geological Setting, and Age." *Science* 12 May 2000: Vol. 288, Issue 5468, pp. 1019–1025 DOI: 10.1126/science.288.5468.1019; **Figure 11.11a**: Guram Bumbiashvili, Georgian National Museum/David Lordkipanidze, Marcia S. Ponce de León, Ann Margvelashvili, Yoel Rak, G. Philip Rightmire, Abesalom Vekua, Christoph P. E. Zollikofer. "Complete Skull from Dmanisi, Georgia, and the Evolutionary Biology of Early Homo." *Science* 18 October 2013: Vol. 342 no. 6156 pp. 326–331 DOI: 10.1126/science.1238484; **Figure 11.11b**: Jay Matternes; **Figure 11.12**: National Anthropological Archive Negative no. 01019100/Smithsonian Museum of Natural History; **Figure 11.13**: The Natural History Museum/Alamy Stock Photo; **Figures 11.14 and 11.15**: Alan Walker; **Figure 11.17**: West Turkana Archeological Project-Mission Préhistorique au Kenya; **Figure 11.21**: R. Potts, Smithsonian Institution; **Figure 11.23**: Kim Hill; **Figure 11.24**: Ariadne Van Zandbergen/Alamy Stock Photo; **Figure 11.27**: Anup Shah/Nature Picture Library; **Figures 11.30a–c**: Francesco d'Errico; **Figures 11.33b–c**: National Museum of Natural History, Smithsonian Institution, Washington, D.C. (Rdg. 1-2) Courtesy of Kathy D. Schick and Nicholas Toth, CRAFT Research Center, Indiana University; **Figure 11.34**: Biosphoto/Superstock; **Figure 11.35**: Manuel Dominguez-Rodrigo; **Figure 11.36**: National Museum of Kenya. Photograph courtesy of Alan Walker; **Figure 11.38a**: Biosphoto/Superstock; **Figure 11.38b**: James Tyrrell/

Gallo Images/Getty Images; **Figure 11.39**: Robert Boyd & Joan Silk; **Figure 11.40**: Joan Silk; **Figures 11.41 and 11.42**: Robert Boyd; **Figure 11.44**: Wendy Stone/Corbis via Getty Images.

Drawn art: **Figure 11.6**: Figure 5.10, © 1999 by Kathryn Cruz-Uribe from *The Human Career: Human Biological and Cultural Origins, Second Edition* by Richard G. Klein. © 1989, 1999 by The University of Chicago. Reprinted by permission of the University of Chicago Press; **Figure 11.7a–d**: Figures 4.2 (© 1999 by Kathryn Cruz-Uribe), 4.23, 5.10 (© 1999 by Kathryn Cruz-Uribe), 7.2 from *The Human Career: Human Biological and Cultural Origins, Second Edition* by Richard G. Klein. © 1989, 1999 by The University of Chicago. Reprinted by permission of the University of Chicago Press; **Figure 11.44**: Figure 4.41 from *The Human Career: Human Biological and Cultural Origins, Second Edition* by Richard G. Klein. © 1989, 1999 by The University of Chicago. Reprinted by permission of the University of Chicago Press; **Figure 11.46**: Figure from *The Human Career: Human Biological and Cultural Origins, Second Edition* by Richard G. Klein. © 1989, 1999 by The University of Chicago. Reprinted by permission of the University of Chicago Press.

CHAPTER 12

Photos: **Figure 12.CO**: Javier Trueba/MSF/Science Photo Library/Science Source; **Figure 12.8**: Javier Trueba/MSF/Science Photo Library/Science Source; **Figure 12.9**: William Jungers, Stony Brook University; Figure 12.10: Brumm, A., Aziz, F. van den Bergh, G.D., Morwood, M.J., Moore, M.W., Kurniawan, I., Hobbs, D.R. Fullagar, R. "Early stone technology on Flores and its implications for *Homo floresiensis*," 2006. *Nature* 441: 624–628; **Figure 12.12**: Javier Trueba/MSF/Science Photo Library/Science Source; **Figure 12.14**: Kennis& Kennis/Natural History Museum, London; **Figure 12.18a**: Damian Kuzdak/Getty Images; **Figure 12.18b**: Aleksander Bolbot/Alamy Stock Photo; **Figure 12.19**: Len Rue, Jr./Science Source; **Figures 12.20 and 12.21**: Joao Zilhao; **Figure 12.22**: James Steele, Margaret Clegg, and Sandra Martelli, "Comparative Morphology of the Hominin and African Ape Hyoid Bone, a Possible Marker of the Evolution of Speech." *Human Biology* 2013 85 (5), 639–672; **Figure 12.23**: Erik Trinkaus; **Figure 12.24**: Joan Silk; **Figure 12.27**: Eric Delson; **Figure 12.28**: Berger, Lee et al. "*Homo naledi*, a new species of the genus *Homo* from the Dinaledi Chamber, South Africa" eLife 2015;4:e09560. https://elifesciences.org/content/4/e09560/article-info CC by 4.0 Attribution; **Figure 12.29**: Natural History Museum, London/Science Photo Library/Science Source.

Drawn art: **Figure 12.3a, b**: Figures 5.22, 5.26, © 1999 by Kathryn Cruz-Uribe, from *The Human Career: Human Biological and Cultural Origins, Second Edition* by Richard G. Klein. © 1989, 1999 by The University of Chicago. Reprinted by permission of the University of Chicago Press; **Figure 12.5**: Figure 6.24 from *The Human Career: Human Biological and Cultural Origins, Second Edition* by Richard G. Klein. © 1989, 1999 by The University of Chicago. Reprinted by permission of the University of Chicago Press; **Figure 12.6**: Figure 5.32, © 1999 by Kathryn Cruz-Uribe, from *The Human Career: Human Biological and Cultural Origins, Second Edition* by Richard G. Klein. © 1989, 1999 by The University of Chicago. Reprinted by permission of the University of Chicago Press; **Figure 12.13**:

Figure 6.48, © 1999 by Kathryn Cruz-Uribe, from *The Human Career: Human Biological and Cultural Origins, Second Edition* by Richard G. Klein. © 1989, 1999 by The University of Chicago. Reprinted by permission of the University of Chicago Press.

CHAPTER 13

Photos: **Figure 13.CO**: Javier Trueba/MSF/Science Source; **Figure 13.3**: Housed in National Museum of Ethiopia, Addis Ababa. Photo ©2001 David L. Brill/Brill, Atlanta; **Figure 13.4**: Image courtesy of Prof Christopher Henshilwood/University of Bergen, Norway; **Figure 13.5a**: Curtis Marean/Institute of Human Origins, ASU; Figure 13.5b: Antiquity Publications Ltd/Figure 3 from "Early Mesolithic flint-tipped arrows from Sweden." Lars Larsson & Arne Sjöström, *Antiquity* Volume 085 Issue 330 December 2011/National Heritage Board/Riksantkvarieämbetet; **Figure 13.7**: The Granger Collection, NYC; **Figure 13.8**: Figure 3 from Bouzouggar, A. et al. (2007). "82,000-year-old shell beads from North Africa and implications for the origins of modern human behavior." *PNAS* 104:9964–9969; **Figure 13.9**: Pierre-Jean Texier, Diepkloof Project (MAE), CNRS, UMR 5199-PACEA/Redrawn from Figure 1 in Texier et al. (2009). "A Howieson's Poort tradition of engraving ostrich eggshell containers dated to 60,000 years ago at Diekloopf Rock Shelter, South Africa." *PNAS* 107, 6181; **Figure 13.10**: Erlend Eidsvik/Centre for Development Studies/University of Bergen; **Figure 13.11**: Liu W, Martinon-Torres M, Cai Y-j, Xing S, Tong H-w, Pei S-w, Sier MJ, Wu X-h, Edwards RL, Cheng H, Li Y-y, Yang X-x, de Castro JMB, Wu X-j. "The earliest unequivocally modern humans in southern China." 2015. *Nature* 526, 696–699 (29 October 2015) doi:10.1038/nature15696; **Figure 13.19**: figure 4 from Mellars, P. et al. "Genetic and archaeological perspectives on the initial modern human colonization of southern Asia." *PNAS* 2013 v110 no. 26 10699–10704 and Mellars P., "Going east: New genetic and archaeological perspectives on the modern human colonization of Eurasia." 2006, *Science* 313(5788):796–800.13; **Figure 13.21**: From V. V. Pitulko et al., "The Yana RHS Site: Humans in the Arctic before the Last Glacial Maximum," 2004, *Science* 303:52–56; **Figure 13.24**: Jean-Michel Labat/AUSCAPE All rights reserved; **Figure 13.29**: Jeff Pachoud/AFP/Getty Images; **Figure 13.30**: INTERFOTO/Alamy Stock Photo.

Drawn art: **Figure 13.1**: Figure 7.2 from *The Human Career: Human Biological and Cultural Origins, Second Edition* by Richard G. Klein. © 1989, 1999 by The University of Chicago. Reprinted by permission of the University of Chicago Press; **Figure 13.6**: Drawing: "An atlatl is a tool that lengthens the arm," from The Testimony of Hands: Atlatls (http://hands.unm.edu/atlatls.html). Reprinted by permission of James Dixon; **Figure 13.19**: Figure from P. Mellars (2006) "Going East: New genetic and archaeological perspectives on the modern human colonization of Eurasia." *Science* 313(5788), 796–800. Reprinted with permission from AAAS; **Figure 13.26**: Figure 34.8 from Soffer, Olga, "The Middle to Upper Patheolithic Transition on the Russian Plain," from Mellars, Paul; *The Human Revolution*. © 1989 Edinburgh University Press. Reprinted by permission of Edinburgh University Press and Princeton University Press; **Figure 13.27**: Figure 7.22 from *The Human Career: Human Biological and Cultural Origins, Second Edition* by Richard G. Klein. © 1989, 1999 by The University of Chicago. Reprinted by

INDEX

Page numbers in *italics* refer to figures and tables.

abductor muscles, 236, *237*
Abzhanov, Arkhat, 61
accession numbers, 239
Aché, 277, *277*, *278*, 280, 417, *417*
Acheulean tool industry, 273–74, 302, 326, 345
achondroplasia, 12
activator protein, 47, *48*
active metabolism, energy requirement and, 126
activity patterns in primates, 130, *130*
Adapidae, *217*, 217–18, *218*
adaptation, 91, 127, 209–10, 389
  behavior and, 65–66, 326–27
  competition and, 11–12
  complex, 12–17
  constraints on, 68–75
  cooperation and, 417–18
  correlated characters and, 68–70
  culture as, 414–15
  before Darwin, 3–5
  Darwin on, 5–6, 11–12, 60–61, 62, 143, 209
  dietary, *70*, 70–71
  digestive, *117*
  disequilibrium and, 70–71
  eyes and, 4, 14–15, *15*
  genetics in, 62, 63, 67–68
  individual selection and, 11–12
  local *vs.* optimal, 74–75
  postulates of, 6
  by primates, 119
  sexual selection and, 155
  variation and, 6, 12–17
  in variation maintenance, 63–65
adaptive radiation, *90*, 90–91
adenine, 38, *39*, 49
Aegyptopithecus, 227
Aegyptopithecus zeuxis, *219*, 221, *221*
Afar depression, Ethiopia, 246
affiliative contacts, 179, *181*
Africa, 134, 209, *209*, 210, *210*, 217, 218, 222, 226, 375, 380, 382, 408
  anatomically modern humans in, 300, 306, 316, 323–26, *325*, 333
  biological habitats of, *299*
  decreased genetic variation and increased distance from, 337, *337*, 338, *338*
  deforestation in, 139, *139*
  East, 170, *209*, 214, 226, 228, 235, 246, 251, 262, 284, 329

East African Rift, 226
  emergence of *H. sapiens*, 320, *320*
  H. erectus in, 297
  H. heidelbergensis in, *300*, 300–3, *301*
  hominin species in, 234, 261
  hominoid evolution in, 227–29
  Kalahari Desert of, *277*, 398
  lactase persistence in, 368
  Middle Stone Age in, 327
  Miocene climate of, 226, 228
  Mode 2 tools in, 275
  North, 219, 221
  ornaments and decorative carving in, *329*, 329–30, *330*
  patterns of genetic variation in, *372*, 372–73, 380, *381*
  Pleistocene climate of, 262, *262*, 298–99
  primate conservation, 137
  primates in, 123, *124*, 223
  route and timing of human expansion out of, 318, *319*, 343–44
  savannas in, *209*
  tool technologies and hominin invasion to Eurasia from, 275, *275*
  West, 137, 139, 269, *270*, 312, 360, 361, 364, 382, *382*
African Americans, 380
African ancestry, 382, *382*
African wild dogs, 418
Afrikaners, 372
Afropithecus, *227*
age at reproduction, *253*
aggression, redirected, 198
aging. *see* senescence
Agricultural Experiment Station, University of Illinois, 64
agriculture, 139, 372, 390
alanine, *42*, 44
alarm calling, 134, 171–72, *172*, 173–74, *174*, 411
Alberts, Susan, 148, 162
Alemseged, Zeresenay, 246
Algeripithecus minutus, 219
alkaloids, 126
alleles, 29–30, *30*, 191, 364, 391–92
  dominant, 30
  gene frequency and, 54
  in linkage, 33, 36–37
  ratio of, 32–34, *33*, *34*
  recessive, 30
  in recombination, 32–36
  sampling variation and, 71–72
Allen, Woody, 149
Allia Bay, Kenya, 245, 250

alliances, 180
allopatric speciation, 86–88, *87*, 320
Alperson-Afil, Nira, 302
Altai Neanderthal, 315, 340, 344
Altamira, Spain, *347*
alternative splicing, 45–46, *46*
Altmann, Jeanne, 177
altruism. *see also* kin selection
  alarm calling and, 171–72, *172*, 173–74, *174*
  in behavior, 170–72, *171*, *172*, 184–86, *185*, *186*
  coalition formation and, 170–71, *171*, 180, 180–82, *182*, 186, 199
  grooming and, 169–70, *170*, 177, *179*, 179–80, *185*, 186, 199
  group-level explanations, problems with, 171–72
  group selection and, 173
  Hamilton's rule and, 173–75, *176*, 179, 180, 181, 184
  natural selection and, 169, 172–73
  in primates, 169–70, *170*, *174*, *179*, 184–86, *185*, *186*
  reciprocal, 184–86, *185*, 390, 404, 420
  social behavior and, 171, 173, 174–76, 180–81
Amboseli National Park, Kenya, *89*, 150, 160, 197
amino acids, 97, *97*, 357, 358
  chemical backbone of, *42*
  codon variants of, 43
  in primate nutrition, 126
  protein in sequence of, 43, *43*
  tRNA attached to, 44, *45*
aminoacyl-tRNA synthetases, 45
Amish, 371, *371*, 372
Amud, 326
Anabaptist sects, 371, 372
analogous characters, 98
Anbarra, *281*
ancestral characters, *97*, 98–101, *99*, *100*
angiosperms, 214, *215*, 216
Anoiapithecus, 228
Antarctica, 210, *210*, 218
antelope, 250, 284, *285*, 291, 292, 308
anthrax, 139
anticodons, 44
Antón, Susan, 269
ants, 418
apatite crystals, 213
apes, 82, 92, *93*, 94, 100, *101*, *105*, 110, 111, *115*, *117*, 118, 119, 121, 122–23, 127, 138, *249*, 250

apes *(continued)*
    anatomical features distinguishing
        monkeys from, 122, 226, *226*,
        229, *229*
    arboreal Miocene, bipedalism
        in, 242–43
    associative learning and, 199–200
    brain size in, 193–96
    distinguishing characteristics
        between modern humans and, 234
    early evolution of, 223, 226–30, *229*
    foraging by, 196, 276
    intelligence of, 196
    kin recognition by, 177
    knee joint of, *237*
    knowledge about kinship relationships
        by, 197–98
    locomotion of, *94*, 94–95, *95*
    observational learning by, 412
    physical and social cognition in,
        201–2, *202*
    teeth of, 221
Apidium phiomense, 219
Arabia, 218
Aramis, 238, 239
arboreal primates, 94, 96, *96*, 123, *123*,
    127, 134, 139, 214, 242
archaic *Homo sapiens*, 316, 320
Arctic Circle, 343, *343*
Arctic exploration, Franklin Expedition
    (1846), 409
Arcy-sur-Cure, France, 311, 345
Ardi (ARA-VP-6/500), 239, *239*
Ardipithecus, 257
Ardipithecus kadabba, 238, *238*
Ardipithecus ramidus, 238, 238–42, *239*,
    240, 242, 243, 250, 251
area-volume ratios, geometry of,
    76, 76–77
Argentina, 221, 272
arginine, *42*
argon-40, 213
argon-argon dating, 213, 257, 268,
    325, 327
Arnhem, *281*
arrow, *328*
art
    of anatomically modern humans, 327,
        329, 329–30, *330*
    cave, 342, 350, *350*
    of Middle Stone Age, *329*, 329–30, *330*
    of Upper Paleolithic, 349–51, *350, 351*
artificial selection, 19, *19, 22*
Asa Issie, 246, 250
Asfaw, Berhane, 239, 247
Asia, 134, 139, 217, 223, 226, 228, 229,
    335, 339
    anatomically modern humans in, 337,
        339, *339*, 340
    biological habitats of, *299*

deforestation in, 139
    extinction of primates, 135, *135*
    primates in, 123
    Upper Paleolithic tool tradition in, 343
asparagine, *42*
aspartic acid, *42*
associative learning, examples of, 199
astrochimps, *190*
Atelidae primates, 119
Atlantic dog whelk, *15*, 17
atlatl, 328, *328*
Aureli, Filippo, 180
Aurignacian tools, 343, 344–45, *345*,
    350, 351
aurochs, 306, 308
Austad, Steven, 192
Australia, 210, *210*, 218, 342, *342*
    anatomically modern humans in, 323,
        331, 336, 341–43
    Lake Mungo, 331, 342
    marsupial fauna of, *16*, 16–17
Australopithecus (australopithecines),
    244, *245*, 245–53
    Au. anamensis, 244, *244, 245*, 245–46,
        250, 273
    Au. deyiremeda, 244, *245*, 251
    Au. garhi, 244, *245*, 247, 248, 258, *258*
    Au. sediba, 244, *245*, 248, *248*
    maturation rate of, 253
    teeth of, 248–49, *249*
Australopithecus afarensis, 244, *245*,
    246, 246–47, *247*, 251, 254, 255, 257,
    258, *258*
    arboreality of, 251–52
    bipedalism of, 248, 251
    knees of, *237*
    modern humans compared with, 248,
        249, 250
    pelvis of, *236, 242*
    skull of, 246, *247*
    teeth of, *238, 249*
Australopithecus africanus, 244, *245*,
    248, *248*, 255, 258, *258, 265*, 273
    bipedalism of, 248, 251
    brain of, 248
    diet of, 255
    maturation rate of, 248
    postcranial skeleton of, 248
    sexual dimorphism in, 248
    skull of, 248, *248, 254, 265*
    teeth of, *249*, 255
Australopithecus deyiremeda, 247,
    247, 251
Australopithecus robustus, 255
Australopithecus sediba, 248, *248*
Australopiths, *235, 237*
    brain size of, 263, *263*
Awash Basin, Ethiopia, 238, 246, *246*,
    247, 270
aye-ayes, 111, *112, 115*, 194

baboons, 122, *127*, 132, 138, 139, 199,
    291, 312, 408, 420
    birth rates of, 148, *149*
    coalitions of, 170, *171, 180*, 181,
        182, *182*
    ecology of, *125, 126*
    gelada, *112*, 136, 137, 160, 161, *161*,
        164, 165, *165, 194*
    grooming by, *179*
    habit diversity and, *89*, 89–90
    hamadryas, 137, 155
    infanticide by, 164, *165*, 165–66, *166*
    kin recognition, 177, *177*
    learning mechanisms, adaptive
        modifications and, 414–15
    mate guarding by, 170–71, *171*
    maternal ranks among, *182*
    mating systems of, 143, *145*, 148, 154,
        161, *162, 163*
    number of births per female, *149*
    rank relationships and, 198–99
    reciprocal altruism and, 185, 186
    relationship maintenance, 180
    sexual dimorphism in, *157*, 252
    social behavior of, *197*
    suckling times for, *155*
    weaning conflicts and, 184
bachelor males, 157–58, 161
Bacho Kiro, Bulgaria, 346
backbone, *251*
Backwell, Lucinda, 283
Baghdad, 384
Bahr el Ghazal, Chad, 246
balanced polymorphism, 364
    calculating gene frequencies for,
        365, *365*
bald eagle, *145*
bamboo, 275
Bamshad, Michael, 383
Barro Colorado Island, Panama, *131*
Barton, Robert, 150
basal metabolic rate, 126, *126*
bases, 38, *39*
Batadomba-lena Cave, Sri Lanka, 343
Bateson, William, 60
bats, *91*, 91–92, *92*, 209, 214, 219
Beagle, HMS, 5, *6*, 395
bears, 347
Beehner, Jacinta, 161, 166, 198
bee larvae, 252
behavior
    adaptation and, 65–66, 326–27
    altruism in, 170–72, *171, 172*, 184–86,
        185, 186
    in archaeological record, 318, 326–30
    artistic, *329*, 329–30, *330*
    of chimpanzees, 410, *410*
    complexity of, in modern
        humans, 326–27
    cooperative, *417*, 417–25, *419, 420, 425*

culture and, 330

evolution and, *65*, 65–68, *66*, *67*, 318, 324, 327, 330, 387–88, 394, 395, 401, 403–4

fitness-enhancing, 415

genetic fitness and, 145

kin biases in, 179–83

in Middle Stone Age, 327

natural selection and, *65*, 65–68, *66*, *67*, 389

nature-nurture question and, 388, 415

observational learning and, 412–13, *413*, 414, 415

of primates, 109, 110–11, *113*, 130, *131*, 131–32, 202

ranging, *131*, 131–32

reconciliatory, 180–81, *181*

self-directed, 180–81

sexual selection and, 156, *156*

social (*see* social behavior)

social facilitation and, 412

speciation and, 82

symbolic, 327–28, 329, 330, 342

third-party sanctions and regulation of, 422–23

behavioral flexibility hypothesis, 194, 196

Beja, 368, *369*

Belanger's tree shrew, *209*

Bell's Karongo, 287, 291

"benefit," use of term, 145–46

Berelekh, 343, *343*

Berger, Lee, 248, 317

Bergman, Thore, 161, 198

Berman, Carol, 179

Beyrich's slit shell, eye cup of, *15*

biface tools, 273, 275, 327, *327*, 328

bilateral symmetry, 116

Binford, Lewis, 308

binocular vision, 112, *114*

biochemical pathways, 41

biological species concept, 83–84

biology, culture and, 415–16

bipedalism, *94*, *95*, 98, *98*, 209, 210, 236–37. *see also* locomotion

in *A. afarensis*, 248, 251

in *A. africanus*, 248

in *A. anamensis*, 246

adaptive advantages of, 242–43

in australopiths, 251

foramen magnum and, 235

in hominins, 234, 235, 236, 241, 242, *243*, 245, 248, 251, *251*, 252, 253, 255

hominins distinguished from hominoids, 236

in *P. robustus*, 244

pelvis and, 236, *236*, *237*, 241–42, *242*

torque in, *237*

bipolar technique in tools and toolmaking, 270

birds, 91, 105, 131, *145*, 146, 159, 214, 410

bison, 308, *310*, 343, 347, 350

"Black Skull," *253*, 254

blades, 327, 344, 346, *346*

blending inheritance, 21–22, 63, *63*

blind copying, cumulative cultural evolution and, 413

Blind Watchmaker, The (Dawkins), 13

Bloch, Jonathan, 215

Blombos Cave, South Africa, 327, *327*, 328, 329, *330*

blue monkeys, *11*, 137, 139, 160, *179*

Blumenbach, Johann, 110

Blumenschine, Robert, 290, 291

Blurton Jones, Nicholas, 277

BMP2, 61, 69

BMP4, 61

BMP7, 61, 69

body size, adaptive variation in, *376*, 376–77

body weight, 360

average basal metabolism and, *126*

Boesch, Christophe, 137, 162

Boise, Charles, 256

bolas, 272

Bolivia, 221

bone, hyoid, 312, *313*

bone tools, 328, *328*, *329*

bonnet macaques, *146*, *148*, *176*, *177*, 199, *199*

bonobos (*Pan paniscus*), 123, 196, 252, 356, 357, 408. *see also* chimpanzees, common (*Pan troglodytes*)

classification of, *103*, 103–4, *104*, 105

communities of, 124–25

genomes of, 356

phylogeny of, *92*

Borgerhoff Mulder, Monique, 402, 403

Borneo, 119, 123, 139, 193, *193*, 331

Borries, Carola, 152

Bose basin, China, 275, *275*

Botswana, *133*, 164, 166, 198, 398, 414

Bouri, Ethiopia, 247

Bouzouggar, Abdeljalil, 329

bovids, 250, 284, *285*

Boxgrove, England, 301

Boyer, Doug, 215

Boykins, Earl, 388

brachiation, as form of locomotion, *123*

brain, brain size, 209, 359, 360

of *A. africanus*, 248

of *A. garhi*, 244

of *A. sediba*, 244

of anatomically modern humans, 20, *195*, 234

of *Ar. ramidus*, 239

in australopiths, 244, 253

components of brain, 194, *195*

in dolphins, 114

of early *Homo*, 261, 263, *263*

early reproduction, life spans, and, 192

evolutionary analyses of, 390

fetal brain growth and development, 147

foraging and, 281–82

of *H. erectus*, 267, *267*

of *H. ergaster*, 320

of *H. floresiensis*, 304

of *H. heidelbergensis*, 300, *300*, 303, *304*

HAR1 and, 360

of hominins, 235, 239, 244, 245, 248, 250

of *Homo erectus*, 263, *263*

intelligence and, 196, *197*

of KNM-ER 1470, 263, *263*

life span and, 189–90

in modern humans, 234, 408

in monkeys and apes, 193–96

of Neanderthals, 306, 307

of *P. aethiopicus*, 254

of plesiadapiforms *vs.* strepsirrhines, *216*

in primate intelligence, 114

in primates, 112, *113*, 120, *196*

Brain, C. K., 292

Brain, Robert, 283

Bramble, Dennis, 269

Brazil, 140, 222, 382, *382*

bridewealth, 402–3

Brooks, Alison, 327, 328

Broom, Robert, 244, 255

Brown, Kyle, 328

Brues, Alice, 384

Brunet, Michel, 235

BSN49/P27, 268

buffalo, 250, 274

Bulgaria, 346

Burger, Joachim, 369

burials, 349, *349*

burins, 344, *345*, 346

Buss, David, 396, 397, 399, 400

butchery, hand axes and, 274, 275

butchery sites, 293

Byrne, Richard, 196

caffeine, 126

California abalone, *15*

Call, Josep, 200

C-14010 allele, 368

callitrichids, reproductive inhibition in, 392

Callitrichinae, 120

Cambridge study, *372*

camera-type eyes, 4, 74–75, *75*

canalized environment, 389

canalized mate-guarding trait, 66

"candidate gene" approach, positive selection and, 369

canines, *113*, 116, *116*, 156, 158, *158*, *216*, 219, 234, 235, 238, *238*, 240, *240*, *241*, 245, 248, *248*, *249*, 252, *252*, 253, 255, 265, *265*
cannibalism, 135
capsicin, 126
capuchin monkeys, 119–20, *120*, *131*, 136–37, 164, 199, 408
    behavioral variation in, 410
    extracted foods and, 194
    grooming by, *179*
    home ranges of, *131*
    social learning in, 413, 414
    third-party information in coalitions and, 199, *199*
    white-faced, *130*, 162, 413
carbohydrates, 126, 127, *127*
carbon-12 (radiocarbon) dating, 213
carbon-14 (radiocarbon) dating, 213, 214, 342
carbon isotopes, 250, 256
Caribbean islands, 222
caribou, 347, 409
carnivores, 219, 309
Carpolestes simpsoni, 216, *216*
Carroll, Scott, 65, *65*, 66, 67
Cartmill, Matt, 215
Caspari, Rachel, 349
Catarrhini primates, *115*, 119, 121
Caucasus Mountains, 266, *266*
cave art, 342, 350, *350*
caves, 317
Cayo Santiago, 179, *179*, 200, 201
Cebidae primates, 119–20
cells
    chromosomes in, *28*, 28–29
    division of, 28–29
    enzymes and chemical composition of, 39, 40–41, *41*
    mitochondria in, 314, 332
    nucleus of, 28, *28*
cellulose, 41, 127
Cenozoic era, 207, *208*, 211
Central America, 139, 218
CEPH data set, race and, 383
cercopithecines. *see* Old World monkeys
Cercopithecoidea primates, 121–22
cerdopithecoids, hominoids *vs.*, 122
cerebellum, *195*
cerebrum, *195*
cetaceans, 410, 412
chacma baboons, 161
Chad, 235, 246
character displacement, *87*, 88, *88*
characters (traits)
    analogous *vs.* homologous, 99–100
    canalized *vs.* plastic, 66
    correlated, 68–70
    in defining primates, 111–14, *112*, *113*, *114*, 191
    derived, 99

of finches, 9, *9*, 10–11, *87*, 88, *88*
life history, 192
maladaptive, 70, 74
in Mendelian genetics, 26, 32–35, *34*, *35*
out-groups and, 101
phenotype and expression of, 61–62
recombination and, 32–33
sexual selection and, 156
shared by primates, 111–14, *112*, *113*, *114*
single genetic locus and, 361–63
in speciation, 86–88
Châtelperronian tool industry, 345, *345*
checkerspot butterflies (*Euphydryas editha*), 86, *86*
cheetahs, 289, *290*, 293
chemistry, 41, *41*, 76
Cheney, Dorothy, 186, 197, 198, 312
chickens, domestic, 97, *98*, 360
childhood propinquity, 393
Chile, 221
chimerism, 183
chimpanzees, *155*, 229, 230, 233, 408
    backbone of, *251*
    behavioral variation in, 410, *410*
    bipedalism and, 236, *238*, 243, *243*
    brain size of, 235
    cognitive abilities in, *194*
    diet of, 250
    endangered, 137
    extracted foods and, 194, *195*
    genomes of, 356, 357, 358
    human lineages and, 357–59, 360
    intelligence of, 194, *195*, *196*, *200*, 200–1, *201*
    jaw shape of, *264*
    knees of, *237*
    language of, 312, 313
    level of expression of genes in prefrontal cortex of, 359, *359*
    life expectancy of, *253*
    male dominance, 162
    mate guarding by, 170–71
    mating systems of, 152, *153*, 162, *163*, *392*
    pelvis of, 236, *236*
    predation by, *134*
    protein coding genes in humans and, 357
    reciprocal altruism and, 185, *185*, 186
    relationship maintenance, 180
    senescence in, *191*
    social learning and, 412, 413, 414
    in space, *190*
    teeth of, 235, 240, *240*
    tool use by, 196, *196*, 269, *270*
    weaning conflicts, 184
chimpanzees, common (*Pan troglodytes*), 84, 93, *101*, 101–2, *102*, 122, 123, 124–25, 128, 143

arboreality of, 239
classification of, *103*, 103–4, *104*, 105
communities of, 124–25, *125*
computing genetic distance between humans and, *101*, 101–2, *102*, 103, 105
diet of, 240
endangered, 137
food sharing by, 278, 280, *280*
foraging by, 276, *276*, 277
genomes of, 357, 358
hunting by, 269
inbreeding and, 392, *392*
knuckle walking and, 94, *94*, *95*
mating system of, *153*
maturation rate of, 244
morphology of, 82, *82*
observational learning by, 412
pelvis in, *242*, 242–43
phylogeny of, *92*, *93*
predation by, 132, 134, *134*
reproductive isolation of, 82, 84
sexual dimorphism and, 240–41
skull of, *249*
social organization of, 137
teeth of, *249*
tool use by, 82, 125, 143, *196*
Chimpanzee Sequencing and Analysis Consortium, 357
China, 139, 219, *245*, 343, 344, 393, 400, 401, 411, *411*
    Bose basin, 275, *275*
    Dali, 303
    Daoxian Cave, 331
    Hexian, 303
    Maba, 303
    Tianyuan Cave, 331
    Yingkou, 303, *304*, 320
Chlororapithecus abyssinicus, 229
chocolate, 126
chorion (membrane), 183
chromosomes, 28, *28*, *29*, 31, *370*
    in cell division, 28–29
    crossing over process and, 35, *35*, 36–37
    definition of, 28
    in diploid organisms, 28, *29*
    homologous pairs of, 28, *29*
    in Mendel's experimental results, 29–32
    proteins in, 37
    repeated DNA sequences on, 49
    X, 332, 340
    Y, 332, 333, 335, 373
circumcision, Kipsigi girls and, *403*
cladistic taxonomy (or cladistic systematics), 104, *104*, 105
Clark, J. Desmond, 271
Clarke, Ronald, 246
cleavers, 273

climate and climate change, *210*, 210–11, *211*, 212, *212*, 298, *298*, 305, 343
 bipedal locomotion and, 233–34, 243, *243*
 of Eocene epoch, 216
 in fossil record, 209, 211, 325
 human expansion out of Africa, 318, *319*
 of Miocene epoch, 226, 228–29, 233
 of Oligocene epoch, 218, 219, *219*
 of Pleistocene epoch, 262, *262*, 297–99
 Pliocene, 230
 tool technologies, hominin invasions from Africa to Eurasia and, 318, *319*
clothing, 348, 409
Clovis points, 328
Clutton-Brock, Tim, 158
coalition (alliance) formation, 170–71, *171*, *180*, 180–82, *182*, 186
 intelligence and, 198, 199, *199*
codons, 43, *45*, 357
coefficient of relatedness (*r*), 175, *175*, *176*
collagen, 42
collected foods, 276, *276*
Colobinae, 121
colobine monkeys, 117, 250
colobus monkeys, 121, *121*, 239, 276
 black-and-white, 158
 olive, *134*
 red, *129*, 132, 134, *134*
 teeth of, *117*
Colombia, 221
color vision, of primates, 112
Combe Grenal, France, 309
combinatorial control, of gene expression, 47–48
comparative method, 94, 96, *96*, 111
competition
 adaptation and, 11–12
 kinship among females and, 183
 life history and, 192
 male-male, in non-pair-bonded groups, 160–62
 sexual dimorphism and, 156, 157
 sociality and, 135
 in social life of primates, 180
complex adaptations, 12–17
compound eyes, 74–75, *75*
conflict, in social life of primates, 180
Congo, 139, 252, 328, *329*
conservation, primate, 135, 137–40, *138*
conspecifics, 111
contextual cues, kin recognition and, 176–79
continental drift, 209–210, *210*, 216, 222, 226
continuous variation, 12, 22, 60–62
contraception, 399
Convention on International Trade in Endangered Species of Wild Fauna and Flora (CITES), 139
convergence, 16–17

convergent evolution, 97–98, *98*, 111, 223, 303
cooperation, 417–25
 adaptation and, 417–18
 among large groups of unrelated individuals, 418–20, *419*, *420*
 as evolutionary puzzle, 423–24
 nonhuman primates and, 417
 reciprocity and, 420
 regulation of, 421–22
 third-party enforcement of culturally evolved moral norms and, 422–24
Cords, Marina, 179
cores, 270, *270*, 272, *272*, *273*, 284, *303*, 305, *306*
 deep-sea, 212, *212*
corn, 64–65, *65*
cornea, 4
correlated characters, 68–70
correlated response, to selection, 69–70, *70*
Correns, Carl, 27
cortex, 272
cortical bone, 236, 238
cortisol, *166*
Cosmides, Leda, 390
"cost," use of term, 145
cowbirds, 411–12
crabs, 302
cremation, 331
Cretaceous, 214
Crick, Francis, 37
Croatia, 315, 316, 380
Crockett, Carolyn, 161
crocodiles, *133*, 305
Crompton, Robin, 242
crosses, in pea plants, 26
crossing over, 35, *35*, 36–37
crowned hawk eagles, 132–33, *133*, 134
crural index, 308, *309*
Csibra, Gergely, 414
cuckoldry, 135
Cueva Antón, Spain, 311, *311*
Cueva de los Aviones, Spain, 311, *311*
cultural group selection hypothesis, 424
culturally acquired information, 409–10
culture
 as adaptation, 414–15
 behavior and, 330, 410, *410*
 biology and, 415–16
 definition of, 410
 end of human evolution and, 425–26
 environmental variation and, 360
 environment and, 414–15
 evolution and, 408–14, *409*, *410*, *411*, *413*
 human cooperation and, 418–21
 incest prohibition in, 394
 maladaptive beliefs and, 416
 male selection and, 400–1, *401*
 in nonhuman primates, 417

 observational learning and, 412–13, *413*, 414
 race concept and, 383–84
 social facilitation and, 412
 social learning and, 412
Curtis, Garniss, 268
Cuvier, Georges, 110
cysteine, *42*
cystic fibrosis (CF), 363, 391
cytoplasm, *45*
cytosine, 38, *39*
Czech Republic, *325*, 348

Dagosto, Marian, 216
Daka, Ethiopia, 264
Dakikia child, 313
Dali, China, 303
Daoxian Cave, China, 331
Daphne Major Island, 7–8, *8*, 9, 10, 17, 61, 62, 68, *68*, 70, *70*, 81
Dart, Raymond, 248, *248*
Darwin, Charles, 64, 155, 173, 307, 395
 on adaptation, 5–6, 13, 61–62, 143, 209
 background of, 5
 on classification of humans, 110
 on evolution, 5–6, 7, 8, 10, 13, 19–20, 60
 on natural selection, 6, 21–22, 62, 64
 postulates of, 6, 8, 21, 173
 on sexual selection, 155
 on species, 10, 81, 86
 variation explanation difficult for, 21–22
Darwin, Emma Wedgwood, 395, *395*
Darwinius masillae, 218, *218*
Darwin's finches. *see* finches
Dawkins, Richard, 13–14
deception, *200*, 200–1, *201*
deep sea cores, 212, *212*
deer
 fallow, 302, 308
 red, 155, *156*, 308, *310*, 347
deforestation, *123*, *139*, 139–40
Democratic Republic of Congo, 124
Denisova Cave, Siberia, 315, 339
Denisovans, 316
 genome, 333, 338–39
 interbreeding and, 338, *339*
dental formula, 116, *117*, 220, 221
dental morphology, 116–17, *117*
deoxyribonucleic acid. *see* DNA (deoxyribonucleic acid)
derived characters, *97*, *99*, 99–100, *100*
d'Errico, Francesco, 283
Descent of Man, The (Darwin), 110
development, 75
developmental constraints, 75, 147
de Vries, Hugo, 27, 60
de Waal, Frans, 180
diabetes, 366

Diamond, Jared, 365
Diana monkeys, 134, *135*
dictator game, 421
Diepkloof Rock Shelter, South Africa, 329, *330, 341*
diet, human, disequilibrium and, *70,* 70–71
digestion, 371
Dikika
    child skeleton, 246, *247*
    tools found at, 270, *270*
Dinka, *425*
Dinklage, Peter, 12
dinosaurs, 90–91, 207
diploid organisms, 28, *29*
directional selection, 358, 363
Dirks, Paul, 248
disastema, 248, *249*
discontinuous variation, 12–13, 22
disease
    genetically transmitted, 356
    primates and, 139
disequilibrium, 70–71
dispersal, inbreeding avoidance and, 392
diurnal primates, 111, *130*
divergence dates, genetic distance and, 102–3
divine creation, 5
division of labor
    food sharing and, 253, 275, 280, *280*
    foraging and, 278, *278*
divorce, in minor marriages, 393, *393*
dizygotic (fraternal) twins, 374–75
Dmanisi, Republic of Georgia, 266, *266, 267,* 269
DNA (deoxyribonucleic acid), 37–43, *39, 40,* 332
    alternative splicing, 45–46, *46*
    enzymes and, 39–41, *41*
    in eukaryotes, 44
    in genes, 38–43
    genetic distance and, 101
    mitochondrial, 314
    of Neanderthals, 314, 315
    in origin and spread of anatomically modern humans, 332–41
    positive selection and sequences of, 369–70
    protein codes of, 38–40, *39, 40,* 357–59
    replication of, *40*
    sequences of, 38–39, *39,* 43–44, 49
    structure of, 38–39, *39*
    transposable elements of, 357
DNA sequence data, genetic distance and, 101
Dobzhansky, Theodosius, 61, 388
dogs
    domestication of, 19
    wild, 289
    wolves as ancestors of, 19, *22*

dolphins, 114, *114*
dominance hierarchies, 151, *151,* 182, 198
    in female primate mating systems, 150, *152,* 152–54, *153*
    linear, 151
    male reproductive success and, 162, *162, 163*
    in social behavior, 180, 182
    transitive, 151
dominance matrix, 151, *151*
dominance relationships, 151
dominant alleles, 30
Domínguez-Rodrigo, Manuel, 291
Douglas, Gabrielle, 361, *361*
Drakensberg Mountains, South Africa, 89
drift-mutation equilibrium, 336, *336*
Drimolen, South Africa, 255
Drosophila (fruit flies), 28
Dryopithecus, 228
Dubois, Eugène, 267, 268, *268*
duck-billed platypus, 97, *97,* 98, *98*
dugongs, *91,* 91–92, *92*
Dunbar, Robin, 180, 194
Durbin, Richard, 357
dusky titi monkey, *130*
dwarfism, evolutionary, 304–5
Dydek, Margo, *360,* 361

eagles, crowned hawk, 132–33, *133,* 134
East Africa, *209*
East African Rift, 226
Ebola virus, 139
ecological intelligence hypothesis, 194, *194*
ecological species concept, 84–86
Efe, 252
egg and genetics, 28, *32*
egg laying, *98*
egocentric empathy, 394
Egypt, 392
    Fayum depression of, 219, *219,* 221, 223
Ehrlich, Paul, 86
electron-spin-resonance dating, 213, 214, 326
elephants, 190, *192,* 209, 284, *284,* 302, *304,* 305, 308, 384
    dwarf, *304,* 305
    stone tools and butchering of, 272, 274
elk. *see* red deer (elk)
embryo, *100*
emulation, 412
Enattah, Nabil, 368
endocranial volume, 250
Engh, Anne, 153
England, 378, 379
environment
    canalized *vs.* plastic, 66, 389
    culture and, 414–15
    in fossil record, 209, 211
    life history and, 192, 193

    reasoning and, 110
    Upper Paleolithic peoples compared with Neanderthals and, 347–49
environmental covariation, 374
environmental variation, 62, 360, 361, 373
    height and influence of, 377–79, *378, 379*
environment of evolutionary adaptedness (EEA), 390, 404
enzymes
    DNA and, 39–41, *41*
    in regulation of genes, 41, 47–48
Eocene epoch, *208, 211,* 216, *217,* 219, 223
Eosimias, 219
equids, 284
equilibrium, among populations, 9
Eritrea, 301
Erus, Justus, 257
Escherichia coli, 44, 47, *48*
essentialism, 11
Estrada, Alejandro, 135
estrus, 158, *162*
Ethiopia, 160, 164, 229, 246, *246,* 263, 266, 284, *318*
    Afar depression of, 246
    Awash Basin of, 238, 246, *246, 247,* 270
    Daka, 264
    Herto, 318, 325, 326, *326*
    Konso-Gardula, 264
    Omo-Kibish Formation of, *318,* 325, *326*
ethnic groups, 380
eukaryotes, 44–47, 49
Eurasia, 210, *210,* 218, 226, 326
    anatomically modern humans in, 227, 261, 274, 315, *339*
    biological habitats of, *299*
    expansion of hominins throughout, 261
    H. erectus in, 261, 266, 267, 297, 303–4
    H. heidelbergensis in, *300,* 300–2, *301,* 320
    modern human spread across, *335,* 336
    Neanderthals in, 297
    Pleistocene climate of, 298, *299*
    spread of hominins to, 299, 300, 315
    tool technologies and hominin invasions from Africa to, 318, *319*
Europe, 228, 229
    anatomically modern humans in, *335,* 336, 343
    hominins in, 228
    lactase persistence in, 368–69
    primate evolution in, 216–17
European Americans, 380
eusocial insects, 418
event trees, 31, *32, 34,* 56, *57*

evolution, 100
  of altruism, 172
  behavior and, *65*, 65–68, *66*, *67*, 318, 324, 327, 330, 387–88, 394, 395, 401, 403–4, 414–15
  climate change and, 210
  of cognitive complexity, 194
  of complex adaptations, 12–17
  of complex characters, 20
  constraints on, 75, 76–77
  continental drift and, 209–10, *210*
  convergent, 97–98, *98*, 111, 223, 303
  culture and, 408–14, *409*, *410*, *411*, *413*
  Darwin on, 5–6, *7*, 8, 10, 13, 19–20, 60
  end of, 425–26
  of eye, 4, *4*
  genetic variation and, 361
  genotypic frequencies and, 54–55
  of lactase persistence, 368
  of locomotion in apes, *94*, 94–95, *95*
  of mate guarding, *65*, 65–68, *66*, *67*
  molecular basis of, 37–38
  phylogenetic reconstruction and study of, 93
  process not synonymous with, 230
  psychology of human mating strategies and, 395–96
  rates of change in, 17–21
  of reproductive strategies, 145–47
evolutionary dwarfism, 304–5
evolutionary taxonomy (or evolutionary systematics), 104, *104*, 105
exons, 44–46, *46*
expressed variation, *64*
extinction, 135, 137–40
extracted foods, 194, *195*, 276, *276*
extractive foraging, 276, 277, *277*, 278, 282, 283–84
eyes
  adaptation and, 4, 14–15, *15*
  of *C. simpsoni*, 215, *215*
  compound *vs.* camera-type, 74–75, *75*
  evolution of, 17, *17*, 20, *20*
  of fish, 4, *4*, 17, *17*
  of modern humans, *4*
  of plesiadapiforms, *216*
  of primates, 112, *114*

Faben, 314, *314*
facial recognition, 177
faithful copying, cumulative cultural evolution and, 413
falciparum malaria, 364, *364*, 366, *367*, 369, 382
fallow deer, 302, 308
familiarity, kinship and, 176
family, taxonomic, 104
father-daughter matings, 162–63
fats, 126, *127*
fat-tailed dwarf lemurs, 111

Fayum depression, Egypt, 219, *219*, 221, 222, 223
fecundity, 12
felids, 134
femur, 235, *235*, 236–37, *237*, 238, *238*, 241, 251, 252
fertility, 395, *396*
  age-specific rates of, 148, 152
  in minor marriages, 393, *393*
Fessler, Daniel, 394
F_0 generation, 26
F_1 generation, 26, *27*, 31, *31*, *34*, 56
F_2 generation, 26, *27*, 30, *31*, 32, *34*, 57
fighting, 130, *131*, 161, *162*
finches, 18, *18*
  adaptive radiation of, *90*, 90–91
  allopatric speciation and, 87, *87*
  blending inheritance, 21
  Cactus, *7*
  characters of, 9, *9*, 10–11, *87*, 88, *88*
  correlated characters of, *68*, 68–69, *69*, *70*
  evolution of, *84*, 84–86, *85*
  gene flow between, 83, *83*, *84*, 84–86, *85*
  genetic drift and, 74
  honeycreeper, *91*
  interspecies mating between, 85
  large ground (*G. magnirostris*), 18, *18*, 85, *85*
  medium ground (*G. fortis*), *7*, 7–11, *9*, *10*, *11*, 12, 17–18, *18*, *84*, 85, *85*
  morphology of, 8–10, 18, *61*, 61–62, *62*, 64, 81, 88, 169
  reproductive isolation of, 83, *83*
  small ground (*G. fuliginosa*), 85, *85*, *88*
  species boundaries and, 86
fire use, *291*, 291–92
fish, 146, 302, 410
  eye of, 4, *4*, 17, *17*
Fisher, Ronald A., *60*, 61, 63
fishing, 342–43
fitness-enhancing behavior, *198*, 415
fixation, of populations, 74
flakes (tool), *270*, 270–71, *271*, 272, *272*, *273*, 274, 284, 303, 308, 328, 346
  cortex of, 272, *272*
Flatz, Gebhard, 368
flint, 346
flint knappers, 272, *272*
FLK Zinjanthropus, 287
Flores, Indonesia, *304*, 304–5
Florisbad cranium, 316, *316*
flute, 351
Foley, Robert, 318
folivores, 117, *117*, 128, 129, 218, 220
folk classification schemes, 382, *382*
"follower" males, 161
food, distribution of, *125*, 125–30
food resources, categories of, 276

food sharing, 390, 391, 423
  among chimpanzees, 278, 280, *280*
  meat eating and, 278
  by modern humans, 278, 279, 280
  sexual dimorphism and, 282
foragers, technologies of, 409, *409*
foraging, 145
  by apes, 196, 276
  by australopiths, 252
  brain size and, 281–82
  capuchin monkeys and, 413
  by chimpanzees, 82, 276, *276*, 277
  by gorillas, 276
  home bases and, 292–93
  by modern humans, 275, 276, *276*, 280–1, *281*, 326–27, 347, 390, *390*, 408, 417, *417*
  by Oldowan toolmakers, 276–86
  by orangutans (*Pongo pygmaeus*), 276
  ranging patterns and, 128–29
  by rats, 390, *390*
  self-sufficiency and, 280–81, *281*
  sexual division of labor and, 278, *278*
  slow maturation and, 282
foraging societies
  human mating strategies and, 395
  warfare and, 419, *420*
foramen magnum, 235, 248
forebrain, 194, *195*
fossas, 132
Fossey, Dian, 123
fossil record, 17–20, 100–1, 209
  anatomically modern humans in, 324, 325, 330, 331, *331*, 339
  ancestral characters in, 100–1
  climate change in, 209, 211, 298–99, 325
  continental drift in, 209–10
  dating methods and, 211, 213–14
  footprints in, 251, *251*
  H. erectus in, 298
  H. ergaster in, 320, *320*
  H. heidelbergensis in, *300*, 300–1
  on Haplorrhini evolution, 218–19, 221–2
  hominins in, 229, 235, *235*, 245
  incompleteness of, 224, 225, *225*
  missing links in, *224*, 224–25, *225*
  Neanderthals in, 306, 324
  New World fossil evidence, *222*
  Old World monkeys in, 230
  P. boisei in, 256
  primates in, 217, 218, *218*
  tools in, *270*
founder effect, 371
FOXP2 gene, 313, 358, 363
France, 309, 310, *325*, 327, 345, 346, 350, *350*, 351
Franklin, John, 409, *409*
Franklin, Rosalind, 37
free riders, 420, 422, 423

Freud, Sigmund, 394, 404
frugivores, 116, *117*, 128, 129, 215, 217, 218, 220, 221, 228, 241
    dentition and digestive tracts of, 117, *117*
fruit flies (*Drosophila*), 28, 49

Gabunia, Leo, 266
galagos, 116, *116*, *118*, 119, 127, 217, 269
Galápagos Islands, 7, *7*, 10, 17, 18, 21, 61, 70, *84*, 85, 86, 87, 90, *90*
Galdikas, Birute, 123
Game of Thrones, The, 12
gametes, 26, *35*, 55–56, *72*, 73, 145, 183
    haploid, 28, *29*, 31
    meiosis and, 28, *29*, 31
Gamova, Ekatarina, 361, *361*
Garber, Paul, 160
Gebo, Daniel, 226
gelada baboons, *112*, 136, 137, 160, 161, *161*, 164, 165, *165*, *194*
gene flow, 83–84
    character displacement and, 88
    between Darwin's finches, 83, *83*, *84*, 84–86, *85*
    in human history, 383
    migration patterns and, 305, 324, 373, *373*
    reinforcement and, 88
gene frequency
    calculating, 54, *54*, *57*, 365, *365*
    evolution and, 54–55, 61, 62
    genetic drift and, 71–74
    Hardy-Weinberg equilibrium and, 57–59
    natural selection and, 54, 59–60
    random mating and, 55, 58, 59
    sexual reproduction, 55–60
    stability reached by, 57
genes, 26, 49, 416
    calculating frequencies, 365, *365*
    on chromosomes, 29–30, 37
    combinatorial control and, 47–48
    crossing over, 35, *35*, 36–37
    DNA in, 38–43
    FOXP2, 313, 358, 363
    language and, 313
    mutation of, 55
    natural selection and, 54–55
    phenotypic traits and interactions between environment and, 388–89
    pleiotropic effects of, 69
    in populations, 54–55
    positively selected, 358
    recessive, 363
    regulatory, 39, 47–49, 358
    senescence and, 191
genetic determinism, 388
genetic distance, 333
    among humans and three great ape species, *101*, 101–1, *102*

geographical distance and, 373, *373*
    phylogeny and, *101*, 101–3, *102*
    racial groupings and, 381–82
genetic diversity, 355–84. *see also* variation
    among groups (*see* genetic variation among groups)
    in complex phenotypic traits, 373–79, *374*, *376*, *378*
    explanations of, 355–56
    within groups (*see* genetic variation within groups)
    influenced by single genes, 361–63
    migration patterns reflected in, 371–73, *372*
    race and, 381–82
genetic drift, 47, 55, 81, 316, 366, 383, 387
    anatomically modern humans and, 358
    gene frequency and, 71–74
    isolated populations and, *73*, 73–74, 371–72
    maladaptation and, 74
    population size and, 72–73
    variation and, 71, *71*, 336, *336*
genetic fitness, 191
    behavior and, 145
genetic markers, 356, 362
genetics
    in adaptation, 62, 63, 67–68
    blending in, 21–22, 63
    cell division in, 28–29
    in continuous variation, 60–62
    Mendelian, 25–37
    modern synthesis of, 61
    molecular, 37–49
    population, 53–77
genetic variation, *334*, 374. *see also* variation
    definition of, 360
    explaining, 355–56
    geographic distance from Africa, 337, *337*, 338, *338*
    in height, *360*, 361
    mutation and, 333, 336
    origin of modern humans and, 331
    worldwide patterns of, 372–73, *373*
genetic variation among groups, 361, 366–73
    body size and, *376*, 376–77
    causes of, 366–73
    environmental variation on stature, 377–79, *378*, *379*
    genomewide association studies, stature and, 377–78
    misconceptions about nature of, 376–77
    race and, 382, 383
    stature among human populations, 377

genetic variation within groups, 361, 363–64, 366
    causes of, 363–66
    height and, 374, *374*, 375
    race and, 382, 383
    twins and, 374–75, *375*
gene trees, 333, *334*
genome, 33
    African, 338
    Australian, 336, *337*
    bonobo, 356
    chimpanzee, 315, 356
    Denisovans, 315, *315*, 316, *316*, 333, 338–39
    European, 315
    human, 315, 316, 356
    in Neanderthals, 315, 333, 338–39
    sequencing, 356–57
genomewide association studies, 375, 377
genotypes, 30–31, *31*, 53, *337*, 337–38, 382, 383
    alternative, 54
    body weight and, 77
    frequency of, 54–55
    random mating and, 55–58, *58*, 59–60
    sexual reproduction and, 55–58, *58*
genotypic frequencies, 54–55
    random mating and, 55–58, *58*, 59–60
genus, 103, *103*
geographical distance, genetic distance and, 373, *373*
geological timescale, *208*
Geospiza
    G. fortis (medium ground finch), 7, *7*–11, *9*, *10*, *11*, 12, 17–18, *18*, *84*, 85, *85*
    G. fuliginosa (small ground finch), 85, *85*, 88
    G. magnirostris (large ground finch), 18, *18*, 85, *85*
Gergely, George, 414
Germany, 302, 351, *351*
gestural communication system, 312
gibbons, *92*, 92–93, *93*, *103*, *104*, 122, *123*, 136, 139, 177, 230
    mating system of, 143, 158
    skywalker hoolock, 138
    as territorial, 123, *123*, 131, *131*
    white-handed, 159, *159*
Gilgil, Kenya, 182
Gingerich, Philip, 19
glacial periods, 210, *210*, 262, 298, 299, *299*, 305
glucose, 41, 47, *48*
glutamate, *42*
glutamic acid, *42*, 43, *43*
glycine, *42*
glycogen, 41
goats, wild, 308
golden bamboo lemurs, 140

golden lion tamarins, 140, *183*
Gombe, Nigeria, 278, 279
Gombe Stream National Park, Tanzania, *89*, 124, 125, 152, *153*, *155*, 160, *196*, 278, 279, 314, *314*, 392, 412
Gona, 239, 268, 269, 270
Gondwanaland, 210, *210*
Goodall, Jane, 124
gorillas, 92, *92*, 105, 110, *117*, 122, 123–24, *124*, *131*, 139, 140, 149, 196, 229, 230, 233, 239, 240, 242, 252, 356, 357
  classification of, *103*, 104, *104*, 105
  foraging by, *129*, 276
  genetic distance, *101*, 101–2, *102*
  grooming by, *179*
  jaw shape of, *264*
  knuckle walking and, 94, *94*, *95*
  life expectancy of, *253*
  lowland, 124
  mating system of, 156, 158
  morphology of, 82, *82*
  mountain, 123–24, *124*, *129*, 140, 152, 156, 164, 196
  number of births per female, *149*
  reproductive isolation of, 82, 84
  resting, *130*
  sexual dimorphism in, 156, 252
  silverback, 124
  tool use by, 269
Grand Canyon, complexity of, 5, *5*
Grant, Peter, 7, 8, 9, 10, 17, 18, 61, 62, 68, 70, 85
Grant, Rosemary, 7, 8, 9, 10, 17, 18, 61, 62, 68, 70
Gravettian tool tradition, 345
gray langurs, *121*, *152*, 160, 164, *164*
great apes (Pongidae), *93*, *101*, *104*, 123, 139, *147*, 230. *see also specific species*
  endangered, 137
  life history of, 193
  sex differences in canine dimensions in hominins and, 240, *241*
  social intelligence hypothesis and, 196
Greece, 229, 300
Greenland, 305, *306*
grooming, 111–12, *113*, 130, 153, 154, *154*, 156, 159, *159*, 166
  altruism and, 169–70, *170*, *177*, *179*, 179–80, *185*, 186, 199
Grotte de Pigeons, Morocco, 329
Grotte due Renne, France, 345
group selection, 172, 173
growth rate, energy requirement and, 126
guanine, 38, *39*
guenons, *134*, 219
guereza colobus monkey, 121, *121*
Guinea, 124
guinea pigs, 219
gum and gummivores, 117, *117*, 127, 128
guts, of primates, *117*, 117–18

Gwi, *281*
gymnosperms, 214

habitat destruction, 118, *123*, 139–40
habitat distribution, when humans left Africa (72 ka to 60 ka), *342*
Hadar, Ethiopia, 246, 252
Hadza, *70*, 277, *278*, 280, 290
hafted tools, 303
Haile-Selassie, Yohannes, 238, 246, 247
Haldane, J. B., *60*, 61, 63
Ham, *190*
hamadryas baboons, 137, 155
Hamilton, William D., 170, 172–73
Hamilton's rule, 173–75, *176*, 179, 180, 181, 184
hammer stone, 270, *271*, 272
Hammon, Becky, *360*, 361
Han, *337*
hand axes, 273, *273*, 274–75, *275*, 302, 303
handedness, 308
Hanihara, Tsunehiko, 338
Hanuman langurs, *121*, 162
haplogroup, 333, 344
haploid cells, 28, *29*
Haplorrhini primates, 112, 223
  evolution of, 218–19, 221–23
  in taxonomy of living primates, 115, *115*, 118, *119*, 119–21, *120*, *121*
  teeth of, *116*
haplotypes, *335*, 369
HAR1, 359, 360
HAR202, 359
Hardy, Godfrey Harold, 57
Hardy-Weinberg equations, 362, *362*, 363
Hardy-Weinberg equilibrium, *57*, 57–58, 59, 61, *61*, 62
Hare, Bryan, 200
Harpending, Henry, 398
Harvey, Paul, 158
Haselton, Martie, 399, 400
Hawaii, Japanese immigrants in, 378–79, *379*
Hawaiian archipelago, *91*
hearths and hearth building, 292, 310, 328, 348, *348*
heat stress, 243
heat-treated tools, 328
height
  environmental variation and, 377–79, *378*, *379*
  genetic differences and, 375, 388
  genetic variation and, 374, *374*, 375
Heistermann, Michael, 165
hemoglobin, 43, *43*, 361
hemoglobin A, 361, *365*
hemoglobin E, 367
hemoglobin S, 361, 363, 365, *365*, 366, *367*

Henrich, Joseph, 421
Henshilwood, Christopher, 329
Henslow, John Stevens, 5
herbivores, 309, 346–47
Herero, 398
heritability, of phenotypic traits, 374
Herrmann, Esther, 201, 202
Herto, Ethiopia, 318, 325, 326, *326*
heterozygotes, 30
heterozygous alleles, 29, 30, *30*, 364
Hexian, China, 303
hidden variation, *64*, 64–65
Hill, Kim, 276, 277, 417, 422, 424
Himalayas, 226
hindbrain, *195*
hind-limb dominated locomotion, primates and, *113*
hippopotamuses, 219, 284, 308, 325
Hirschhorn, Joel N., 377, 378
histidine, *42*
Hiwi, 277, *278*, 280
Hobbes, Thomas, 417, *417*, 423
home bases, 292–93, 310
home ranges, *131*, 131–32, 136, *136*
hominids (Hominidae), 104, *104*, 105, 122–23
  fire use by, *291*, 291–92
  as larger-bodied apes, 123
  Oldowan, 291
  tool use by, 291
hominins, 111, 234, 320, 388
  in Africa, 234, 297, 316, 318
  arboreality of, 250
  Ardipithecus, *238*, 238–42, *239*, *240*, *242*, 243, 250
  bipedalism and, 234, 235, 236, 241, 242, *243*, 245, 248, 251, *251*, 252, 253, 255
  Bouri, 247
  brain and brain size of, 235, 239, 244, 245, 248, 250
  carcasses processed by, 291–92
  climate change and, 233–34, 243, *243*
  convergence in evolution of, 257
  Dmanisi, 266, *266*, *267*, 269
  domestic lives of, *292*, 292–94, *293*
  in Eurasia, 275, 320
  fire use by, *291*, 291–92
  food sharing and, 279–80, *280*
  in fossil record, 229, 234
  at kill sites, 285, 287
  of Late Pleistocene, 303–16, *304*
  of Lower Pleistocene, *266*, 266–67
  maturation rate of, 234, 244, 253
  of Middle Pleistocene, 300–1, 303, 306, 316
  Oldowan, 270–71, 292–94
  Orrorin tugenensis, 235, 238
  parallelism in evolution of, 257–58
  phylogenies of, 257–58, *258*, 320
  sagittal crest of, 254, *254*

hominins (continued)
    as scavengers, 288–90, 289
    self-sufficiency after weaning, 280
    sex differences in canine dimensions
        in great apes and, 240, 240
    sexual dimorphism in, 252–53, 269
    skulls of, 235, 235, 244, 248–49, 249,
        253, 253–4, 254, 255, 255, 257, 257,
        258, 263, 263, 264, 265, 300
    species, 244
    taxonomic scheme for, 244, 244
    teeth of, 235, 238, 238, 240, 240–41,
        241, 244, 245, 247, 248, 249, 250,
        253, 255, 255–56, 256, 263, 265
    as toolmakers, 271, 273
    traits distinguishing modern humans
        from, 230
    Woranso-Mille, 246
hominoids (Hominoidea), 104, 104,
    121, 122–25
    emergence of, 223, 227–30
    in Eurasia during Miocene
        epoch, 228–29
    life expectancy of, 253
    phylogeny of, 92, 92–93, 103, 104
    Proconsul species, 227, 227, 228, 239
    suspensory adaptations and, 228
Homo, 257, 258, 258, 261, 304, 305
    early, 245, 262–64
    H. sapiens (see humans, anatomically
        modern; humans, modern;
        Neanderthals)
    questions about classification of
        earliest members of, 320
Homo erectus, 244, 245, 262, 264–69,
    294, 297
    body shape of, 291
    brain of, 266
    brain size of, 263, 263
    diet of, 265
    in Eurasia, 261, 266, 266, 267–68,
        299, 303–4
    H. heidelbergensis in coexistence with,
        303–4, 304
    maturation rate of, 269
    as meat eater, 287–88
    morphology of, 265, 265
    phylogeny of, 264–65, 291
    running ability of, 269
    skull of, 263, 263, 264, 264–65, 265
    toolmaking by, 273–74, 326
Homo ergaster
    brain of, 320
    classification of, 320
    emergence of modern humans and,
        320, 320
    in fossil record, 320, 320
    skull of, 258
Homo floresiensis, 304, 304–5, 305
Homo habilis, 244, 263, 264

Homo heidelbergensis, 300, 300–2, 301,
    306, 313, 325, 326
    body shape of, 306
    brain of, 303, 304
    in Eurasia, 300, 300–2, 301
    H. erectus in coexistence with,
        303–4, 304
    hunting by, 302
    plant and animal resources
        used by, 302
    skull of, 300, 300, 316
    toolmaking by, 302, 325
homologous characters, 98
homologous pairs, 28
Homo naledi, 317, 317
Homo neanderthalensis, 258
Homo rudolfensis, 244, 263, 264
homozygotes, 29
homozygous alleles, 29–30, 33, 364
honey, 252, 269
honeycreeper finch, 91
horses, 209, 284, 302, 306, 308, 343,
    347, 350
housing, Central Inuit, 409
Howieson's Port tool industry, 329
howler monkeys, 112, 119, 136, 139, 162
    red, 161, 164, 182–83
Hoyle, Frederick, 13
Hrdy, Sarah Blaffer, 163, 166
Hugo, 191
Human Genome Diversity Project,
    338, 372
humans, anatomically modern, 384
    in Africa, 300, 306, 316, 323–26,
        325, 333
    art and symbolic expression of, 327,
        329, 329–30, 330, 349–51, 350, 351
    in Asia, 336, 337, 339, 339, 340, 343
    in Australia, 323, 331, 336, 341
    behavior of, 326–27
    bipedalism and, 98, 209
    brain of, 20, 195, 234
    chimpanzee lineages and, 37,
        357–59, 360
    clothing of, 348
    expansion out of Africa, 330–41,
        331, 334
    in fossil record, 324, 325, 330, 331,
        331, 339
    genetics and spread of, 333, 335, 335
    genetic variation in, 331, 333, 334,
        355–56, 360, 360, 361, 361–
        64, 366–73
    genome of, 315, 316, 356
    knee joint, 237, 237
    language and, 312
    life expectancy of, 349
    long-distance exchange networks
        and, 327
    in Middle East, 326

    in migration from Africa, 324, 331,
        332, 335, 337, 337
    morphology of, 324, 324–26, 325, 326
    Neanderthals and, 309
    origin and spread of, 330–44
    pelvis of, 236, 236
    phylogeny of, 298, 333
    plant foods and, 347
    as primates, 110
    religion and, 327
    ritual burial by, 348, 349, 349
    shelters and communities of,
        347–48, 348
    skull of, 265, 324, 325, 325, 326, 342
    subsistence economies of, 346–47
    toolmaking of, 326–28, 327, 328,
        344–45, 345, 346
    upright posture and, 241–42
    variation in, 355–56
    vocal apparatus, 313
humans, modern, 97
    A. afarensis compared with, 248,
        249, 250
    in Africa, 324
    allopatric speciation and, 320
    ancestral characters and, 98–101
    archaic, 316, 320
    behavioral evolution of, 387–88
    brain size of, 408
    children of, 202, 202
    classification of, 103, 104, 104–5
    common Neanderthal ancestry
        with, 340–41
    complex adaptations in, 209
    computing genetic distance between
        chimpanzees and, 101, 101–2, 102,
        103, 105
    culture (see culture)
    cumulative cultural evolution
        and, 414–15
    disequilibrium in characters of, 70–71
    distinguishing characteristics
        between contemporary apes and,
        234
    food gathering, 70
    food sharing by, 278, 279, 280
    genetic distance between three great
        ape species and, 101, 101–1, 102
    genomes of, 356, 357
    hunting and foraging by, 276, 277, 277,
        280–81, 281
    inbreeding avoidance in, 391–94, 392
    level of expression genes in prefrontal
        cortex of, 359, 359
    life expectancy of, 253
    mental mechanisms of, 391
    natural classification schemes
        and, 380
    Neanderthals' genetic distance
        from, 340–41

pelvis, 236, *236*
phylogeny of, 92, 94, *95*, 97, *97*, 98, *98*
physical and social cognition in, 201–2, *202*
protein coding genes in chimpanzees and, 357
psychology of mate preferences, 395–96
skulls of, 324, *324*
teeth and jaws of, *249*
traits distinguishing modern hominoids from apes, 234
variation in, 360–61
variety of lifeways among, 392
humerus, 252
Hunt, Kevin, 243
hunted foods, 276, *276*
Hunter, Rick, 317
hunter-gatherer societies, *423*, 423–24
cooperation and, 417, *417*
hunting, 139, 275
by anatomically modern humans, 277, *277*
by Central Inuit, *409*, 409–10
food sharing and, 278–80
by *H. heidelbergensis*, 302
kill site formation and, 285
by Neanderthals, 308–9, *310*
scavenging and, 288–90
wild primate populations and, 139
Hupa tribe, *419*
Hurtado, A. Magdalena, 276
Hutterites, 371
Huxley, Thomas Henry, 110, 307
hybrid zone, 89
hydrogen bonds, 38, *39*
hyenas, 285, 287, 289, *289*, 290, 309, *310*
Hylobatidae (lesser apes), *93*, 122–23
hyoid bone, 312, *313*

ice cores, 305, *306*
Ida, 218, *218*
Ileret, Kenya, 263, *264*, 266, 268
ilium, 236, *237*, 241–42
imitation, 412, 413, *413*, *414*
inbred matings, 391
inbreeding avoidance, 135, 391–94, *392*, 404
incest, third-party attitudes toward, 394
incisors, *113*, 116, *116*, *216*, 218, 219, 220, 235, 240, 245, 248, 255, 265, 267, 268, 301, 307
independent assortment, 26
index of refraction, 4
India, 139, 152, *152*, 210, *210*, 341, *341*, 381, *381*
individual selection, 11–12
Indonesia, 140, *245*, *268*, 304, *304*
indri, *115*, *195*, 220, *220*

infanticide, 135, 152–53, 163–66, *165*, *166*, 169
controversy over, 164, 166
female counterstrategies for, *164*, 164–65, *165*, 166
by monkeys, 122, 164
infant mortality, 148
information, culturally acquired, 409–10
infraorders, 118, 119
inheritance
blending, 21–22
blending *vs.* Mendelian, 63, *63*
discontinuous, 60–61
role of chromosomes in, 26–37
Initial Upper Paleolithic (IUP), 344, *345*
insectivores, 116–17, *117*, 128, *128*, 129, *129*, 196, 209, 218, 219, 220
dentitin and digestive tract of, 117, *117*
insects, 74, 75, 214, 418
Institute of Contemporary Evolution, 65
insulin, 41, 366
insulin-dependent diabetes, 366
intelligence
behavioral flexibility hypothesis of, 194, 196
brain size and, 114, 196, *197*
coalition formation and, 198, 199, *199*
cumulative cultural adaptation not byproduct of, 414
deception in, *200*, 200–1, *201*
ecological hypothesis of, 194, *194*
extractive foraging hypothesis of, 196
kinship relations and, 197–98
of primates, 114, *190*, 198
social hypothesis of, 194, 196
theory of mind in, 200
interbreeding, 83, *83*, 85, 87, 89, 338, *339*, 340
interglacial periods, 298, 305, 318
International HapMap Project, 370
intersexual sexual selection, 156
interspecific associations, 134
intrasexual selection, 156–59, *157*, *158*
introns, 44–46, *46*, 49, 363
Inuit, 344, *409*, 409–10, 415
"investing" males, 156, 159–60
Iraq, *307*, 311
iris, 4
Irula, *337*
Isaac, Glyn, 292
ischium, 241
islands, body size and, 304
isolated populations, genetic drift and, *73*, 73–74
isoleucine, *42*
isotopes, 212, 213, 214, 250
nitrogen, 309
Israel, 292, 302, *325*, 326, 393
Italy, 228, 345, 376
Ivory Coast, 133, 137

Taï Forest, 124, 125, 134, 139, 162, *163*, 280, *280*

jacanas, 146
jackals, 289
Jadera haematoloma (soapberry bug), *65*, 65–68, *66*, *67*, 389
Japan, 148, *148*, 377
Japanese macaques, 148, *149*, 164
Java, 267, 268, *268*, 303
jaws, 263, *264*
Jenkin, Fleeming, 21–22, 64
Jerimalai, Timor, 342
Johannesburg, 248
Johanson, Donald, 246
Jolly, Alison, 112

Kabwa (Broken Hill) cranium, 300, *300*, 301
Kalahari Desert, Africa, *277*, 398
Kanapoi, Kenya, 245, 250
kangaroos, 16, 242, *252*, 253
Kanyawara, 124
Kaplan, Hillard, 276, 277, 280
Kapsalis, Ellen, 179
Kapthurin Formation, Kenya, 327, 329
kapunji monkey, *139*
Karisoke Research Center, 123
Katanda, Congo, 328, *329*
Kebara, 326
Keefe, Richard, 398
Keeley, Lawrence, 274
KE family, *362*, 362–63
Kelley, Jay, 253, 268
Kenrick, Douglas, 398
Kenya, *125*, 139, 182, 235, 244, 327, 329
Amboseli National Park, *89*, 150, 160, 197
Ileret, 263, *264*, 266
Kipsigis of, 402–3, *403*
Koobi Fora, 262, 268, 272, *272*, 284, 287
Lake Turkana, 245, *245*, 246, 253, *253*, 257, 263, *263*, 264, 268, 270, *419*, *419*, 420, *420*, 422
Losidok site, 227
Olorgesailie, 264, 274
Rift Valley, 229, 402
Tugen Hills, *245*
Kenyapithecus, 228
Kenyathropus platyops, 244, 251, 257, 273
of *H. erectus*, 273–74
keratin, 42
Kibale Forest, Uganda, 124, *129*, 133, 170, 185
kibbutz, 393
kibbutz age-mates, 393–94
kill sites, 282, *285*, 285–86, 290, 293
Kimeu, Kimoya, 268, *269*
King, Martin Luther, Jr., 383

kin recognition, 176, 178
   contextual cues in maternal
      recognition, 176–77
   contextual cues in paternal
      recognition, 177
   facial resemblances and, 176, 176, 178
   in social behavior, 179, 179–83,
      180, 182
kin selection, 172–84, 404
   contextual cues in, 176–79
   domestic arrangements and, 392
   Hamilton's rule of, 174–75, 184
   parent-offspring conflict and, 184
   phenotype and, 176
   polyandrous marriage and, 392
   in primates, 172–74, 174, 176, 176–77,
      177, 178
Kipsigis, 402–3, 403
Klamath River, 418
Klasies River, South Africa, 326, 341
Klein, Richard, 257, 258, 266, 320,
   320, 330
knapping, 270, 303, 303, 327
knees, 237, 237
KNM-ER 1470, 263, 263
KNM-ER 1808, 287, 287
KNM-ER 1813, 263
KNM-ER 2598, 265
KNM-ER 3733, 264, 264
KNM-ER 42700, 268
KNM-WT 15000, 268–69, 269
KNM-WT 17000, 254
knuckle walking, 94, 94, 95, 242
Koenig, Andreas, 152
Köhler, Wolfgang, 194
Koisan, 335
Komodo dragons, 305
Konso-Gardula, Ethiopia, 264
Koobi Fora, Kenya, 262, 268, 272, 272,
   284, 287
Kosovo, 384
Kromdraai, South Africa, 255
!Kung, 277, 281, 376, 396

La Chapelle-aux-Saints, France, 310, 311
lactase persistence, 368, 368, 369, 369,
   371, 380
lactase-phlorizin hydrolase (LHP), 368
lactation, 75, 98, 109, 146, 278
   female reproductive behavior and, 148
   infanticide and, 164
   parental care and, 146, 147
lactose, 47, 48, 367–68, 368, 371, 380,
   388
Laetoli, Tanzania, 245, 246, 251, 316
La Ferrassie, France, 310, 325
Lahr, Marta, 318
Lake Malawi, 263
Lake Mungo, Australia, 331, 342
Lake Tanganyika, Kenya, 89, 124,
   125, 410

Lake Turkana, Kenya, 245, 245, 246,
   253, 253, 257, 263, 263, 264, 268, 270,
   419, 419, 420, 420, 422
Laland, Kevin, 194, 196
Lamalera, 422
Lancaster, Jane, 276
land-for-debt swaps, 140
language
   as adaptation, 330
   of Neanderthals, 313
   origins of, 312–13
langurs, 121, 136, 154, 164, 169, 199
   gray, 121, 129, 152, 154, 160, 164, 164,
      166, 170
   hanuman, 162
   mating system of, 152, 152, 153, 165
Lannister, Tyrion, 12
Laos, 331
large ground finch (Geospiza
   magnirostris), 18, 18, 85, 85
Laron syndrome, 305
larynx, 313
Lascaux cave paintings, France, 350–51
Latin America, deforestation in, 139
Laurasia, 210, 210
LCT, 368
leaf clipping, 312
leaf monkeys, 111, 112, 121
Leakey, Jonathan, 262
Leakey, Louis, 262
Leakey, Louise, 263
Leakey, Mary, 246, 251, 255, 256,
   262, 284
Leakey, Meave, 245, 257, 263
Leakey, Richard, 262, 263, 265
leaping locomotion, 216
learning, natural selection and, 282, 389
Le Chauvet Cave, France, 350, 351
Ledi Garu, 263
Lee, Sang-Hee, 349
leister (fishing spear), 409, 409
Le Moustier, France, 310
lemurids, 116, 116
Lemuriformes, 115, 118, 118
lemurs, 112, 132, 217
   dwarf, 218
   fat-tailed dwarf, 111
   fork-marked, 137
   golden bamboo, 140
   mouse, 118, 138, 147
   pygmy mouse, 110
   ring-tailed, 111, 112, 118
   social learning in, 413
   teeth of, 116
lens of an eye, 4
leopards, 132, 133, 134, 134, 252,
   289, 290
lesser apes (Hylobatidae), 93, 122–23
leucine, 42
Levallois tool technique, 303, 303
Levant, 344, 345

Lévi-Strauss, Claude, 394, 404
Liang Bua, 304, 305
Lieberman, Daniel, 269
Lieberman, Debra, 394
Lieberman, Philip, 313
life expectancy
   of anatomically modern humans,
      253, 349
   brain size and, 189–90
   foraging and, 282
   of hominoids, 253
   of Neanderthals, 311
   of primates, 193
   of Upper Paleolithic peoples vs.
      Neanderthals, 349
life history, of primates, 193
life history theory, 190–93
limpet (Patella sp.), 15
linkage, genes and, 33
linked loci, 36
Linnaeus, Carolus, 91, 110
lions, 132, 133, 156, 157, 169, 190, 209,
   289, 289, 309, 350, 408
lizards, 304
local adaptations, 74–75
loci, 33, 375, 382–83, 391
   continuous variation and, 60–62
   linked and unlinked, 36
   microsatellite, 338, 338
   mutation and, 63
   in recombination, 36
   statue and, 377
Lockwood, Charles, 255
locomotion, 209, 223, 226. see also
   bipedalism
   brachiation, 123
   evolution of, 94, 95, 96
   hind-limb dominated, 113
   quadrupedal, 94, 94, 209, 215, 221,
      242, 243, 243
   suspensory, 226, 228, 228, 229, 242
   vertical clinging and leaping, 118,
      118
logging, 139
Lomako, 124
Lomekwi, Maat, 270
longevity, 191
   big brains and, 189–90, 192–93, 193
   female fitness and variation in, 149,
      149, 150
long noncoding RNAs (lncRNAs), 49
long-tailed macaques, 131, 152, 162
Lonsdorf, Elizabeth, 412
Lordkipanidze, David, 266, 267
lordosis, 251
lorises, 112, 116, 116, 119, 218
Lorisiformes, 118, 119
Losidok, Kenya, 227
"lost European explorer experiment,"
   409, 409
lowland gorillas, 124

Lucy, 246, *246*, *247*, *250*
Lufengpithecus, 228
Luhea processing techniques, 413
lysine, *42*

Maasai, 376
Maba, China, 303
macaques, 122, 134, 150, *176*, 177, *177*, 182, 312
    bonnet, *146*, *148*, *176*, *177*, 199, *199*
    brain of, *195*
    coalitions of, 181
    Japanese, 148, *149*, 164
    level of expression of genes in prefrontal cortex of, 359, *359*
    long-tailed, 131, *152*, 162
    mating system of, 161, 162, 392
    reciprocal altruism and, 185
    rhesus, 177, *178*, 200–1
Machigenga, Peru, 251
MacLarnon, Ann, 313
MacLatchy, Laura, 226
macroevolution, 81–82
macropods, 242
Madagascar, 118, 132, *135*, 138, 140
Magdalenian tool industry, 345
magnetic fields, 214
Mahale Mountains, 124
Makapansgat, 248
maladaptations, 70, 74, 416
Malapa, 248
malaria, 364, *364*, 366, 367, 369
male-male competition, 160–63, *161*, *162*, *163*
Mal'ta, Siberia, 349
mammals, 91, *91*, 109, 111, *113*, 116, 137
    average life span of species of, 225
    body size and gestation length in, *147*
    brain of, 190
    limited cooperation among, 417
    placental, 16, 207
    sexual reproduction in, 144
    therapsid ancestors of, 207
mammoths, 343, 347, 348, *348*, 350, *350*
    wooly, 302
mandible, 116
mangabey, 220, *220*
Manú National Park, Peru, *130*
marmosets, 116, *116*, 119, 120, *121*, 127, 136, 137, *148*, 160, *160*, 219
    kin selection in, 183
    mating system of, 152, 158, 160, *160*
marsupials, *16*, 16–17, 190, *191*, 207, 221, 342
Martin, Robert, 95, 111, 224, 225
Mata Menge, 305
mate defense territoriality, 132
mate guarding, 389
    evolution of, *65*, 65–68, *66*, *67*
    by male primates, 159, *159*, 162, *162*, 170–71, *171*

Mathew, Sarah, 419, 422
mating systems and mate selection, 130, 143–67, 391–401
    of chimpanzees, *392*
    controversy over evolutionary analyses of, 401
    culture and, 400–1, *401*
    dominance hierarchies in, 151, *151*
    evolution of reproductive strategies in, 145–47
    female reproductive strategies in, *147*, 147–48, *148*, 149, *149*, 152–55
    of gorillas, 156
    inbred, 391
    infanticide and, 135, 152–53, 163–66, *165*, *166*
    intersexual selection in, 156
    intrasexual selection in, 156–59, *157*, *158*
    male strategies in, 155–59, *156*, *157*
    male tactics in, *159*, 159–63, *160*, *161*, *162*, *163*
    misunderstandings between men and women, 399–400, *400*
    number of sexual partners, 399, *399*
    outbred, 391
    parental care in, *145*, 145–47, *146*, 154–55, *155*
    parental investment theory and, 397–98
    paternal care in, 145–47, *146*, 159–60
    preferred ages of partners in, 398, *398*
    of primates, *136*, 137, 145–67, *146*, *147*, *148*, *153*, *156*, *157*, *158*, *160*, *161*, *162*
    psychology in, 395–96
    questionnaire on desirability of traits, 396–97, *397*
    sexual dimorphism in, 156–58, *157*, *158*
    sexual selection in, 156, *156*
    social behavior in, 153–54, *154*
    social consequences of, 401–3, *403*
Matopo Hills, Zimbabwe, *89*
matrilineage rank, 182, *182*
Mauer, Germany, 301
Mauran, 308
maxilla, 116
Mayr, Ernst, 11, 61
Mbuti, 252, *292*, 335
McBrearty, Sally, 327
McGrew, William, 269
meat eating
    archaeological evidence for, 284–88
    food sharing and, 278, 279
    by *H. erectus*, 287
Mediterranean Sea, 218, 226
medium ground finch (*Geospiza fortis*), 7, 7–11, *9*, *10*, *11*, 12, 17–18, *18*, *84*, 85, *85*
medulla, *195*
meerkats, 410

Mehtakheri, India, 341
meiosis, 28–29, *29*, 35, *35*, 36
Melanesia, 372
Melis, Alice, 186
menarche, 402
Mendel, Gregor, 25–26, *26*, 30, 34, 53, 55, 56
    Darwinian genetics and, 53, 60, 61
    experiments of, 26, 27, *27*, 29–33, *30*, *31*, 34–35
    principles of, 26, 29, 33, 56, 362
menopause, 191
Menzel, Emil, 200, *200*
Mesozoic era, 207, *208*, 214
messenger RNA (mRNA), 44, *45*, *48*
methionine, *42*
Mezmaiskaya, Caucasus Mountains, 315
microevolution, 81
microliths, 328, *328*, 341, 345
Micronesia, 366, 372
Micropithecus, 227
microRNAs (miRNAs), 49
microsatellite loci, 338, *338*
midbrain, *195*
Middle Stone Age (MSA), 327, 328, 329
mineralization, 211
minerals, 126, *127*
Ming, Yao, 388
minor marriages, 393, *393*
Miocene epoch, *208*, 221, 223, 226
    climate change in, 211, *211*, 233
    hominoid development during, 230
mismatch hypothesis, 423–24
Mississippi Delta, indigenous people of, *391*
Mitani, John, 185
mitochondria, 314, 332
mitochondrial DNA (mtDNA), 314, 332, 333, *334*, 335, 344
mitochondrial Eve, 332
mitosis, 28–29, *29*
Mixe, *337*
modern synthesis, 61
Mode 1 technology, 271, 273
Mode 2 technology, 273
Mode 3 technology, 303
Mode 1 tools, 271, 275, 305
Mode 2 tools, *273*, 273–74, 275, 318, *319*
Mode 3 tools, 308, 318, *319*
Mode 4 tools, 327, 345
Mode 5 tools, 328
molars, *113*, 116, *116*, *117*, 120, 122, *220*, 228–29, 234, 235, 238, *240*, 240–41, 245, 247, *248*, *249*, 250, 253, 254, 255, *255*, 256, 257, 268, 307, *308*, 315
Moldova, *348*
molecular clocks, 102
molecular genetics, 37–49, 314, 356
moles, *91*, 91–92, *92*
molluscs, 14, *15*, 75
Mongolia, 343

monkeys, 110, 111, 112, *120, 121,* 121–22, 127, *130,* 133, 138, *139,* 148, *148,* 192, 193. *see also specific species*
 alarm calling by, 171–72, *172,* 173–74, *174*
 anatomical features distinguishing apes from, 226, *226,* 229, *229*
 associative learning and, 199–200
 blue, *11,* 137, 139, 160, *179*
 brain size in, 193–96
 early evolution of, 209, 218, *218,* 230
 extracted food and, *195*
 golden, 180
 infanticide by, 122, 164
 intelligence of, 194, 196
 kin recognition by, 177
 knowledge about kinship relationships by, 197–98
 New World (*see* New World monkeys)
 observational learning by, 412–13
 Old World (*see* Old World monkeys)
 reciprocal altruism and, 185
 reproduction of, *11,* 11–12
 at typewriter, 13–14
monogamy, 137, 144, 159, 392
monozygotic (identical) twins, 374, *375*
moon wrasse, *17*
Moremi Game Reserve, 164, 166
Morgan, T. H., 26, 29
Mormons, 371, 372
Morocco, 329, *329*
Moroto, Uganda, 226
Morotopithecus bishopi, 226, *226,* 227
morphemes, 312
morphine, 126
morphology, 371. *see also* sexual dimorphism
 of anatomically modern humans, 324–25, *325*
 behavior and, 65
 of chimpanzees, 82, *82*
 dental, 116–17, *117*
 Dmanisi hominins, 266, *266, 267,* 269
 of finches, 8–10, *61,* 61–62, *62,* 64, 68–69, 81, 88, 169
 of gorillas, 82, *82*
 of *H. erectus,* 265, *265*
 of *H. floresiensis,* 304, *304, 305*
 of Miocene hominoids, *227*
 of Neanderthals, 307, 308, *308,* 320
 sexual selection and, *156,* 156–59, *157*
 species and, 82
mortuary practices, 326
most recent common ancestry (MRCA), 332, 335, 336, 340
motor neurons, 48
mound builders, Mississippi Delta, *391*
mountain gorillas, 123–24, *124, 129,* 140, 152, 156, 164, 196
mouse, 359

mouse lemurs, 118, 138, 147
Mousterian tool industry, 308, 327, 344, 345
MSA (Middle Stone Ages), 327, 328, 329
multicellular organisms, gene regulation and, 49
multiparous, 148
Mumba, Tanzania, *341*
Mumbwa Cave, Zambia, 328
muriquis (woolly spider monkey), 119, *120, 129,* 140, 180
music, 351
musk oxen, 306, 343
mutation, 81, 102, 333, 364, 369, 387
 in anatomically modern humans, 358
 genetic frequency and, 55
 genetic variation and, 333, 363–64
 loci and, 63
 nonrecombining sections of DNA and, 332
 parental care and, 146
 variation and, 63–64, 336
mutation-drift equilibrium, 336, *336*
mutualism, *170,* 170–71
myoglobin, 95, 97, *97*

Nacholapithecus, 228
Nadel, Dani, 347, 348
Nägeli, Karl Wilhelm von, 26
Nakalipithecus nakayamai, 229
naked mole rat, 419, *419*
NASA, *190*
Native Americans, 328, 376, 419, *419*
natural classification system, 380
naturalistic fallacy, 166
natural selection, 38, 61, 81, 143, 209, 233, 363, 383, 387, 400, 416
 altruism and, 169, 172–73
 balanced polymorphism and, 364
 behavior and, *65,* 65–68, *66, 67,* 389
 bipedalism and, 242–43
 body size and, 376, *376*
 correlated characters and, 68–70
 Darwin on, 6, 21–22
 Darwin's finches as examples of, *7,* 7–11
 disequilibrium and, 70–71
 DNA and, 38, 47, 357–58, 361, 369
 environment and, 26–28, *27, 28, 30,* 30–33, *31, 32, 33, 34,* 34–35, *35, 36,* 36–37, 53, *54,* 60, 62
 in genetic frequency, 54, 59–60
 in genetics of continuous variation, 61–62
 genetic variation and, *337,* 338, 340, 364–69
 hidden variation and, *64,* 64–65
 inbreeding and, 392
 individual, 11–12
 intermediate steps favored by, 14–17
 learning and, 282, 389

 life history and, 192
 local *vs.* optimal adaptations and, 74–75
 morphology and, 215
 parental care and, 146
 phenotypes and, 59, 60
 random variation and, 13–14
 reciprocal altruism and, 185
 regulatory genes and, 47
 senescence (aging) and, 191
 sexual selection and, 155–56
 strategies and, 144
 territoriality and, 132–33
 in variation maintenance, 63–65
Natural Theology (Paley), 5
nature-nurture question, 388, 415
Nauru, 366
Navarrete, Carlos, 394
Neanderthals, 305–16, *308*
 body shape of, 307, *309*
 brain of, 306, 307
 burial of dead by, 310, 349
 classification of, 320–21
 common human ancestry with, 340–41
 crural index, 308, *309*
 disappearance of, 323–24
 DNA of, 314–15, 332, 333
 emergence of, 306
 in Eurasia, 309
 in Europe, *301*
 face of, 307
 fossils of, 306–7, 326
 genome in, 315, 333, 338–39, *339*
 handedness of, 308
 humans' genetic distance from, 307, 315, *315*
 hunting by, 308–9
 injury and disease in, 311, 314, *314*
 interbreeding of, 338, *339,* 340
 language of, 313
 life expectancy of, 311, 314, 348
 morphology of, 306, 307, *307, 308*
 overlap with anatomically modern humans, 345
 personal adornment and, 311, *311*
 population sizes of, 316, *316*
 shelters and home bases of, 310
 skulls of, 306, 307, *307,* 311, *325*
 subsistence economies of, 346–47
 teeth of, 307, *308*
 toolmaking of, 308–9, 327
 Upper Paleolithic people compared with, 347–49
 world distribution of, 306–7
Neel, James V., 366
negatively correlated characters, 69
negative selection, 359
neocortex, 194, *195*
neocortex ratio, 194
neoteny, 359

Nepal, *129*, 152, 164

neurons, 48

New Guinea, 304, 326, 336, *337*, 339, 342

New World monkeys, 119, *120*, 121
evolution of, 219, 221–23, *222*
teeth of, 116, *116*, 221

Ngaloba cranium, 316

Ngandong, Java, 303

Ngeneo, Bernard, 263

Ngogo, 124, 185

Ngorongoro Crater, Tanzania, *157*

Niah Cave, Borneo, 331

niches
created by flowering plants, 214
in speciation, *90*, 90–91

Nilsson, Dan-Eric, 20

Nishida, Toshisada, 124

nitrogen-14, 213

nitrogen isotopes, 309

nocturnal primates, 111, 217, *217*

noncoding RNA (ncRNA), 49

non-insulin-dependent diabetes (NIDD), 366

"noninvesting" males, 146

nonrecombining part of Y chromosome (NRY), 332

nonsynonymous substitutions, 358

North America, 210, *210*, 218, 223, 324, 376
primate evolution in, 216–17

Northern Africa, 122, *299*, 329, *369*, 383

nucleotides, 357, 358, 368

nucleus. *see* cells, nucleus of

Nuer, 376, *425*

nursing, 154

observational learning, 412–13, *413*, 414, *414*, 415

obsidian, 329

occipital torus, *265*, *300*

Oceania, 372

oceans, 210, *210*
deep-sea cores and temperatures in, 212, *212*
global temperatures and, *306*

Odzala-Kokoua National Park, 139

offspring
reproduction and quality of, 191–92

OH 7, 262, *262*

Ohalo II, 347, 348

oils, 126, *127*

Okavango Delta, Botswana, *133*, 198, 414

Old Order Amish, 371, *371*, 372

Oldowan toolmakers, 273
archaeological evidence for meat eating, 284–88, *286*
domestic lives of, 292–94
evidence for complex foraging by, 276–86
hunters or scavengers?, 288–90

Oldowan tools, 270–71, *271*, *272*, 272–73, 275, 284, 292

Olduvai Gorge, Tanzania, 255, 256, 262, 263, 264, 270, 284, *284*, *285*, 286, *286*, 291, 292–93, *293*

Olduvai Hominin, 255

Olduvai Hominin 7, 262

Old World monkeys, 21, *117*, 119, 219, 239, 243
in fossil record, 230
grooming in, 180
mating system of, 150
teeth of, *116*, *117*, 221

olfactory, 112, *113*

Oligocene epoch, *208*, *211*, 218–19, *219*, 222, 223

oligopithecids, 219, *219*, 221

Olorgesailie, Kenya, 264, 274

Omo Kibish 1, *318*

Omo-Kibish Formation, Ethiopia, 325, *326*

Omomyidae, *217*, 217–18, *218*

On the Origin of Species (Darwin), 21, 81, 91

opossums, 190, *191*, 192, 219

opposable thumb, primates and, *113*

optimal adaptations, 74–75

orangutans (*Pongo pygmaeus*), 94, *94*, *101*, 101–2, *102*, *103*, 104, *104*, 122, 123, *123*, 125, 136, 140, 196, 228–29, 230
behavioral variation in, 410
bipedalism and, 243, *243*
endangered, 137
foraging by, 276
hominoid relative of, 228
life history strategies of, 193, *193*
phylogeny of, *92*, *93*
physical and social cognition in, 201–2, *202*
sexual dimorphism in, 252
sociality of, 196
tool use by, 269

orbital convergence, 215

orbits (eye sockets), 215, 217

Oreopithecus, 228

organelles, 44

ornaments, *329*, 329–30, *330*

Orrorin tugenensis, 235, *235*, 238, *238*, 239, 241

ostrich eggs/eggshells, 329, *330*, 341, *341*

Ouranopithecus, 229

outbred matings, 391

out-groups, 101, 358

ovulation, *164*

Owen, Richard, 91, *91*

owl monkeys, 119, 120, 147, 160, 217, 221

oxygen, in sea water, 210, *210*

Pääbo, Svante, 314, 315, 357

Packer, Craig, 156

pair-bonding, 136, *136*, 137, 144, *145*, 158, 159–60

Paleocene epoch, *208*, *211*, 215

paleontologists, 114, 211

paleontology, methods, 211, 213–14

Paleozoic era, *208*

Paley, William, 5

Palombit, Ryne, 159, 166

Panama, *131*

Pangaea, 210, *210*, 214

Pan paniscus. see bonobos (*Pan paniscus*)

Pan troglodytes. see chimpanzees, common (*Pan troglodytes*)

Paraguay, 277, *277*

Paranthropus
P. aethiopicus, 244, 253–54, *254*
P. boisei, 244, 255–56, *256*, 273
P. robustus, 244, 255, *255*, 256, *256*, *265*, 273, 291

parapatric speciation, 89, *89*, 90

parapithecids, 219, *219*, 221

parental investment theory, mate preferences and, 397–98

parenting
culture and, 393, 395
in mating systems, *145*, 145–47, *146*, 154–55, *155*, 393, 394, 397–98
mutations and, 146
natural selection and, 146
tradeoffs and, 190
unequal parental investment, 145–46

parent-offspring conflict, 184

Parra, Flavia, 382

Partner Institute for Computational Biology, 359

passive hammer technique in tools and toolmaking, 270

pastoralism, 368–69, *369*, 398, 402

Patagonia, 221, 376

patas monkeys, 160, 162

paternal care, 159–60

Patne, India, *341*

PAX6, 49

peacocks, 155, *156*

peas, Mendel's experiments with, *26*, 26–28, *27*, 29–32, *30*, *31*, *33*, 34–35, 37, 53, *54*, 60, 62

Pelger, Susanne, 20

pelvis and bipedalism, 236, *236*, *237*, 241–42, *242*

Permian period, 207

Perry, Susan, 162, 199, 413

personal adornment, 311, *311*

Peru, *130*, 251

Petralona cranium, 300, *300*

Phayre's langur, 139

phenemes, 312

phenotypes, 30–31, *31*, *33*, 34, *34*, 35, *36*, 38, 47, 53, 357, 382
blending genes in, 63
expression of characters and, 61–62

phenotypes *(continued)*
  heritability and, 374
  in kin selection, 176
  natural selection and, 59, 60
  optimal, 74–75
phenotypic matching, 176
phenotypic traits, 388–89
  complex, variation in, 373–79
  genetic and environmental influences
    on, 360–61
phenotypic variation, geographical
  distance from Africa and
  reduction in, 338
phenylalanine, *42*
phenylketonuria (PKU), 54, *54*, 55, 56,
  59–60, 69, 363, 391
Philippines, 119
photoreceptors, 14–15, *15*
photosynthesis, 250
phylogenies
  of anatomically modern humans,
    298, 333
  ancestral characters and, *97*,
    98–101, *99*, *100*
  of chimpanzees, *93*, 94, *94*, *95*
  classification and, *103*, 103–5, *104*
  in comparative method, 94, 96, *96*
  convergence in, 97–98, *98*
  definition of, 92
  genetic distance in, *101*, 101–3, *102*
  of *H. erectus*, 298, 320, *320*
  of *H. ergaster*, 320, *320*
  of *H. heidelbergensis*, 320, *320*
  of hominins, *225*, 257–58, *258*, 320
  of hominoids, *92*, 92–93
  of hypothetical lineage, 225, *225*
  of modern humans, 94, *95*
  of Neanderthals, 320
  of primates, 94, 96–97, *97*
  reconstruction of, 93–95, 97–105
  speciation and, 81–105
  taxonomy of, 93–95, *94*, *95*
physics, 76
Pickford, Martin, 235
picks, 273
Pierolapithecus, 228
Pierolapithecus catalaunicus, 228,
  229
pigeons, 199
  domestication of, *19*, 19–20
pigs, 214, 284
Pinnacle Point, South Africa, *328*
Pitheciidae primates, 119, 121
PKU (phenylketonuria), 54, *54*, 55, 56,
  59–60, 69
placental mammals, 16, 207
plastic environment, 389
plastic mate-guarding trait, 66
Platyrrhini primates, *115*, 119, 136
playing, 130, *130*
pleiotropic effects, 69

Pleistocene epoch, *208*, 230, 415
  climate of, 262, *262*
  Late, 303–5, 326–30
  Lower, 262, *266*
  Middle, 262, *262*, 297, 298–99, *299*,
    303, 306, *311*, 316, 318, 320–21, 324
  Upper, 262, *262*, 298, 304, *307*
plesiadapiforms, 215, 215–16, *216*
Pliocene epoch, *208*, *211*, 230, 234, *262*
pneumatized, 248, *249*
poaching, 137
Poeciliopsis, 20, *20*
Poland, 346
polio, 314, *314*
Pollard, Katherine, 359, 360
polyandry, 137, 392
polygynandry (promiscuity), 137, 160
polygyny, *136*, 137, 160, 392
  of Kipsigis, 402–3, *403*
Polynesia, 372
Pongidae. *see* great apes (Pongidae)
Pope, Teresa, 161, 182
population genetics, 53–77
population sizes, 316, *316*, 336, *337*
porcupines, 219
porphyria variegata, 372
Portugal, 310, 382, *382*
positively correlated characters, 68
positively selected genes, 358
positive selection, since
  human-chimpanzee split, 359–60
postcranial skeleton
  of anatomically modern humans, 324
  of *Au. afarensis*, 251
  of *Au. africanus*, 248, 251
  of *Au. garhi*, 247
  of early *Homo*, 264
  of Eocene primates, 218, *218*
  of *H. erectus*, 268
  of *H. floresiensis*, *305*
  of *Paranthropus*, 254, 255
potassium-40, 213, 214
potassium-argon dating, 213, 214
pottos, 116, *116*, 134
Potts, Richard, 274, 293, 294
Precambrian era, *208*
precision grip, of primates, 111, *113*
predation and predators
  alarm calling and, 134, 171–72,
    172, 312
  by chimpanzees, 132, 134, *134*,
    270, *270*
  defenses and, 134
  grooming and, 179
  kill sites and, *285*, 285–86, 290, 293
  by leopards, 132, *133*, 134, *134*
  life history and, 192
  in primate ecology, 127, 132–34,
    133, *134*
  scavenging by, 288–90
  sociality and, 134–35

Predmostí 3, *325*
Predmostí, Czech Republic, 348
prefrontal cortex, neoteny and, 359, *359*
pregnancy, 147–48
prehensible thumb, primates and, *113*
prehensile tails, 119, *120*
premolars, *113*, 116, *116*, *117*, 121, 219,
  220, 221, 229, 235, 238, *238*, 240, 245,
  249, 250, 265
pressure flaking, *327*, 328
Preutz, Julia, 269
primary structure, 42
primates, 28, 67, 408
  activity patterns of, 130, *130*
  adaptations by, 119
  altruistic behavior in, 169–70, *170*,
    174, *179*, 184–86, *185*, *186*
  arboreal, 94, 96, *96*, 123, *123*, 127,
    134, 139, 214, 242
  in Asia, 123
  Atelidae, 119
  behavior of, 109, 110–11, *113*, 130, *131*,
    131–32, 202
  biogeography, *114*, 114–15, 121
  brain of, 112, *113*, 120, 147, 189–
    90, 193–96
  Callitrichinae, 120
  Catarrhini, *115*, 119, 121
  Cebidae, 119–20
  Cercopithecoidea, 121–22
  characters in definition of, 111–14,
    112, *113*, *114*, 191
  coalition formation by, 199, *199*
  cognitive evolution in, 194, 196
  color vision of, 112
  conservation of, 135, 137–40, *138*
  deceptive behavior in, *200*, 200–1, *201*
  dietary requirements of, 126–27, *127*
  disease and, 139
  diurnal, 111, *130*
  diversity within order of, 110–11,
    112, 118–25
  early evolution of, 209, 214–19, *215*,
    216, *217*, *218*
  Ebola virus and, 139
  ecology of, 125–34
  endangered species of, 135, *135*,
    137–40, *138*
  extracted foods and, 194
  eyes of, 112, *114*
  feet of, 111, *113*
  foraging challenges for, 128–29
  in fossil record, 220, 221, 222, *222*
  grooming by, *179*, 179–80
  guts of, *117*, 117–18
  hands of, 111, *113*
  Haplorrhini, 112, 115, *115*, 118,
    119, 119–21
  as herbivores, 127, 129
  Hominoidea, 123–25
  humans as, 110

Hylobatidae, *93*, 122–23
inbreeding avoidance in, 392–93
as insectivores, 128, *128*, 129, *129*
intelligence of, 114, *190*, 198
interspecific associations, 134
kin selection in, 172–74, *174*, *176*,
    176–77, *177*, *178*
knuckle walking of, 94, *94*, *95*
lactation in, 75, *145*, 146, 147
language of, 312
life history of, 112, 193
mating systems of, *136*, 136–37,
    145–67, *146*, *147*, *148*, *153*, *156*, *157*,
    158, *160*, *161*, *162*
nocturnal, 111, 217, *217*
nutrition in ecology of, *125*, 125–29,
    126, *127*, *128*, *129*
parental care in, 120, *145*, 147–48, *148*
phylogenies of, *94*, 94–95, *95*
Pitheciidae, 119, 121
Platyrrhini, *115*, 119, 136
precision grip, 111, *113*
predation and, 132–34, *133*, *134*
prehensile tails of, 119, *120*
ranging behavior of, *131*, 131–32
reasons for study of, 109–11
reciprocal altruism in, 184–86, *185*
reconciliatory behavior in,
    180–81, *181*
Rungwecebus, 138
senescence (aging) in, 191, *191*
shrew-like ancestor of, 209
sociality in, 134–35, 136–37, *137*
social organization among,
    136, 136–37
Strepsirrhini, 112, 114, 127, 136, *147*,
    216, 217, 223
Tarsiiformes, *115*, 119, *119*
taxonomy of, 115, *115*, 118
teeth of, *113*, 114, *116*, 116–17, *117*,
    157
terrestrial, 94, 96, *96*, 127, 134
territoriality in, 132–33
primiparous, 148
Proconsul africanus, *227*
Proconsulidae, 227
proconsulids, 227
Proconsul species (early hominoids), 227,
    227, 228, 239
prokaryotes, 44
proline, *42*
propliopithecids, 219, *219*, 221
Propliopithecus chirobates, *219*
protein coding genes
    differences between humans and
        chimpanzees, 357
    DNA in, 39–43
proteins, 49. *see also* enzymes
    in amino acids, *42*, 42–43, *43*
    in chromosomes, 37
    mRNA in synthesis of, 44, *45*

non-coding DNA in synthesis
    of, 49–50
primary structure of, 42
in primate nutrition, 126, 127, *127*
tertiary structure of, 42
tRNA in synthesis of, 44
proximity, kinship and, 176
Prugnolle, Franck, 338
psychoanalysis, 394
psychological mechanisms,
    special-purpose, 390, 391
psychology, evolutionary, 401
    in inbreeding avoidance, 391–94,
        392, 404
    learning predisposition and, 390, *390*
    mate preferences and, 395–96
    mismatch hypothesis and, 423–24
    personal qualities of ideal mates,
        396, *396*
    reasoning ability and, 390–91
    reciprocity and, 390
pubis, 241
Punnett square, 32, *33*, *34*, 35, *36*, *58*
Pusey, Anne, 152, 156
pygmy chimpanzees. *see* bonobos (*Pan
    paniscus*)
pythons, *133*

Qafzeh, Israel, *325*, 326
quadrupedalism, 242, 243, *243*
quadrupedal locomotion, 94, *94*, 209,
    215, 221
Quichua, *422*

race concept
    classification schemes for, 379–83,
        380, *381*, *382*
    culture and, 383–84
    as flawed, 379
racism, race concept and, 384
radioactive decay, 213
radiocarbon (carbon-14) dating, 213
radiometric dating methods, 211, 213–14
rafts, bamboo, 411, *411*
rain shadow, 226
Ramachandran, Sohini, 338
Ramnagar, 152, 164
random mating, genotypic frequencies
    and, 55–58, *58*, 59–60
raptors, 132, 134
Rasmussen, Tab, 216
rats, 199, 305, 359, 390, *390*
Reader, Simon, 194, 196
reasoning
    by analog, 110
    by homology, 110
recessive alleles, 30, 391–92
recessive genes, 363
reciprocal altruism, 184–86, *185*, 390,
    404, 420
reciprocity, cooperation and, 420

recombinant DNA technology, 44
recombination, 32–37, 387
reconciliatory behavior, in primates,
    180–81, *181*
red deer (elk), 19, 155, *156*, 308, *310*, 347
red howler monkeys, 161, 164, 182–83
redirected aggression, 198
red ocher, 329, *330*
Reed, Kaye, 263
reelin, 360
referential meaning, 312
regulatory genes, 39, 47–49, 358
Reichard, Ulrich, 159
reindeer, 306, 346, 347, 350
reinforcement, 88
relative dating methods, 214
religion, 384
repressor protein, 47, *48*
reproduction
    offspring quality and, 191–92
reproductive effort, energy requirement
    and, 126, 190–91
reproductive isolation, 83, 84, *85*, 85–86
reproductive strategies, evolution
    of, 145–47
reproductive system, 371
Republic of Georgia, *245*, 266, *266*, *267*
resource defense territoriality, 132
resting, 130, *130*
Reznick, David, 20
rheas, 146
rhesus macaques, 177, *178*, 200–1
rhinoceros, 284, 302, 308, *350*
ribonucleic acid. *see* RNA
    (ribonucleic acid)
ribosomes, 44, 49
Richerson, Peter, 410
Rieseberg, Loren, 85
Rift Valley, Kenya, 229, 266
Rightmire, G. Philip, 320, *320*
ring-tailed lemurs, 111, *112*, *188*
Rising Star Cave, 317, *317*
RNA (ribonucleic acid), 39, 44, 360
    messenger, 44, *45*, *48*
Robbins, Martha, 152
Roberts, Eila, 165
rock climbing, 416, *416*
rock shelters, 310
rodents, 221, 223, 302, 410
Romania, 331, 339
Ross, Corinna, 183
Rungwecebus primates, 138
running, 269
Russia, *324*, 339, 344, 348
Rwanda, 123, *129*, 140, 164

saber-toothed cat, 17, 293
sagittal crest, 254, *254*, 265
Sahara Desert, 298
Sahelanthropus tchadensis, 235, *235*,
    238, 239, 241

Sahul, 306, 342, *342*
Saint-Acheul, France, 273
Saint-Césaire, France, 345
saki monkeys, 121, 221
salmon, 190, 347, 418–19, *419*, 420
Saltzman, Wendy, 392
Sambungmachan, Java, 303
Samburupithecus kiptalami, 229
sampling variation, *71*, 71–72, *72*
sandpipers, spotted, 146
Sangiran 17, *268*
Santos, Laurie, 200
São Tomé, 382
Sarajevo, 360
scapulae, 226, 246, 308
scavenging, hunting and, 288–90
Schaafhausen, Hermann, 306
Schick, Kathy, 272, 274
Schmitt, David, 399
Schoningen, Germany, 302
Schwartz, Gary, 253, 268
sciatic notch, 241–42, *242*
scratching, *181*
sea horses, 146, *146*, 156
seals, 409
seashells, as personal adornment, 311, *311*
secondary compounds, 126–27, 129
selection. *see also* natural selection; sexual selection
    artificial, 19, *19*, 22
    correlated response to, 69–70, *70*
    detecting from DNA sequences, 358–59
    group selection, 172, 173
    individual, 11–12
    intersexual, 156
    intrasexual, 156–59, *157*, *158*
    life history and, 192
    stabilizing, 9
selection-mutation balance, 364
selective sweeps, 369
    DNA sequences and, 369–70
    haplotype length and, 369, *370*
self-directed behaviors, 180–81
Semaw, Sileshi, 239
Senegal, 269
senescence, 191, *191*
Senut, Brigitte, 235, 238
Sepher, Joseph, 394
Serbia, 380
Serengeti National Park, Tanzania, *157*
serine, *42*
sex ratio, 65, *66*, 66–67, *67*
sexual dimorphism, 111, *136*, 165, 218, 240, 245, *249*, 254. *see also* morphology
    in *A. afarensis*, *249*, 251
    in *A. africanus*, 251
    in australopiths, 252–53
    food foraging and, 282
    food sharing and, 282

in gorillas, 252
in *H. erectus*, 269
in hominids, 240
mating systems and, 156–58, *157*, *158*
in orangutans, 252
in *P. aethiopicus*, 254
in *P. robustus*, 255
in *Proconsul* species, 227
sexual reproduction
    blending in, 63
    female strategies in, *147*, 147–50, *148*, *149*, *150*, *152*, 152–54, *153*
    genotypic frequencies and, 55–58, *58*, 59–60
    hidden variation and, 64
    male strategies in, 155–59, *156*, *157*
    male tactics in, *159*, 159–63, *160*, *161*, *162*, *163*
    reproductive trade-offs, 154–55
sexual selection
    behavior and, 156, *156*
    characters and, 156
    definition of, 155
    intersexual, 156
    intrasexual, 156–59, *157*, *158*
    in mating systems, 156–59
    natural selection and, 155–56
sexual selection infanticide hypothesis, 164, 166
Seyfarth, Robert, 186, 197, 198, 312
Shanidar 1, 314, *325*
Shanidar Cave, Iraq, *307*, 311, *325*
sheep, wild, 308
shells, *329*
shelters, 310, 328
Shepard, Alan, *190*
Shimelmitz, Ron, 292
shrews, 209, 215
Shultz, Susanne, 134
siamangs, *93*, 123, *123*, *131*, 147, 160
    classification of, *103*, 104
Siberia, 343, *343*
    Denisova Cave fossils, 315, *315*, 316, 339
    Mal'ta, 349
sickle-cell anemia, 42, 361, *364*, 369, 380
Sifakas, *118*
silcrete, 328
Sillen, Andrew, 292
Sima de los Huesos, 306, *307*
Simien Mountains, 164
Simpson, George Gaylord, 61
single-nucleotide polymorphism (SNPs), 370
Sivapithecus, 228
Skhul Cave, Israel, 326
skin color, 380, *380*
skulls, 318, *318*, 320
    of *A. africanus*, 248, *248*, *254*, 265
    of *A. sediba*, *248*

of anatomically modern humans, *265*, 324, 325, *325*, *326*, 342
of *Ar. ramidus*, *240*
of Dikika child, *247*
of Dmanisi hominin, 267, *267*
of early *Homo*, 263, *263*
of *H. erectus*, *258*, 264, 264–65, *265*, *267*, 268
of *H. ergaster*, *258*
of *H. floresiensis*, 304, *305*
of *H. heidelbergensis*, *300*, 300–1, 306, *316*, 325, *326*
of hominins, 235, *235*, 244, 248–9, *249*, 253, 253–4, *254*, 255, *255*, 257, *257*, *258*, 263, *263*, *264*, *265*, *300*
of *Kenyanthropus platyops*, 257, *257*
of KNM-ER 1470, 263, *263*
of KNM-ER 1813, 263
of KNM-ER 2598, 265
of KNM-ER 3733, 264, *264*
of modern *Homo sapiens*, *316*
of Neanderthals, 306, 307, *307*, 311, *318*, *326*
of *P. aethiopicus*, 254, *254*
of *P. robustus*, 255, *265*
phenotypic variation and, 338
of *Sahelanthropus tchdensis*, *235*
sutures of, 311
skywalker hoolock gibbon, 138
sleeping, 130
sloths, 221
slow loris, 139
small ground finch (*Geospiza fuliginosa*), 85, *85*, 88
snakes, 134
SNP chips, 375
SNPs (single-nucleotide polymorphism), 370
Snyder-Mackler, Noah, 161
soapberry bug (*Jadera haematoloma*), *65*, 65–68, *66*, *67*, 389
social behavior
    altruism in, 170, 173, 174–76, 180–81
    competition in, 135
    costs and benefits of, 134–35
    dominance hierarchies and, 154, *154*
    Hamilton's rule, 173–75, *176*, 179, 180, 181, 184
    kin selection in, 179–83, *180*, *182*, *183*
    in primate group organization, 134–35, 157–58
    in primate mating systems, 154, *154*
    reciprocal altruism in, 184–86, *185*
social facilitation, 412
social intelligence hypothesis, 194, 196
sociality, brain size in monkeys and apes and, 193–94
social learning
    brain evolution and, 190
    culture and, 412

social life, cumulative cultural adaptation not byproduct of, 414
social networks, Middle Stone Age, 329
social organization, *136*, 136–37, 159, 240
solitary primates, 136, *136*
Solo River, Java, 267
Solutrean points, France, 328
Solutrean tool tradition, 345, 346, *346*
Sommer, Volker, 152, 166
"Sonic Hedgehog," 48
South Africa, 244, *245*, 246, 248, 255, 263, 283, 316, 317, *330*
    Afrikaners of, 372
    Blombos Cave, 327, *327*, 328, 329, *330*
    Diepkloof Rock Shelter, 329, *330*, *341*
    Drimolen, 255
    Klasies River Mouth, 326, *341*
    Kromdraai, 255
    Malapa, 249
    Pinnacle Point, *328*
    Still Bay, 327
    Swartkrans, 255, 264, 283, 291, *291*
South America, 139, 210, *210*, 218, 223, 324, 376
    primate evolution in, 221–22
Southeast Asia, 366–67
space travel, chimpanzees and, *190*
Spain, *311*, 316, 347
    Altamira, *347*
    seashell jewelry found in, 311, *311*
    Sima de los Huesos, 306, *307*
    Trinchera Dolina, 302, 306
spears, 269, 272, 274, 277, 302, *343*, 346, *409*
species, speciation, 81–105
    in adaptation, 11–12
    allopatric, 86–88, *87*, 320
    asexual, 86
    biological concept of, 83–84
    classification of, 91–93, *92*, *103*, 103–5, *104*
    Darwin on, 10, 81
    in Darwin's explanation of variation, 21–22
    ecological concept of, 84–86
    endangered, 135, *135*, 137–40, *138*
    genetic distance and, *101*, 101–3, *102*
    morphology and, 82
    niches in, *90*, 90–91
    origin of, 86–91
    parapatric, *89*, 89–90, *90*
    sympatric, 89–90, *90*
specific language impairment (SLI), *362*, 362–63
speech, 312, 358
sperm
    genetics and, 31–32, *32*, *33*
    production, 158
spherical gradient lens, 4
spheroids, 272

spider monkeys, 119, *120*
spiny dye-murex, *15*
spliceosomes, 49
Spoor, Fred, 262, *262*, 263
spotted sandpipers, 146
springhares, 242
squid, 17, *17*
squirrel monkeys, *113*, 119, 120, *120*, 131, *131*, 137, 221
Sri Lanka, *342*, 343, 384
stabilizing selection, 9, 64
Stanford, Craig, 279
Stanford study, *372*
starvation, food sharing and reduction in, 278
stasis, 11
stereoscopic vision, 112, *113*, *114*
Sterkfontein, 248, 255, 263
Still Bay points, bifacial, 327, *327*, 328
Strait of Gibraltar, 226
"strategy," use of term, 144
stratum (layer), 213
Strepsirrhines, 136
Strepsirrhini primates, 112, 114, 127, 136, *147*, 193, *216*, 217, 223
    brain of, *195*
    in taxonomy of living primates, 115, *115*, *118*, 118–19, *119*
    teeth of, *116*, 117
stress, index of, *181*
structuralist anthropology, 394
subnasal prognathism, 248, *249*
subsistence economies
    anatomically modern humans of, 346–47
    foraging groups and, 280
suckling times, *155*
Sudan, *425*
sufajas, 149
suids, 284
Sulawesi, 119
Sultan, *194*
Sumatra, 123, 137, 139, 193, *193*
Sunda, *342*
Sundaland, 306
superfamily, 104
suspensory locomotion, 226, 228, *228*, *229*, 242
Sussman, Robert, 216
Sutton, Walter, 29
sutures, 311
Suwa, Gen, 229, 239, 240
Swartkrans, South Africa, 255, 264, 283, 291, *291*
Sweden, 400, 401
Swisher, Carl, 268
sympatric speciation, 89–90, *90*
synonymous substitutions, 358
Systema Naturae (Linnaeus), 110
systematics, 95
    cladistic *vs.* evolutionary, 104–5

Szalay, Fred, 216
Szeletian tool industry, 345

T. asiatica, 288, *288*
T. saginata, 288, *288*
T. solium, *288*
Tabun, 292, 326
Taenia, 288
Taieb, Maurice, 246
Taï Forest, Ivory Coast, 124, 125, 133, 134, 139, 162, *163*, 280, *280*
Taiwanese minor marriages, 393, *393*
takeovers, *162*
    attempts, 161, *161*
    collective defense against, 183
    females and terminated pregnancies, 166, *166*
T-13910 allele, 368
tamarins, 116, *116*, 119, 120, 127, *129*, 136, 137, *148*, 160, *160*, 183
    golden lion, 140, *183*
    mating systems of, 152
Tam Pan Ling Cave, Laos, 331
tannins, 126
Tanzania, 138, *157*
    Gombe Stream National Park, *89*, 124, 125, *125*, 152, *153*, *155*, *160*, *196*, 279, 314, *314*, 392, 412
    Laetoli, *245*, 246, 251, 316
    Mahale Mountains, 124
    Mumba, *341*
    Olduvai Gorge, 255, 256, 262, 263, 264, 270, 284, *284*, *285*, 286, *286*, 291, 292–93, *293*
    Serengeti National Park, *157*
tapetum, 217
tapeworms, 288, *288*
taphonomy, 285–86, 290, 291, 293
tarsiers, 116, *116*, 118, 119, *119*, 137, 217, 220, *220*
Tarsiiformes, *115*, 119, *119*
Tasmania, 342
Taung child, 248, *248*
taurodont roots, 307, *307*
taxonomy, 93–95, *94*, *103*, 103–5, *104*
    cladistic, 104, *104*, 105
    evolutionary, 104, *104*, 105
    of living primates, 115, *115*, 118
Taylor, Andrea, 193
Tay-Sachs disease, 356, 363, 364, 365, 391
technologies, adaptive, 327–28
teeth
    of *A. afarensis*, *238*, 249
    of *A. africanus*, 255, 256, *256*
    of *A. anamensis*, 245
    of *A. garhi*, 247, *247*
    of *A. zeuxis*, 221
    of *Ar. kadabba*, 238, *238*
    of *Ar. ramidus*, 238, 239–41, *240*
    of *Australopithecus deyiremeda*, 247

teeth (continued)
    in australopiths, 244, 248–49,
        249, 250
    bones marked by, 285, 286, 287,
        287, 290
    of chimpanzees, 235, 240, 240
    of chimpanzees, common (Pan
        troglodytes), 249
    in dietary adaptations, 116–17
    of Dikika child, 247
    of early Homo, 261
    enamel on, 191, 213, 229, 250,
        253, 308
    facts revealed by, 220
    of H. erectus, 265, 265
    of hominins, 235, 238, 238, 240, 240–
        41, 241, 244, 245, 247, 248, 249, 250,
        253, 255, 255–56, 256, 263, 265
    of K. platyops, 244, 257
    of Miocene apes, 234
    of modern humans, 234, 331
    of Neanderthals, 307, 308
    of Omomyidae, 217
    of Orrorin tugenensis, 235–36
    of P. aethiopicus, 244
    of P. boisei, 256, 256
    of P. robustus, 255, 255, 256
    of Paranthropus species, 244
    of primates, 113, 114, 116, 116–17,
        117, 158
    of Sahelanthropus tchadensis,
        235, 235
    of Strepsirrhini primates, 116, 117
    taurodont roots, 307, 307
    zygomatic arch of, 228
temporalis muscle, 254, 254
termites, 125, 194, 195, 269, 283, 283,
    412, 413
terrestrial primates, 94, 96, 96, 127, 134
territoriality
    benefits and costs of, 132
    mate defense and, 132
    in primate ecology, 132–33
    resource defense and, 132
territories, definition of, 131
tertiary structure, 42
testes, 82, 159, 159
Tethys Sea, 218, 226
Texier, Pierre-Jean, 329
theory of mind, 200, 408
therapsids, 207, 208
thermoluminescence dating, 213, 214, 326
third-party relationships, 197, 198, 199
third-party sanctions, behavior
    and, 422–23
threonine, 42
Thrinaxodon, 208
thymine, 38, 39, 44, 49
Tianyuan Cave, China, 331
tibia, 267, 301, 308

tigers, 132
time budgets, 130
Timor, 342
Tishkoff, Sarah, 368
titi monkeys, 121, 158, 160, 177
Tobias, Phillip, 246
Tomasello, Michael, 200
Tooby, John, 390
tools and toolmaking
    Acheulean, 273–74, 302, 326, 345
    of anatomically modern humans, 323,
        327, 327–28, 328, 329
    animal bones associated with, 284,
        284–84, 285
    Aurignacian, 343, 344–45, 345,
        350, 351
    in Australia, 270, 342
    in Awash basin, Ethiopia, 270
    bipolar technique, 270
    blade, 344, 346, 346
    bone tools, 283, 283, 328, 328, 329
    burins, 344, 346, 346
    of Central Inuit, 409, 409
    Châtelperronian, 345, 345
    of chimpanzees, 82, 125, 143, 196,
        269, 270
    cut marks on, 285–86, 286, 287,
        287, 346
    in Dikika, 270, 270
    in foraging, 196
    Gravettian, 345
    by H. heidelbergensis, 302, 325
    of H. erectus, 273, 275
    of H. floresiensis, 305
    hafted, 303, 328
    heat-treated, 328
    of hominins, 269–70
    of Homo, 261
    Howieson's Port, 329
    Levallois, 303, 303
    long-distance movement of resources
        and, 329
    Magdalenian, 345
    Middle Paleolithic, 344
    Mode 1, 271, 273, 305
    Mode 2, 273, 318, 319
    Mode 3, 303, 308, 318, 319
    Mode 4, 327, 345
    Mode 5, 328
    Mousterian, 308, 327, 344, 345
    of Neanderthals, 327
    Oldowan, 270–71, 271, 272,
        272–73, 275
    by orangutans (Pongo pygmaeus), 269
    passive hammer technique, 270
    right-handers, 272, 272
    scrapers, 345, 346
    Solutrean, 345, 346, 346
    stone, 269–70, 270, 271, 273, 325,
        342, 346

    Szeletian, 345
    for termiting, 125, 194, 195, 269,
        283, 283–4
    Uluzzian, 345, 345
    of Upper Paleolithic, 344–46, 345, 346
    wear patterns on, 274, 283, 283
toothcomb, 218
torque, 236, 237
Toth, Nicholas, 272, 274
toxins, 126
trachea, 313
tradeoffs, life history theory and, 190–93
traditions, social learning and, 412
traits. see characters (traits)
transfer RNA (tRNA), 44, 45, 314
transitive dominance, 151
transposable elements, 357
tree climbing, 252
Tree of Life, 91–93
tree shrews, Belanger's, 209
Triassic period, 207
Trinchera Dolina, Spain, 302, 306
Trinil, 268
Trinkaus, Erik, 325
Trivers, Robert, 170, 184
tropical forests, 128
    destruction of, 123, 139, 139–40
tryptophan, 42
Tschermak, Erich, 27
tuberculosis, 365
tubers, 277, 282, 283, 291
Tucker, Steven, 317
Tugen Hills, Kenya, 245
turban shell, 15
Turkana (nomadic herders), 419, 419,
    420, 420, 423
Turkanapithecus, 227
Turkey, 229
turtles, 302
Tutin, Caroline, 269
Tuttle, Russell, 251
twins, 148, 160, 374–75, 375
    chimerism and, 183
tyrosine, 42

uakari monkeys, 121
Uganda, 170, 226
    Kibale Forest, 124, 129, 133, 185
Ukraine, 348
ultimatum game, 421, 421–22
Uluzzian tool industry, 345, 345
ungulates, 221
unlinked loci, 36
Upper Paleolithic people, 343
    burials of, 348
    cave painting of, 349–51, 350, 351
    clothing for, 348
    diets of, 346–47
    foraging of, 347
    injury and disease in, 349

life expectancy of, 349
  Neanderthals compared with, 347–49
  population density of, 348–49
  ritual burials and, 349, *349*
  subsistence economy of, 346–47
  toolmaking of, 344–46, *345, 346*
uracil, 44
uranium-lead dating, 213
Ust'-Ishim, Russia, 344

valine, *42*, 43, *43*, 361
van den Bergh, Gerrit, 305
van Noordwijk, Maria, 152
van Schaik, Carel, 152, 164, 193
variants, 26
variation, 47. *see also* genetic diversity;
  genetic variation
    in adaptation, 6, 12–17
    in anatomically modern humans, *360*,
      360–61, *361*
    behavioral plasticity and, 65–68
    in complex phenotypic traits, 373–79
    continuous, 12, 22, 60–62
    Darwin on, 21–22
    discontinuous, 12–13, 22
    environmental, 62, 360, 361, 373
    expressed, *64*
    genetic drift and, 336, *336*
    geographic patterns of, 320, *320*,
      324–25, *325*
    group selection and, 173
    hidden, *64*, 64–65
    human, dimensions of, *360*,
      360–61, *361*
    loci and, 60–62
    maintenance of, 63–65
    mutations and, 63–64, 336
    random, 13–14
    recombination and, 33
    sampling, *71*, 71–72, *72*
    sexual reproduction and, 64
Venezuela, 161, 164, 182, 277
vertebral canals, 313

vertebrates, 48, 75, *92*
vertical clinging and leaping, 118, *118*
vervet monkeys, 122, *122, 129, 130*, 132,
  134, 182, 197, 198, 199, 312
    alarm calling, 134
    coalition formation and, 186
    mating system of, 150
    reciprocal altruism and, 185, *186*
    social learning in, 413
Vilas Ruivas, Portugal, 310
Vindija, Croatia, 315
Virchow, Rudolf, 307
Virginia opossum (*Didelphis
  virginiana*), *191*
Virunga Mountains, *124*, 164
vitamin A poisoning, 287
vitamins, 126, *127*
viviparity, 109
vocal communication system, 312–13
Voight, Benjamin, 370, 371
Volcanoes National Park, Rwanda, *129*
vultures, 290, *290*

Walker, Alan, 253, 287
wallabies, 242
Wallacea, 304
walrus, 409
Wamba, 124
Ward, Carol, 230
warfare, as large-scale
  cooperation, 419–20
warthogs, 291
water, 126, *127*
waterbirds, 219
Watson, James, 37
Watts, David, 185
weathering, 293, *293*
Wedgwood, Josiah, 395
Wedgwood, Josiah II, 5
Weinberg, Wilhelm, 57
West Africa, 137, 139, 269, *270*, 312, 360,
  361, 364, 382, *382*
Westermarck, Edward, 393, 394

whales, 209, 412
Wheeler, Peter, 243
White, Tim, 239, 242, 246, 247, 325, 326
Whiten, Andrew, 150, 413
Widdig, Anja, 177
wild dogs, 289
wildebeests, 284, *286*
Wilkins, Maurice, 37
Winkler, Paul, 152
Wolf, Arthur, 393
wolves, 16, *16*, 347, 408
    dogs descended from, 19, *22*
Women's National Basketball Association
  (WNBA), *360*, 361
woodworking, 274
woolly mammoth, 302, 306
woolly rhinoceros, 302, 306, 347
woolly spider monkey. *see* muriquis
  (woolly spider monkey)
Woranso-Mille, 246
Wrangham, Richard, 291, 292
Wright, Sewall, *60*, 61, 63
Wynne-Edwards, V. C., 173

X-rays, 63

Ya'aqov, Gesher Genot, 302
Yakut, *337*
Yana River, 343, 409
Yingkou, China, 303, *304*, 320
Yoruba, 336
Yugoslavia, 380
Yurok, 418–19, 420

Zaire, 124
Zambia, 300, 301, 328
zebras, 291
Zinjanthropus boisei, 255
*Zoology of the Voyage of H.M.S. Beagle,
  The* (Darwin), 7
zygomatic arches, 228
zygotes, 28–29, *30, 32*, 33, 34, 55–56, *57*,
  58, 59, 374